# Wed Again!

## ...is he back in her heart?

# Wed Again!

**THE SIX-MONTH MARRIAGE**
by
**Penny Jordan**

**A RELATIVE BETRAYAL**
by
**Anne Mather**

**LOVERS IN THE AFTERNOON**
by
**Carole Mortimer**

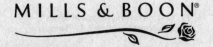

**MILLS & BOON**®

*All the characters in this book have no existence outside the imagination
of the author, and have no relation whatsoever to anyone bearing the
same name or names. They are not even distantly inspired by any
individual known or unknown to the author, and all the incidents are
pure invention.*

*WED AGAIN!*
© by Harlequin Enterprises II B.V., 2001

*The Six-Month Marriage, A Relative Betrayal* and *Lovers in the
Afternoon* were first published in Great Britain by Harlequin Mills &
Boon Limited in separate, single volumes.

*The Six-Month Marriage* © Penny Jordan 1985
*A Relative Betrayal* © Anne Mather 1990
*Lovers in the Afternoon* © Carole Mortimer 1985

ISBN 0 263 82772 0

*05-0104*

*Printed and bound in Spain
by Litografia Rosés S.A., Barcelona*

**Penny Jordan** has been writing for over twenty years and has an outstanding record: over one hundred and fifty novels published including the phenomenally successful A PERFECT FAMILY, TO LOVE, HONOUR & BETRAY, THE PERFECT SINNER AND POWER PLAY which hit *The Sunday Times* and *The New York Times* bestseller lists. Penny Jordan was born in Preston, Lancashire, and now lives in a beautiful fourteenth-century house in rural Cheshire.

**Look out for THE MISTRESS PURCHASE
by Penny Jordan
in Mills & Boon Modern Romance™, April 2004**

# THE SIX-MONTH
# MARRIAGE
### by
### PENNY JORDAN

# CHAPTER ONE

'SAPPHIRE, you haven't heard a word I've said. What's wrong?' Alan asked her.

The densely blue, dark lashed eyes that were the reason for Sapphire's unusual name turned in his direction, her brief smile not totally hiding the concern in their dark blue depths.

'I've had a letter from home this morning, and apparently my father isn't well.'

'Home?' Alan gave her a strange look. 'Funny, that's the first time I've heard you call it that in the four years that you've worked for me. Before it's always been Grassingham.'

Frowning slightly, Sapphire left her desk, pacing restlessly. It was true that in the four years she had worked in London she had tried to wipe her memory clean of as much of the past as she could, and that included any foolishly sentimental references to the border village where she had grown up as 'home', but in times of crisis, mental conditioning, no matter how thorough, was often forgotten. Her father confined to bed and likely to remain a semi-invalid for the rest of his life!

Unconsciously she stopped pacing and stared through the large window of her office, but instead of seeing the vista of office blocks and busy London streets all she could see was her childhood home; the farm which had belonged to many generations of Bells and which had been handed

5

down from father to son from the time of Elizabeth the First. But of course *her* father had no son to carry on farming the land he loved, that was why... Sapphire gnawed worriedly at her bottom lip. In the Borders people adapted to social changes very slowly. Those who lived there had a deeply ingrained suspicion of 'new ideas', but had she wanted to do so, she knew that her father would have encouraged her to undertake the agricultural degree needed to successfully run a farm the size of Flaws. However, although she had grown up on the farm she had had no desire to take over from her father.

Flaws valley was one of the most fertile in the area, and should her father decide to sell, there would be no shortage of buyers. But how *could* he sell? It would break his heart. After her mother had left him he had devoted himself exclusively to the farm and to her. Her mother. Sapphire sighed. She could barely remember her now, although she knew that she looked very much like her.

It was from her American mother that she had inherited her wheat blonde hair and long lithe body, both of which were viewed with a touch of scorn in the Borders.

'She's the looks and temperament of a race horse,' one neighbour had once commented scornfully to her father, 'but what you need for these valleys is a sturdy pony.'

Acutely sensitive, Sapphire had grown up knowing that the valley disapproved of her mother. She had been flighty; she had been foreign; but worst of all she had been beautiful with no other purpose in life but to *be* beautiful. Although she had been fiercely partisan on her father's behalf as a child—after all she too had shared his sense of rejection, for when her mother left with her lover there had been no question of taking a four-year-old child with her—older now herself Sapphire could understand how the valley had stifled and finally broken a woman like her mother, until there had been nothing left for her other than flight.

A farmer's hours were long hours, and her mother had craved parties and entertainment, whereas all her father wanted to do in the evenings was to relax. Her mother was dead now, killed in a car accident in California, and she... Despite the warmth of her centrally heated office Sapphire shivered. She knew she had never been wholly accepted by her peers in the valley and that was why she had responded so hungrily to whatever scraps of attention she had been given. A bitter smile curved her mouth and she looked up to find Alan watching her worriedly.

Dear Alan. Their relationship was such a comfortable one. She enjoyed working for him, and after the emotional minefields she had left behind her when she left the valley, his calm affection made her feel secure and relaxed. Their friends looked on them as an established couple although as yet they weren't lovers, which suited Sapphire very well. She wasn't sure if she was strong enough yet to involve herself too intimately with another human being. As she knew all too well, intimacy brought both pleasure and pain and her fear of that pain was still stronger than her need of its pleasure. Divorce was like that, so other people who had been through the same thing told her. Along with the self-doubts and anguish ran a deep current of inner dread of commitment.

'Alan, I'm afraid I'm going to have to ask for time off so that I can go and see my father.'

'Of course. If we weren't so busy, I'd drive you up there myself. How long do you think you'll need? We've got quite a lot to get through before the end of the month and we're away for all of March.'

Alan's small import business had been very successful the previous year and he was rewarding himself and Sapphire with a month's holiday cruising round the Caribbean; an idyll which Sapphire sensed would culminate in them becoming lovers. Without saying so outright Alan had intimated that he wanted to marry her. Her father seemed to have sensed it too because in his last letter to her he had teased her about the 'intentions' of this man she wrote about so often. She had written back, saying that they were 'strictly honourable'.

'Don't worry too much.' Alan comforted, misunderstanding the reason for her brief frown. 'If your father's well enough to write. . .'

'He isn't.' Sapphire cut in, her frown deepening.

'Then who was the letter from?'

'Blake.' Sapphire told him brittly.

When Alan's eyebrows rose, she added defensively, 'He and my father are very close. His land runs next to Flaws Farm, and his family have been there nearly as long as ours. In fact the first Sefton to settle there was a border reiver—a supporter of Mary Queen of Scots, who according to local rumour managed to charm Elizabeth enough to be pardoned.'

'Do you still think about him?'

For a moment the quiet question threw her. She knew quite well who the 'him' Alan referred to was, and her face paled slightly under her skilful application of makeup. 'Blake?' she asked lightly, adopting the casual tone she always used when anyone asked her about her ex-husband. 'We were married when I was eighteen and we parted six months later. I don't think about him any more than I have to, Alan. He was twenty-six when we were married, and unlike me he knew exactly what he was doing.'

'I hardly recognise you when you talk about him,' Alan murmured coming across to touch her comfortingly. 'Your voice goes so cold. . .'

'Perhaps because when I talk about Blake that's how I feel; terribly cold, and very, very old. Our marriage was a complete disaster. Blake was unfaithful to me right from the start. The only reason he married me was because he wanted Flaws' land, but I was too besotted—too adolescently infatuated with him to see that. I thought he loved me, and discovering that he didn't. . .'

She shuddered, unable to go any further; unable to explain even now the terrible sense of disillusionment and betrayal she had experienced when she discovered the truth about her marriage. It was four years since she had last seen Blake— and four years since she had last seen her father, she reminded herself, mainly because she had refused to go home and risk meeting Blake, and her father had been too busy with the farm to come to London and see her. And now this morning she had received Blake's letter, telling her about the pneumonia that had confined her father to bed.

A terrible ache spread through her body. It hurt to know that her father had been so ill and she had not known. He had not written or phoned to tell her. No, that had been left up to Blake, with the curt p.s. to his letter that he thought she should come home. 'Although he doesn't say so, I know your father wants to see you,' he had written in the decisive, black script that was so familiar to her—familiar because of that other time she had seen it; the day she had discovered the love letter he had written to one of his other women. The tight ball of pain inside her chest expanded and threatened to explode, but she willed it not to. She had already endured all that; she wasn't going to allow it to return. There was a limit to the extent of mental agony anyone could be expected to suffer, and she had surely suffered more than her share, learning in the space of six months that the husband she worshipped had married her simply because he wanted her father's land, and that he had not even respected their marriage vows for a week of that marriage. While he left her untouched save for the brief kiss he gave her each morning as he left the farm, he had been making love to other women; women to whom he wrote intensely passionate love letters—love letters that had made her ache with longing; with pain; with jealousy. Even now she could still taste the bitterness of that anguished agony. She had gone straight from discovering the letters to her father, complaining that she did not believe that Blake loved her. Not even to him could she confide what she had found, and when he questioned her, she had simply told him of Blake's preoccupation; of his darkly sombre moods, of the little time he spent with her.

'I don't know why he married me,' she had cried despairingly, and her father taking pity on her had explained how worried he had been about the future of the farm once he was gone, and how he and Blake had agreed on their marriage, which was more the marriage of two parcels of land than two human beings.

She hadn't told her father about discovering Blake's infidelities, and for the first time in her life she had truly appreciated how her mother must have felt. From that to making the decision to leave Flaws valley had been a very short step. Blake had been away at the time buying a new ram and she vividly remembered, tiptoeing downstairs with her suitcase and out through the large flagged kitchen, leaving a note for him on the table. In it she had said simply that she no longer wanted to be married to him. Her pride wouldn't let her write anything else, and certainly nothing about Miranda Scott who had been one of Blake's regular girlfriends before he started dating her. She had bumped into Miranda in the library and the other girl had eyed her tauntingly as she told her about the night she had spent with Blake the previous week. Blake had told her that he was buying fresh stock and that he would have to stay in the Cotswolds overnight.

She had asked if she could go with him, thinking that away from the farm she might find it easier to talk to him about her unhappiness with their marriage. In the months leading up to it she had been thrilled by the way he kissed and caressed her and had looked forward eagerly to their wedding night, but she had spent it alone as she had all the nights that followed, and that had been one of the

most galling things of all, the fact that her
husband didn't find her attractive enough to want
to make love to her.

But he found Miranda attractive—so attractive
that he had taken her to the Cotswolds with him.

At first when she reached London she had used
an assumed name, terrified that Blake would try to
find her, and terrified that if he did, she wouldn't
have the pride or strength of will to refuse to go
back to him. Not that she was under any illusions
any more that he wanted her. No, he wanted her
father's land!

Those first six months in London had been
bitterly lonely. She had drawn all her money out
of her bank account before leaving the valley and
there had been enough to support her for the first
three months while she took a secretarial course.
Her first job she had hated, but then she had
found her present job with Alan. She had also
enough confidence by then to find herself a
solicitor. She could have had her marriage
annulled—after all it had never been consummated—but she hadn't wanted anyone to know
the humiliating truth—that her husband hadn't
found her attractive enough to want to consummate it—so instead she had patiently waited out
the statutory time before suing for divorce. She
had half expected, even then, some reaction from
Blake but there had been none and their divorce
had become final just five months ago.

Sapphire had been in London seven months
before she wrote to her father. Before leaving the
valley she had posted a letter to him telling him
she was leaving Blake, and saying that nothing
would make her come back.

With hindsight she could see how worried her father must have been when he didn't hear from her, but at the time she had been so concerned with protecting herself both from Blake and from her own treacherous emotions that she hadn't been able to think past them.

'Do you plan to drive North, or will you go by train?'

Jerked out of her reverie by Alan's voice Sapphire forced herself to concentrate. 'I'll drive,' she told him. 'There isn't a direct train service and driving will save time.'

'Then you'd better take my car,' Alan told her calmly, 'I wouldn't feel happy about you driving so far in yours.'

It was true that her battered VW had seen better times, and Sapphire felt the same warm glow she always experienced when Alan was so thoughtful. Being married to him would be like being wrapped in insulating fibre; protected. Protected from what? From her past? From her foolish adolescent craving for the love of a man who was simply using her? That's all over now, Sapphire told herself sharply. Blake means nothing to me now. Nothing at all.

'Look, why don't you go home now and get yourself organised,' Alan suggested. 'You're too strung up to be much use here, and you'll need an early start in the morning. Here are my car keys.' He frowned. 'No, I'll go and fill the tank up first. That should be enough to get you all the way there. And when you arrive, 'phone me won't you? I wish there was some way I could come with you.'

'Dear Alan.' Sapphire rested her head against

his shoulder—a rare expression of physical affection for her. 'You're so good to me.'

'Because you're worth being good to,' Alan retorted gruffly. Expressions of emotions always embarrassed him, and as she withdrew from him Sapphire wondered why she should remember so clearly the sensual seduction of the words Blake had written; words which still had the power to move her even now, and yet Blake too was a man of few words, but then unlike Alan, Blake's words were always pithy and to the point. Blake deplored waste of any kind; a true Sefton; and yet there was something about him that had always attracted and yet frightened her. He had spent several years in the army after leaving university. Perhaps that was where he had developed that hard veneer that was so difficult to get past. Sapphire knew that he had been posted to Northern Ireland, and yet his experiences there were something he never did discuss—not even with her father. When she had commented on it once, her father had simply said, 'There are some things a man can't endure to remember, and so for the sake of his sanity he forgets them. War is one of them.'

An hour later, gripping the cord of the telephone receiver as she waited for someone to answer the 'phone, she felt her stomach muscles contract with tension. According to Blake's letter her father didn't know he had written, so she must try to pretend that she knew nothing of his illness. The ringing seemed to last for ever, and for one dreadful moment Sapphire pictured her father lying in bed, listening to the demanding sound, too ill to do anything about it, but then the receiver was lifted, the ringing abruptly cut off. Relief made her voice hesitantly husky, 'Dad, it's Sapphire.'

The cool male voice, edged with taunting mockery, wasn't her father's, and the tiny hairs on her arm stood up in prehensile alarm as she recognised it.

'Blake?'

'How very flattering that you should recognise my voice so quickly after all this time.'

'They say people always remember anything connected with acute trauma,' Sapphire snapped sharply. 'Blake, I've got your letter. My father, how is he?'

'Why don't you come home and see for yourself, or are you still running scared?'

'What of? You? Of course I'm coming h . . . back, but I can hardly arrive without warning Dad to expect me.'

'Very thoughtful. Giving him time to kill the fatted calf is that it? I take it you're coming alone,' he added, before she could respond. 'Flaws Farm only has three bedrooms remember; your father's in one, his housekeeper's in the other, and I'm sure I don't need to tell you how the valley will feel about one of its daughters openly co-habiting with a man she isn't married to—to say nothing of your father's feelings.'

Gritting her teeth Sapphire responded. 'I'm coming alone, but only because Alan couldn't make it. Now may I please speak to my father?'

It was only when Blake put the receiver down that she realised she hadn't asked him what he was doing at Flaws Farm. He had sounded very much at home, and she bit worriedly at her bottom lip.

She had forgotten how freely Blake was used to coming and going in her old home, and if she was forced to endure the constant sight of him how would it affect the calm control she had sheltered behind for so long?

It won't affect it at all, she told herself angrily. Why should it? Blake had effectively killed whatever feelings she had had for him—and they had only been infatuation—a very deep and intense infatuation agreed, but infatuation nevertheless. . .

Five minutes later she was speaking to her father, unable to stop the weak tears rolling down her face. Normally they only rang one another at Christmas and birthdays, and it shocked her to hear the hesitancy in his voice.

'Blake tells me you intend paying us a visit?'

'If you've got room for me. I hear you've got a housekeeper?' Sapphire responded drily.

'Yes, Mary Henderson. You probably remember her from the old days. She used to nurse at the local hospital. She was widowed a couple of years ago, and her husband left a lot of debts, so she had to sell her house and look for a job. Blake recommended her to me. This is still your home Sapphire,' he added in a different voice. 'There's always a room for you here.'

Without saying it he was making her aware of all the times she should have gone home and hadn't, because she hadn't been able to conquer her weakness; her fear of meeting Blake, and discovering that she wasn't as strong as she had believed. What was she really frightened of though? Blake seducing her? Hardly likely—after all he hadn't wanted her when they were married, so why should he want her now?

'Expect me late tomorrow evening,' Sapphire told him. 'Alan's lending me his car, because he doesn't think my old VW is reliable enough.' For some reason Sapphire found the silence that followed oddly disconcerting.

'You'd better use the top road,' her father said at last. 'They've been doing some roadworks on the other one and there've been traffic jams all week just this side of Hawick.'

Mentally revising her plans, Sapphire said her goodbyes. She had planned to drive up the M6 to Carlisle and then take the A7 through Hawick and Jedburgh, rather than using the 'top road' which was shorter but which meant driving along the narrow winding road which crossed and re-crossed the Cheviots.

That night, too wide-awake to sleep, she acknowledged that hearing Blake's voice had disturbed her—dangerously so. The sound of it brought back memories she had struggled to suppress; herself at fourteen watching with shy adulation while Blake worked. Fresh from university he had seemed like a god from Olympus to her and she had dogged his footsteps, hanging on to his every word. Was it then that he had decided to marry her? It was certainly then that he had started to put into practice the modern farming techniques he had learned partially at university and partially during his working holidays in New Zealand into force. Perhap's it was also then that he had first cast covetous eyes on Flaws Farm and mentally calculated the benefits to himself of owning its rich acres in addition to his own. She would never know, but certainly he had been kind and patient with her, carefully answering all her shy questions, tactfully ignoring her blushes and coltish clumsiness. She remembered practically falling off her pony one day straight into his arms, and how she had felt when they closed round her, the steady beat of his heart thumping into her thin chest. From that day on she had started to weave the fantasies about him that had taken her blissfully into their marriage.

At eighteen she had known very little of the world—had only travelled as far as Edinburgh and Newcastle and had certainly not got the sophistication to match Blake. He had left the valley when she was fifteen to join the army and had returned two years later the same and yet different; harder, even more sure of himself and possessed of a dangerous tension that sent frissons of awareness coursing over her skin whenever he looked at her.

The Christmas she was seventeen he had kissed her properly for the first time in the large living room of Sefton House—the large rambling building his great-grandfather had built when a fire had gutted the old farmhouse. There had been a crowd of people there attending a Boxing Day party and someone had produced a sprig of mistletoe. Even now she could vividly remember the mixture of anticipation and dread with which she had awaited Blake's kiss. She had known he *would* kiss her. He had kissed all the other girls, but the kiss he gave her was different, or so she had told herself at the time. Her first 'grown-up' kiss; the first time she had experienced the potency of sexual desire. His mouth had been firm and warm, his lips teasing hers, his tongue probing them apart.

Restlessly, Sapphire sat up in bed, punching

her pillow. She must get some sleep if she was
going to be fresh for her drive tomorrow. No
doubt if Blake were to kiss her now she would
discover that his kisses were nothing like as
arousing as she remembered. She had been an
impressionable seventeen-year-old to his twenty-
five already halfway to worshipping him, and
during the brief spring days he had cashed in on
that adoration, until by summer he filled her every
thought. He had proposed to her one hot
summer's day beside the stream that divided
Sefton and Bell land. Blake had wanted to swim,
she remembered, in the deep pool formed by the
waterfall that cascaded into it. She had objected
that she hadn't brought her suit and Blake had
laughed at her, saying that neither had he. She had
trembled as revealingly as a stalk of wheat before
the reaper, not troubling to hide her reaction. He
had pulled her to him, kissing her; caressing her
with what she had naively taken to be barely
restrained passion. God how ridiculous she must
have seemed. Blake's actions couldn't have been
more calculated had they been programmed by
computer, and whatever passion there had been
had been for her father's lands and nothing else.

'Damn Blake, this is all his fault,' Sapphire
muttered direfully the next morning, as she ate a
hurriedly prepared breakfast. Ten o'clock already,
and she had hoped to leave at eight, but she hadn't
been able to get to sleep until the early hours and
then when she had done she had slept restlessly,
dreaming of Blake, and of herself as they had
been. Now this morning there was a strange ache
in the region of her heart. She couldn't mourn a

love she had never had, she reminded herself as she had done so often during those first agonising months in London, and Blake had never loved her. It had been hard to accept that, but best in the long run. She had once suffered from the delusion that Blake loved her and the penalty she had paid for that folly had warned her against the folly of doing so again.

It was eleven o'clock before she finally managed to leave. The day was crisp and cold, a weak sun breaking through the clouds. February had always been one of her least favourite months—Christmas long forgotten and Spring still so far away, and she was looking forward to her holiday. There was something faintly decadent about going to the Caribbean in March.

A John Williams tape kept her company until she was clear of the City. Blake had had very catholic tastes in music and in books, but it was only since coming to London that her own tastes had developed. Music was a key that unlocked human emotions she thought as she slowed down to turn the tape over. Alan's BMW was his pride and joy, and although she appreciated his thoughtfulness in lending it to her, she was slightly apprehensive with it.

She had planned to stop for lunch somewhere round Manchester, but oversleeping had altered her schedule, and she glanced at her watch as she travelled north and decided instead to press on to Carlisle and stop there.

She found a pleasant looking pub a few miles off the motorway and pulled up into the car park, easing her tired body out of the car. As she walked in the bar she felt the sudden silence descending on the room, and suppressed a wry grimace. She had forgotten how very conservative northern men were. Even now very few women up here entered pubs alone, but she shrugged aside the sudden feeling of uncertainty and instead headed for the bar, breathing in the appetising smell of cooking food.

The menu when she asked for it proved to be surprisingly varied. She ordered lasagne and retreated to a small corner table to wait for it to be served. While she waited she studied the people around her; mostly groups of men, standing by the bar while their womenfolk sat round the tables. So much for women's lib, she thought drily, watching them. If she had stayed at home she could well have been one of these women. And yet they seemed quite happy; they were fashionably dressed and from the snatches of conversation she caught even the married ones seemed to have jobs, which to judge from their comments they enjoyed.

A chirpy barmaid brought the lasagne and the coffee she had ordered. The pasta was mouth-wateringly delicious. She hadn't realised how hungry she had been, Sapphire reflected as she drank her coffee, reluctant to leave the warmth of the pub for the raw cold of the February night outside, but she was already late. At last, reluctantly, she got up and made her way to the car, unaware of the way several pairs of male eyes followed her tall, lithe body. She had dressed comfortably for the journey, copper coloured cords toning with a coffee and copper sweater, flat-heeled ankle boots in soft suede completing her outfit. She had always worn her hair long, but in London she had found a hairdresser who cared about the condition of his clients' hair and now hers shone with health, curving sleekly down on to her shoulders.

The BMW started first time, its powerful lights picking out the faint wisps of mist drifting down from the hills. Living in London insulated one from the elements, Sapphire thought, shivering as she drove out of the car park, and switched the car heater on to boost. She had to concentrate carefully on the road so that she didn't miss the turning which would take her on to the 'top road' and she exhaled faintly with relief when she found it. The mist had grown thicker, condensation making it necessary for her to switch on the windscreen wipers, the BMW's engine started to whine slightly as the road climbed. She had forgotten how quickly this road rose; the Cheviots were gentle hills compared with some, but they still rose to quite a height. It was an eerie sensation being completely alone on this empty stretch of road, her lights the only ones to illuminate the darkness of the bare hills. Here and there her headlights picked out patches of snow and then visibility would be obscured by the mist that seemed to waft nebulously around her.

Despite the heater she felt quite cold. Nerves, she told herself staunchly, automatically checking her speed as the mist started to thicken. Now she noticed with dismay the patches of mist were longer, and much, much, denser. In fact they weren't mist at all, but honest-to-God fog. It was freezing as well. She had thought it might be several miles back when she felt so cold, but now she felt the BMW's front wheels slide slightly, and tried not to panic. The BMW had automatic transmission, but there was a lower gear and she dropped into it, biting her lip as she crawled down a steep hill.

Nine o'clock! Her father would be wondering where on earth she was. Why hadn't she rung him from the pub and told him she was likely to be late? It was useless now chastising herself for not anticipating adverse weather conditions. One of the first things she had learned as a child was not to trust the Border weather, but she had lived in London for so long that she had forgotten. She tensed as the BMW slid sickeningly round a sharp bend, blessing the fact that she had the road to herself. She ought never to have come this way. The traffic jams in Hawick would have been much preferable to this.

How many miles had she come? It felt like hundreds, but it was probably barely ten, and it was at least thirty to Flaws valley. She hadn't reached the highest part of the road yet either.

Trying not to panic Sapphire concentrated on the road, watching the thick grey film in front of her until her eyes ached. The road had no central markings; no cat's eyes, and on several occasions she felt the change in camber, warning her that she was veering too much to one side or the other.

It was a terrible, nightmare drive, and when the road finally peaked, and she was out above the fog, she trembled with relief. Snow still lined the road, this high up, and the tarmac surface shone dull grey with frost. She was over halfway there now.

Gradually the road started to drop down until she was back into the fog. In her relief to be over the top she had forgotten the sharpness of the bends on the downward road. Several times she felt the BMW slide as she cornered, and each time she prayed she wouldn't panic, refusing to give in to the temptation to brake, trying to steer the car into and then out of the skid.

When she eventually saw the sign for Flaws Valley she could hardly believe her own eyes! Elation made her weak with relief as her senses relayed to her the familiarity of the straight road through the village. Everything was in darkness. People in Flaws village kept early hours. Most of them worked on the land and there was nothing in the village to keep them out late at night. And yet as she remembered it she had never suffered from boredom as a teenager; there had always been plenty to do. Harvest Festivals; Christmas parties and pantomime; summer haymaking; barbecues. Lost in her thoughts she turned instinctively into the road that ran past Blake's farm and then on to her father's. A wall loomed up in front of her with shocking suddenness, emerging from the mist, making her brake instinctively. She felt the car skid almost immediately, wrenching the wheel round in a desperate effort to avoid the wall. She felt the sudden lurch as the car left the road and came to rest with its front wheels in the ditch. Her head hit the windscreen, the pull of her seatbelt winding her. The shock of her accident robbed her of the ability to do anything but grasp the wheel and shiver. The front of the car had hit the wall. She had heard the dull screech of metal against stone.

She must get out of the car. Shakily she switched off the ignition and freed herself from her seatbelt. Her forehead felt cold and damp. She touched it, staring foolishly at the sticky red blood staining her fingers as she pulled them away. She had cut herself, but she could move, albeit very shakily. The car door opened easily and she stepped out on to the road, shuddering with shock and cold as the freezing air hit her. What next? She was approximately five miles from home and two from the village. Blake's house was half a mile up the road, but she couldn't go there. The village was her best bet. Shakily she started out, only to tense as she heard the sound of another vehicle travelling down the road. From the sound of it, it was being driven with far more assurance than she had possessed. Its driver seemed to know no fear of the fog or the ice. Instinctively Sapphire stepped back off the road, wincing slightly as she realised she must have twisted her ankle against the pedals. Bright headlights pierced the fog, and she recognised the unmistakeable shape of a Land Rover. It stopped abruptly by the BMW and the engine was cut. The driver's door jerked open and a man jumped out. Tall and lean, his long legs were encased in worn jeans, a thick navy jumper covering the top half of his body. He walked towards the BMW and then stopped, lifting his head, listening as though he sensed something.

'Sapphire?'

Her heart thumping, her body tense Sapphire waited. She had known him immediately, and was shaken by her childish desire to keep silent; to run from him.

'Sapphire?' He called her name again and then cursed under his breath.

She was being stupid, Sapphire told herself, and

added to that she was beginning to feel distinctly odd. Blake's shadowy figure seemed to shift in patterns of mist, the sound of her own heartbeats one moment loud the next very faint.

'Blake ... over here.' How weak her voice sounded but he heard it. He came towards her with the certainty of a man who knows his way blindfolded. As he got closer Sapphire could see the droplets of moisture clinging to his dark hair. His face was tanned, his eyes the same disturbing gold she remembered so vividly. He was so close to her now that she could feel his breath against her skin.

'So you decided to come after all.' He voice was the same; that slight mocking drawl which had once so fascinated her was still there. 'I began to think you'd chickened out. . . What's the boy-friend going to say when he knows you've ruined his car?'

Not one word of concern for her. Not one solicitous phrase; not one comforting touch ... nothing. She knew she had to say something, but all she could manage was a pitiful sound like a weak kitten, her senses acutely attuned to everything about him. She could feel the leashed energy emanating from his body; smell the clean cold scent of his skin. She shivered feeling reality recede and darkness wash over her. As she slid forward she felt Blake's arms catch and then lift her.

'Well, well,' he murmured laconically. 'Here you are back in my arms. The last place you swore you'd ever be again. Remember?'

She tried to tell him that she had never been properly in his arms; that she had never known them as those of a lover, but it was too much effort. It was simpler by far to close her eyes and absorb the delicious warmth emanating from his body, letting her senses desert her.

# CHAPTER TWO

'COME on Sapphire, the shock can't have been that great.' The coolly mocking words broke against her senses like tiny darts of ice as she started to come round. She was sitting in a chair in the kitchen of Sefton House, and that chair was drawn up to the warmth of the open fire. The flames should have comforted her, but they weren't powerful enough to penetrate the chill of Blake's contempt. 'Flaws Valley females don't go round fainting at the first hint of adversity,' he taunted, watching her with a cynical smile. 'That's a London trick you've learned. Or was your faint simply a way of avoiding the unpalatable fact of our meeting?'

She had forgotten this side of him; this dangerous cynical side that could maim and destroy.

'I knew when I came up here that we were bound to meet, Blake.' She was proud of her composure, of the way she was able to meet the golden eyes. 'My faint was caused simply by shock—I hadn't expected the weather to be so bad.' She glanced round the kitchen, meticulously avoiding looking directly at him. She lifted her hand to touch her aching temple, relieved to discover the cut had healed. 'Don't worry,' Blake tormented, 'it's only a scratch!'

She had either forgotten or never fully realised, the intensity of the masculine aura he carried around him. It seemed to fill the large kitchen, dominantly. Droplets of moisture clung to the thick wool of his sweater, his hair thick and dark where it met the collar. His face and hands were tanned, his face leaner than she remembered, the proud hard-boned Celtic features clearly discernible.

The gold eyes flickered and Sapphire tensed, realising that she had been staring. 'What's the matter?' Blake taunted, 'Having second thoughts? Wishing you hadn't run out on me?'

'No.' Her denial came too quickly; too fervently; and she tensed beneath the anger she saw simmering in his eyes. The kitchen was immaculately clean; Blake had always been a tidy man but Sapphire sensed a woman's presence in the room.

'Do you live here alone?'

She cursed herself for asking the impulsive question when she saw his dark eyebrows lift.

'Now why should that interest you? As a matter of fact I do,' he added carelessly, 'although sometimes Molly stays over if it's been a particularly long day.'

'Molly?' She hoped her voice sounded disinterested, but she daren't take the risk of looking at Blake. What was the matter with her? She had been the one to leave Blake; she had been the one to sue for a divorce, so why should she feel so distressed now on learning that there might possibly be someone else in his life? After all he had never loved her. Never made any pretence of loving her. But she had loved him ... so much that she could still feel the echoes of that old pain, but echoes were all they were. She no longer loved

Blake, she had put all that behind her when she left the valley.

'Molly Jessop,' Blake elucidated laconically, 'You probably remember her as Molly Sutcliffe. She married Will Jessop, but he was killed in a car accident just after you left. Molly looks after the house for me; she also helps out with the office work.'

Molly Sutcliffe. Oh yes, Sapphire remembered her. Molly had been one of Blake's girlfriends in the old days. Five years older than Sapphire, and far, far more worldly. She had to grit her teeth to stop herself from making any comment. It was no business of hers what Blake did with his life. As she had already told him she had known they would have to meet during her stay, but not like this, in the enforced intimacy of the kitchen of what had once been their home. Not that she had ever been allowed to spend much time in here. The kitchen had been the province of Blake's aunt, a formidable woman who had made Sapphire feel awkward and clumsy every time she set foot in it.

'What happened to your aunt?' she questioned him, trying not to remember all the small humiliations she had endured here in this room, but it was too late. They all came flooding back, like the morning she had insisted on getting up early to make Blake's breakfast. She had burned the bacon and broken the eggs while his aunt stood by in grim silence. Blake had pushed his plate away with his food only half eaten. She was barely aware of her faint sigh. The ridiculous thing had been that she had been and still was quite a good cook. Her father's housekeeper had taught her, but being watched by Aunt Sarah had made her too nervous to concentrate on what she was doing; that and the fact that she had been trying too hard; had been far too eager to please Blake. So much so that in the end her eagerness had been her downfall.

'Nothing. She's living in the South of England with a cousin. I'll tell her you've been enquiring about her next time I write,' Blake mocked, glancing at the heavy watch strapped to his wrist. 'Look I'd better ring your father and tell him you're okay. I'll run you over there in the morning and then see what we can do about your car.'

'No! No, I'd rather go tonight. My father's a sick man Blake,' she told him. 'I'm very anxious to see him.'

'You don't have to tell me how ill he is,' Blake told her explosively, 'I'm the one who told *you*— remember? Don't expect me to believe that you're really concerned about him Sapphire. Not when you haven't been to see him in four years.'

'There were reasons for that.' Her throat was a tight band of pain, past which she managed to whisper her protest.

'Oh yes, like you didn't want to leave your lover?' His lips drew back in a facsimile of a smile, the vulpine grin of a marauding wolf. 'What's the matter Sapphire? Did you hope to keep your little affair a secret?'

'Affair?' Sapphire sat bolt upright in her chair.

'Yes ... with your boss ... the man you're planning to marry, according to your father. What took you so long?'

'It's only five months since I got the divorce,' Sapphire reminded him stiffly.

'But you could have got an annulment—much,

much faster... Why didn't you? Or was it that by the time you realised that you could, that the grounds no longer existed?'

It took a physical effort not to get up and face him with the truth, but somehow she managed it.

'My relationship with Alan is no concern of yours Blake,' she told him coolly. 'I'm sorry I've put you to all this trouble, but I'd like to get to Flaws as soon as possible.'

'Meaning you'd like to get away from me as soon as possible,' Blake drawled. 'Well my dear that may not be as easy as you think. In fact I suspect that when I ring your father now and tell him you're here, he'll suggest you stay the night.'

'Stay the night? Here with you, when the farm's only five miles up the road, don't be ridiculous.'

She glared at him, her eyes flashing angrily.

'You know it's probably just as well that you and I have had this opportunity to talk Sapphire. Your father's perked up a lot since you told him you were coming back. He hopes you and I will bury our differences and get back together.'

Stunned, Sapphire could only stare at him. 'You must be mad,' she stammered at last. 'We're divorced ... my father...'

'Your father is a very sick man, still as concerned about the future of his family's land as he was...'

'When you married me so that you could inherit it,' Sapphire broke in. 'You took advantage of my naiveté once Blake, but I'm not a seventeen-year-old adolescent in the grips of her first crush now. We're divorced and that's the way we're going to stay.'

'Even if that means precipitating your father's death?'

She went white with the cruelty of his words. 'His death, but. . .'

'Make no mistake about it, your father's a very sick man Sapphire. Very sick indeed, and worse, he's a man with no will left to struggle. You know that he's always wanted to see the two farms united. That was why he wanted us to get married in the first place.'

'If he's so keen for you to have the land, why doesn't he simply give it to you?' Sapphire asked him angrily.

'Because he wants to think some day that a child of ours—carrying his blood as well as mine—will inherit Bell land.'

'Oh so it isn't just marriage you want from me,' Sapphire stormed, 'it's a child as well? I wonder that you dare suggest such a thing when. . .'

'When?' Blake prodded softly when she stopped abruptly. 'When you couldn't bring yourself to touch me when we were married,' she had been about to say, but the pain of that time still hurt too much for her to be able to talk about it.

'When you know that I'm planning to marry someone else,' she told him coolly. 'Blake, I don't believe a word of what you've just said. My father must know that there isn't a chance of you and I getting together again. For one thing, there's simply nothing that such a relationship could offer me.'

'No.' His eyes fell to her breasts, and although Sapphire knew that the bulky wool of her jumper concealed them, she was acutely aware of a peculiar tension invading her body, making her face hot and her muscles ache.

'I would have said that being able to give your father a considerable amount of peace of mind would be a powerful incentive—to most daughters, but then you aren't like most daughters are you Sapphire?' he asked savagely. 'Or like most women for that matter. You don't care who you hurt or how much as long as you get what you want. Look, I don't want to be re-married to you any more than you want it, but I doubt it would be for very long.'

He watched her pale, and sway, with merciless eyes. 'Your father knows already how little time he's got, and whether you want to admit it or not he's very concerned about the future of his land—land which has been in his family as long as this farm has been in mine. Would it hurt either of us so much to do what he wants—to re-marry and stay together until. . .'

'Until he dies?' She hurled the words at him, shaking with pain and anger. 'And for how long do you estimate we should have to play out this charade Blake? You must know, you certainly seem to know everything else.'

'I was the closest thing to family he has left,' Blake told her simply, 'Naturally his doctor . . .' he broke off, studying the quarry tile floor and then raised his head and it seemed to Sapphire that she had been wrong in her original estimation that he hadn't changed. Now he looked older, harder, and she knew with an undeniable intuition that no matter what lies he might tell her about everything else, Blake did genuinely care for her father. Despair welled up inside her. Her father dying. . .

Remorse gripped her insides, her throat tense and sore. She badly wanted to cry, but she couldn't let Blake see her break down.

'Six months or so Sapphire,' he said quietly at last. 'Not a lot to ask you to give up surely? And you have my word that afterwards . . . that we can part quickly and amicably. This time our marriage will be dissolved.'

'And the farm . . . my father's land?'

'I'd like to buy it from you—at the going rate of course, unless your London lover wants to try his hand at farming?'

Just for a moment Sapphire taxed her imagination trying to picture Alan leading Blake's life. Alan would hate it, and she couldn't keep on the farm and work it herself. Even so, all her instincts warned her against agreeing to Blake's suggestion.

'It's a ridiculous idea, Blake,' she told him at last, taking a deep breath.

'You mean you're too selfish to acknowledge its merits,' he countered. 'I thought you might have grown up Sapphire; might have come to realise that there are other things in life apart from the gratification of your own wants, but obviously I was wrong. Come on,' he finished curtly, 'I'll take you 5o Flaws.'

He strode across the kitchen, thrusting open the door without waiting to see if she was following him. Wincing as she got up from the ache in her ankle, Sapphire hobbled to the door. Cold air rushed in to embrace her in its frosty grip. Across the cobbled yard she could make out the bulky shape of the Land-Rover. Blake opened the door and started up the engine. He must be able to see that she was having difficulty walking, Sapphire fumed as she was caught in the beam of the headlights, but he made no effort to help her.

It was only when she reached the Land Rover that he finally got out, walking round to the passenger side to open the door for her. When his hands suddenly gripped her waist she froze, her whole body tensing in rejection, her stiff, 'don't touch me,' making him tense in return. She could feel it in the grip of his fingers, digging through the wool of her jumper to burn into her skin. 'What the hell. . .' For a moment he seemed about to withdraw and then he spun her round, the proximity of his body forcing her back against the cold metal of the Land Rover. 'What is it you're so afraid of Sapphire,' he mocked, his gold eyes searching her too pale face. 'Not me, surely.' His eyes narrowed. 'As I remember it I barely touched you. So it must be yourself.'

'I'm not frightened of anything Blake,' she managed to reply coolly, still holding herself rigid within the grip of his hands. The warmth of his breath lifted her hair, and she was so acutely aware of him that it was a physical agony. Why, oh why had she come back? She had thought herself strong enough to cope, but she wasn't. Blake still had the power to upset and disturb her. He made her feel just as awkward and insecure as he had done when she was seventeen. 'I just don't want you touching me.'

'Frightened I might make you forget all about your London lover?' The soft goading tone of his voice was too much for her. Drawing in her breath on a sharp gasp she said coldly. 'That would be impossible.' She turned away as she spoke, leaning into the Land Rover. Blake's fingers continued to dig into her waist and then he was lifting her, almost throwing her into the seat with a force that jolted the breath from her body and made her aware of her aching bruises.

He didn't speak until he was in the Land-Rover beside her, his eyes fixed on the fog-shrouded lane as he said softly, 'Don't challenge me Sapphire— not unless you want me to accept your challenge. You've come back from London with some fine haughty airs, no doubt meant to keep country bumpkins like myself in their place but it wouldn't take much for me to forget mine Sapphire. There's one hell of a lot of anger inside me towards you, and believe me it would give me great pleasure to give it release.'

Why should Blake be angry? Resentment burned through Sapphire as they drove towards Flaws Farm. She was the one who should be that; and not just angry but bitter too. Blake had never wanted her; he had callously used her adolescent adoration of him, had ruthlessly exploited her feelings, and now he was saying he was angry. He could say what he liked, but there was no way she was going to agree to his outrageous suggestion that they re-marry. Did he think she was totally without intelligence? She knew what he wanted well enough—the same thing he had always wanted. Her father's land. The Seftons and the Bells hadn't always been friendly to one another, and the border reiver had spawned a race of men who all possessed his reckless touch of acquisitiveness. There had been several Seftons who had cast covetous eyes on Flaws farm and thought to make it theirs, but so far none had ever succeeded.

Now she was being foolish, Sapphire chided

herself. Blake was no border reiver, for all that he had inherited his wild ancestors' darkly Celtic looks, and it was true that her father admired and respected him, but surely not to the extent of wanting her, his daughter, to put herself within his power once more?

Sapphire darted a glance at Blake. He was concentrating on his driving, his profile faintly hawkish, his hands assured and knowing as he turned the wheel. There was nothing indecisive or unsure about Blake, she acknowledged. That was what she had admired so much in him as a teenager, and even now, watching him she was conscious of a faint frisson of awareness, a purely feminine acknowledgment of his masculinity. Stop it, she warned herself as they turned into Flaws Farm Lane. Stop thinking about him.

When the Land Rover stopped, she glanced uncomfortably at him. 'Are you coming in with me?'

'Do you really want me to?' he asked mockingly, before shaking his head. 'No, unlike you Sapphire, I'm not hard enough to raise hopes in your father's heart that I can't fulfil. Your father means a lot to me,' he added, startling her with his admission. 'I've always admired him, even patterned myself on him as a youngster I suppose—my own grandfather was too cold and distant—he never ceased mourning my father. I'd give a lot to see your father happy.'

'And even more to make sure that you get Flaws land,' Sapphire threw at him bitterly, 'even to the extent of marrying me. I fell for it once Blake, I'm not going to fall for it again.'

It was only as she struggled across the yard that

she remembered about her luggage, still in Alan's car. It was too late to turn round and call Blake back now, he was already reversing out of the yard. Sighing, Sapphire found the familiar back door and unlatched it. The kitchen was much as she remembered it. Her father used to employ a housekeeper to look after the house, but she had retired just after Sapphire's marriage. For a while he had managed with daily help from the village, but now it seemed he was employing someone else.

The door to the hall opened as Sapphire stepped into the kitchen and a woman entered the room. For a second they stared at one another and then the woman smiled tentatively, offering her hand. 'Mary,' she introduced herself, 'and you must be Sapphire. Your father's been worrying about you.'

There was just enough reproof in the calm, softly burred voice for Sapphire to flush and feel at a disadvantage. Mary was somewhere in her late thirties, plumpish with smooth brown hair and warm eyes. The sort of calm, serene, capable woman she had always envied.

'I'm sorry about that.' Quickly she explained how she had been delayed, warmed by the quick sympathy in the hazel eyes.

'May I see my father?' Sapphire asked tentatively. She had been nerving herself for this moment ever since Blake had told her the seriousness of her father's condition, and her palms were damp and sticky as she followed Mary up the familiar stairs. Her father's bedroom had windows that looked out over the hills, but tonight the curtains were drawn to obscure the view.

'It's all right Mary, you can switch the lamp on,' her father's familiar voice growled as Sapphire stood awkwardly by the door in the half light. 'I am awake.'

'Sapphire's here,' Mary told him, snapping on the bedside light. Perhaps it was the warm glow from the lamp but her father didn't look as ill as she had anticipated. Her legs felt shaky as she approached his bed, regret, guilt, and a dozen other emotions clamouring for expression. In the end all she could manage was a choked 'Dad,' and then she was in her father's arms, hugging him tightly, trying not to give way to tears.

'Well now, and how's my lass? Let me have a look at you.' As he held her slightly away from him, studying her features, Sapphire studied his. Her father had always had a tall, spare frame, but now he was gaunt, almost painfully thin, the weathered tanned face she remembered frighteningly pale—a sick-room pallor Sapphire acknowledged.

'Dad, if only I'd known. . .'

'Stop tormenting yourself, I wouldn't let Blake tell you. You're far too thin,' he scolded. 'Mary will have to feed you up while you're here. Borders' men don't like their women skinny.'

'But London men do,' Sapphire responded, withdrawing from him a little, sensing danger.

'You're later than we expected.'

'Umm, I had a slight accident.' Quickly she explained.

'You should have stayed overnight with Blake.'

'I'm sure neither Blake or I would have felt comfortable if I had Dad,' she said quietly. 'We're divorced now.'

'More's the pity.' He frowned, the happiness fading from his eyes. 'You should never have left him lass, but then you were so young, and young things take things so seriously.'

If anyone had asked her only days ago if her father had accepted her divorce Sapphire would have had no hesitation in saying 'yes' but now, suddenly, she knew he had not. She looked away from the bed, blinking back tears she wasn't sure were for her father or herself. As she did so she saw Mary glance sympathetically at her.

'I'll run you a bath,' she offered, 'You must be exhausted.'

'Yes, you go along to bed,' her father agreed. 'We'll talk in the morning.' He closed his eyes, his face almost waxen with exhaustion and fear pierced her. Her father was going to die. Until now she hadn't truly accepted it, but suddenly seeing him, seeing his frailty she did. 'Dad, who's looking after the farm?' she asked him trying to force back the painful knowledge.

'Why Blake of course.' He looked surprised that she needed to ask. 'And a fine job he's doing of it too.'

Mary's hand on her arm drew her away from the bed. On the landing Sapphire turned to the older woman, unable to hold back her tears any longer. 'Why?' she asked bitterly. 'Why did no-one tell me? Get in touch with me, I'd no idea. . .'

Shaking her head Mary gestured downstairs, not speaking until Sapphire had followed her down and they were back in the kitchen. 'Blake said not to,' she said quietly, 'he thought it best. At least at first.'

Blake had thought . . . Blake had said. . . Bitterness welled up inside her coupled with a fierce jealousy as she acknowledged something she

had always kept hidden even from herself. Her
father would have preferred a son ... a male, to
continue the family line and although he loved her,
it was to Blake that he had always confided his
innermost thoughts, Blake who he thought of as a
son ... Blake who he turned to when he needed
someone to lean on and not her.

'There, sit down and cry it all out,' Mary said
gently. 'It must have come as a shock to you.'

'Is it true that ... that my father...' Sapphire
couldn't go on. Tears were streaming down her
face and she dug in her jeans pocket for a
handkerchief. 'He's been a very sick man,' Mary
said compassionately, her eyes sliding away from
Sapphire's. 'His heart isn't too strong and this
bout of pneumonia, but having you home has
given him a real fillip.'

'I never knew how he felt about the divorce until
tonight.' Sapphire almost whispered the words,
saying them more to herself than Mary, but the
other woman caught them and smiled sympathetically. 'Blake means a lot to him,' she agreed,
'he thought that your marriage protected both you
and Flaws land.'

'He worries a lot about the land doesn't he?'
Sapphire's voice was unconsciously bitter.

'And about you,' Mary told her. 'The land is
like a sacred trust to him and he has a strong sense
of duty and responsibility towards it.'

'Strong enough to want to see Blake and me
back together again?' Sapphire asked bleakly.

Mary said nothing, but the way her eyes refused
to meet Sapphire's told her what she wanted to
know.

'You obviously know my father very well,' she

said quietly at last. 'He confides in you far more than he ever confided in me.'

'I'm a trained nurse,' Mary told her, 'and that is how I first came to know your father. When he was first ill he needed a full-time nurse. Dr Forrest recommended me, and your father asked me to stay on as his housekeeper-cum-nurse. The relationship between patient and nurse is one of trust. It has to be. I can't deny that your father, like many people of his generation, doesn't wholly approve of divorce, and he does feel that the land would be properly cared for by Blake, and. . .'

'And that if Blake and I had a son that son would inherit Flaws Farm and would also be half Bell.'

Sapphire signed, suddenly feeling intensely tired. Too much had happened too soon, and she couldn't take it all in.

'There was a 'phone call for you,' Mary added, 'an Alan. I said you'd ring back in the morning.'

Alan! Sapphire started guiltily. She had almost forgotten about him, and even more unforgivably she had forgotten about his car. The BMW was Alan's pride and joy and he wouldn't be too pleased to hear about her accident.

Tomorrow, she thought wearily as she climbed into bed. Tomorrow she would think about what had happened. Somehow she would have to convince her father that there was no chance of her and Blake getting together again. Selfish, Blake had called her. Was she? Her father had very little time left to live . . . six months or so . . . if she re-married Blake she would be giving her father a gift of happiness and peace of mind which surely meant more than her own pride and freedom? She wasn't seventeen any more, held in thrall by her adoration of Blake. She could handle him now as she hadn't been able to do then. A six-month marriage which would be quickly annulled—six months out of her life as payment for her father's peace of mind. What ought she to do?

# CHAPTER THREE

'GOOD morning.' Mary smiled a warm welcome at Sapphire as she walked into the kitchen. 'I was just about to bring you up a cup of tea.'

'Yes, I've overslept disgracefully,' Sapphire said wryly. Time was when she had thought nothing of getting up at half-past five with her father.

'You were exhausted, what with the accident and all. Oh that reminds me, Blake rang. He said not to panic about your luggage. He's bringing it over later when he comes to see your father. He calls in most days,' she added, plugging in the kettle. 'Your father looks forward to his visits, Blake keeps him up to date on how the farm's running.'

'May I go up and see my father?' Sapphire didn't want to think about Blake right now. He had occupied far too many of her thoughts already.

'Of course.' Again Mary smiled warmly. 'Would you like to have your breakfast first?'

'Just a cup of coffee will be fine,' Sapphire assured her. 'I'll go up now.' Before Blake arrives, she could have added, but didn't. Somehow, quite how she didn't know yet, but somehow she was going to have to find a way to explain to her father that she and Blake were parted for good. Even now she could still remember the agony of those first months in London, of having to come to terms with the truth about her marriage; about Blake's feelings for her. He had tolerated her because he wanted the farm. He had never loved her, never desired her and knowing that she had not seen these truths had diminished her self-esteem to such an extent that she had felt somehow as though everyone who saw her or spoke to her, must share Blake's opinion of her. The only way she could escape had been to shut herself off mentally from the rest of the world. There had been days when she felt like dying; days when she would have given anything simply not to wake up in the morning. But all that was past now, she reminded herself. She had overcome the trauma of Blake's rejection; had put the past and all that it held, safely behind her. But she couldn't forget it, she acknowledged. She still occasionally had those terrible dreams when she was forced to witness Blake making love to Miranda, when she had to endure the sound of their mocking laughter. How she had hated herself; *everything* about herself, from her height to the colour of her hair, torturing herself by imagining how many times Blake must have looked at her and put Miranda in her place. The only thing that surprised her was that Blake hadn't married. Those love letters she had found had obviously been meant for Miranda.

No-one, not even Alan knew how totally Blake had rejected her; physically, mentally and emotion-ally. And facing up to that knowledge had driven her almost to the point where she lost her sanity. But she had emerged from it all a stronger person. Being forced to come face to face with the truth had made her re-evaluate herself completely. No man would ever hurt her now as Blake had done. She allowed no-one to come close enough to her to do so.

If Alan did propose to her she would probably accept him. She wanted a family; she and Alan got on well. She would never feel for him what she had once felt for Blake, but then he would never look at her body, imagining it was another woman's, he would never lie to her, or look at her with contempt. Blake was an arrogant bastard, she thought bitterly as she stood at the top of the stairs, poised to enter her father's room. After what he'd done to her, she didn't know how he had the nerve to suggest what he had.

'Sapphire.' Her father greeted her happily, from his chair by the window. The cold March sunshine picked out with cruel clarity the signs of wasting on his face, and Sapphire was overwhelmed with a rush of emotion.

'Dad.' She went over to him, hugging him briefly and then turning away before he could see her tears.

'What's this?' Her eye was caught by the heavy, leather bound book on his lap. 'Don't tell me you're actually reading something, other than a farming magazine,' she teased. Never once during her childhood could she remember seeing her father reading. He had always been an active, physical man more at home in his fields than in the house. It saddened her unbearably to see him like this. Why . . . why? she cried bitterly inside.

'It's the family Bible.' His smile was as she had always remembered it. 'I haven't looked at it since your mother wrote your name inside.'

After her, her mother had not been able to have any more children. Had she too, like Sapphire, sensed how much her father felt the lack of a male heir? Had that in·part contributed to the break-up of their marriage? Questions she would never know the answer to now, Sapphire thought dully, watching her father open the Bible.

His hand trembled slightly as he touched the old paper. 'This Bible goes back as far as 1823, and it lists the birth of every Bell since.' He gave a faint sigh and closed it. 'I had hoped I might see the name of your's and Blake's child added to that list, but now. . .' He turned away dejectedly.

The words Sapphire had intended to say died unspoken. A tight knot of pain closed her throat. She reached out her hand touching her father's shoulder, 'Dad. . .' He turned to look at her, and as though the words were coming from another person, she heard herself saying shakily, 'Blake and I are going to try again. I . . . we . . . we talked about it last night.' She looked out of the window without seeing the view. Could her father honestly believe that what she was saying was true? Perhaps not, but he would accept it *as* the truth because he wanted to believe it was so desperately; just as she had once desperately wanted to believe that Blake loved her.

'You mean the two of you plan to re-marry?'

'We may. . .' What on earth had she got herself into? Panic clawed at her. She *couldn't* marry Blake again. But she had just told her father that she might.

'I suppose if we do it will make the local tongues wag.'

'Not necessarily. I don't think Blake's ever told anyone that you're divorced. Most people think you're still just separated.'

*Why* hadn't Blake told them? Could it be that he was using her father's illness as a lever to force her to fall in with his plans? He would buy the land from her, he had told her, but as her husband he wouldn't need to buy it, and being married to her need not stop him from finding love elsewhere. It hadn't stopped him before.

She *must* tell her father that she had changed her mind, she thought frantically, she must tell him now, before this thing went any further. Even now she couldn't believe that he was dying. He looked ill yes, but. . . But hadn't she learned the futility of·self-deception yet?

'Dad. . .'

'Isn't that the Land Rover?' he asked interrupting her. 'Blake must have arrived.'

'Dad, I. . .'

Both of them turned at the sound of firm footsteps on the stairs, Sapphire unconsciously blending into the shadows of the room as the door was thrust open and Blake strode in. Strangely his eyes met hers almost immediately, as though he had known by instinct where she was.

'Blake, Sapphire's just told me the good news.' If she hadn't known better she might almost have believed the look the two men exchanged was one of complicity, but even as the thought formed it was gone as her father turned his head and the harsh light through the window made her acutely conscious of his illness.

'Has she now.' For a man who spent so much of his live outdoors Blake moved exceptionally gracefully, and far too swiftly. She had no opportunity to avoid him as he walked towards her, lean brown fingers curling round her upper arm. 'And do you approve?'

'Need you ask?'

'Not really.'

'I'm sure you two have lots to discuss.' Sapphire snapped out the words bitterly, resenting their male unanimity. 'I must go and telephone Alan. He doesn't know about his car yet.'

'Or about us,' Blake reminded her, and while the look in his eyes might have been mistaken for one of possessive hunger Sapphire knew it was for her father's land rather than for her.

Outside the room she paused on the landing feeling acutely sick. Why had she said what she had to her father? Heaven only knew, she didn't want to be married to Blake again, no matter how temporarily. And yet her father had been pleased; pleased and relieved and surely for six months. . . Gnawing on her bottom lip she walked down to the kitchen and picked up the 'phone. Alan answered almost straight away.

'Where've you been?' he demanded. 'I expected you to ring hours ago.'

'I overslept I'm afraid. Alan, I had an accident last night and damaged your car.' She waited for his anxious spate of questions to finish before explaining what had happened. 'Don't let them touch the car—these country garages, God alone knows what sort of damage they might do. I'll come up and sort it out myself.'

'Alan no . . .' Sapphire started to say, but it was too late. 'Look I've got to go,' he told her before she could continue. 'I've got an appointment. I'll be up as soon as I can—possibly in three or four days.'

'Everything okay?' Mary nodded to the kettle. 'Fancy a drink? I normally take one up to your dad about now.'

'No ... no thanks, I think I'll go out for a walk.'

'Well, don't go too far,' Mary cautioned her. 'The temperature's dropping and we might well have snow. Snow in March isn't uncommon up here,' she reminded Sapphire dryly when she raised her eyebrows. 'Many a farmer's lost a crop of newborn lambs to the weather. *You* should know that.'

She needed time to think, Sapphire acknowledged as she walked into the cobbled yard and through into the field beyond; time to come to terms with what she herself had set in motion. She couldn't back out now; that much was plain. How could she have been so stupid as to allow Blake to manoeuvre her into this situation?

But it hadn't been Blake's logical, reasoned arguments that had won her over, it had been her father's pain. Guilt was a terrible burden to carry. She shivered suddenly, conscious that her jumper was no real protection against the bitter east wind, but she wasn't ready to go back to the farm yet. Going back meant facing Blake; and that was something she wasn't ready for yet. But she couldn't avoid him forever, and it was getting colder. Reluctantly she turned and re-traced her steps but when the farm came in sight and she saw that the Land Rover was still there, instead of heading for the house she walked towards the large attached barn.

In the days when Flaws Farm had possessed a small dairy herd this barn had housed them but now it was empty apart from the farmyard hens whose eggs were purely for domestic use. She had kept her pony, Baron, in here and had spent many hours grooming him, preparing him for local agricultural shows. They had even won a couple of prizes. Sighing faintly she wandered deeper into the barn stopping beside the ladder into the hayloft. As a teenager she had retreated up there to read and daydream. The sound of familiar footsteps made her body tense. Even without turning round to look she knew who it was.

'Something told me you might be in here.' Blake's voice was mocking. 'You always did use it as a bolt-hole.'

She turned round, trying to blank all emotion out of her features, while Blake studied her with a slow, insolent appraisal that set her teeth on edge. Inwardly shaking with nerves she refused to let him see how much his presence disturbed her. 'Finished?' she asked sourly. 'What exactly were you doing Blake?'

'Just wondering why you choose to wear such masculine clothes.' It was a blatantly challenging statement when coupled with his open study of her, and to her resentment she knew she had already been betrayed into a response to it, even if it was only in the increased stiffening of her muscles.

'These happen to be the only clothes I had this morning. No doubt you like your women dulcet and feminine, compliant and obedient, but I'm not like that Blake. Not any more.'

'No, you're not are you?' There was just a suspicion of laughter trailing in his voice, enough to make her stare back at him aggressively and refuse to give way as he came towards her. 'I also like them aroused and responsive—just as you are at the moment.'

The explosive denial trembling on her lips died as he reached forward, his thumb stroking along her throat to rest on the point where her pulse thudded betrayingly. 'Anger is a form of arousal isn't it?' he mocked lightly. 'And you *are* angry with me, aren't you Sapphire?'

'Not as much as I am with myself,' she told him curtly, drawing away. She wasn't going to give Blake any advantages this time. 'What I said to you last night still holds good, I don't want to marry you.'

'But you told your father that you did.'

'No. I told him that I *was* doing. I didn't mean to, but before I could retract you arrived.'

'And now?' He asked the question softly, watching her with eyes that gave nothing of his own feelings away.

'I'll have to go through with it—you know that. You saw how he reacted. Dear God, even now I can't believe that I'm going to lose him.' She paced distractedly, too strung up to give way to tears and yet needing to release some of her nervous energy.

'And what about the boyfriend—have you told *him*?'

'Alan? No . . . not yet, but he's coming up for his car soon, I'll tell him then.'

'How soon is soon?' Blake asked idly. 'Because in three days' time we'll be married.'

Three days! She looked up at him, not even attempting to hide her shock. 'So soon?'

Blake shrugged his shoulders and against her will Sapphire found herself comparing the masculine breadth of them to Alan's. Even dressed in faded jeans and an old woollen checked shirt Blake possessed a lithe masculine sensuality that

Alan would never have, for all his expensive tailoring Alan believed that appearances were important and Sapphire wouldn't have denied it, but Blake was one of those men who could afford to break life's rules. Angrily she pushed the thought away.

'Why wait?' Blake asked laconically. 'The sooner it's done the happier your father will be.'

'He told me that most people up here don't even know that we're divorced.' Her voice gave away her anger.

'Most people? No-one knows,' Blake corrected, blandly.

'Not even Miranda?'

His eyebrows rose, and Sapphire felt her face flush. What on earth had possessed her to bring Miranda's name up? She had no interest in Blake's love life—it was his own affair.

'Why mention Miranda in particular?' Blake mocked.

'Perhaps because it's the sort of thing a man would tell his mistress,' Sapphire came back curtly. 'After all you told her that our marriage . . . wasn't consummated.'

'How do you know that?' His voice had sharpened, hardened almost, but he had turned slightly away so that Sapphire couldn't see his expression, but she had definitely caught him off guard. Good, she thought, watching him. Obviously he didn't know what Miranda had said to her.

'Because she told me.' She shrugged disdainfully as he turned round and stared at her with cold hard, golden eyes. 'It was at the same time as she told me about the weekend the two of you spent in the Cotswolds actually.' Giving him a cold smile she marched past, heading for the barn door. It would do him good to realise that she wasn't as naive as he had always believed, but just as she drew level with the door his arm snaked out, his fingers curling painfully round her wrist.

'And that, of course, was why you left me?'

'It was *one* of the reasons—there were others.' It was her turn to shrug dismissively. 'But none of that matters now, I merely asked about Miranda so that I could be prepared for any situation that might arise.'

'She doesn't know we're divorced,' Blake told her. 'After my experiences with you I decided I preferred the life of a bachelor.'

'And having a wife tucked away in the background made it all a lot simpler. Yes I can see that. Let me go Blake, I want to go back to the house.'

'Isn't there something you've forgotten?'

She frowned, glancing uncertainly at him.

'Loving partners normally part with a kiss,' he told her mockingly.

'Maybe *they* do, but there's nothing "loving" about our relationship,' Sapphire snapped. 'You didn't want to kiss me four years ago Blake, I can hardly see why you would want to now.'

'No? Perhaps I want to see how much your London lover has taught you.' His head bent towards her and Sapphire immediately tensed trying to pull away, but Blake was still gripping her wrist. His free arm fastened round her, his hand on the small of her back forcing her against him.

A mixture of sensations raced through her as the

heat of his body imposed itself against her; anger; tension, but most of all a resurgence of a familiar vulnerability she thought she had long ago overcome. The knowledge that she hadn't, blinded her to everything else. She trembled against Blake, closing her eyes to blot out his mocking smile trying to convince herself that she was wrong; that the panic storming through her came from anger and not from fear.

But what was it she feared? Not Blake. No, herself, she admitted sensing the downward descent of his mouth, and twisting away to avoid it. Not Blake, but herself, her vulnerability towards him; her. . .

His mouth brushed hers and she tensed. 'Is that *all* you've learned? Not very good,' Blake drawled, as his mouth moved from her lips to her ear. His tongue tip explored the delicate shaping of her ear and panic exploded inside her. She mustn't let him do this to her, she. . . Another moment and he would be kissing her again and this time. . . No she wouldn't let him see that he could evoke a response from her . . . a response that was really surely nothing more than a conditioned echo of the old feeling she had had for him?

His mouth was feathering across her skin towards her lips. Taking her courage in both hands, Sapphire turned to meet it, willing herself to relax. She had dated several men in London before settling for Alan, and surely she had learned enough technique from them to show Blake that she wasn't a frightened seventeen-year-old any more.

Forcing herself to ignore the screaming protest of her nerves Sapphire opened her mouth inviting his deeper invasion, teasing him with the tip of her tongue. She actually felt the sudden tension in his muscles, the quickly controlled start of surprise, but her brief advantage was lost as Blake's arms tightened around her, his mouth taking what she had so recklessly offered, his lips harshly possessive against hers.

If only he had kissed her like this when she was seventeen. The thought surfaced through a whirling jet-stream of jumbled emotions, fiercely clamped down as soon as she acknowledged it, and pushed Blake away.

He let her go, watching her with unblinking gold eyes. Almost as though he willed her to do it, Sapphire ran her tongue over the swollen contours of her mouth. 'Well, well... That was quite something.'

His mouth was wry where she had expected it to be triumphant, because she couldn't deny to herself that there had been a moment in his arms when she had forgotten everything that lay between them and she had responded to him in a way she had never responded to any other man, but if anything he looked angry.

'He's obviously taught you well.' The comment bordered on the harshly accusatory and coming from anyone else Sapphire would have instantly taken exception to it, but sensing that for some reason she had got under his skin she responded lightly. 'And very extensively, I'm not seventeen any more Blake.'

'No, you're not are you,' he agreed, 'so don't expect me to handle you with kid gloves will you?'

'I don't expect you to "handle" me at all Blake—that's part of our agreement—remember?'

'Oh I think I'll be able to, now, but will you?'

He turned on his heel and left before she could speak, and although Sapphire told herself it was relief that made her shake so much that she had to lean against the stairs, in reality she knew that her emotions were far more complex than that.

What had she let herself in for agreeing to re-marry Blake? She had always known he must despise her, but the anger she had just seen, so savage and bitter, that was something she hadn't guessed at. He must want Flaws Farm very badly, she thought bleakly as she made her way on shaky legs back to the house.

'Blake gone?' her father asked, when she walked into his room. Already he looked much better, and Sapphire realised with an aching pang how much her marriage to Blake meant to him.

'Yes.' She couldn't inject any enthusiasm into her voice. 'Never mind.' Her father obviously mistook the reason for her listlessness. 'You'll be seeing him tonight. He's taking you out to celebrate—at least that's what he said to me.'

To celebrate! Sapphire grimaced, inwardly resenting the fact that Blake hadn't said anything to her about going out. Had he done so, she would have refused.

'I can't tell you how much it means to me that the pair of you are getting back together again,' her father said quietly. 'He's a fine man Sapphire. A good strong man, the sort of man you need.'

She made her escape from the room without giving any response, half-blinded by the weak tears threatening to obscure her vision. In her own room she opened the suitcase Blake must have brought up. Even to think of him walking into her room made prickles of antagonism run down her spine. How on earth was she going to live with him for six months when she hated him so much?

She hadn't brought much with her, certainly nothing she could go out in to 'celebrate'—and nothing she could wear to get married in. Fresh tears blurred her eyes as she remembered the dress she had worn the first time they were married. Stupid sentimentality, she derided herself; their wedding had just been another part of Blake's elaborate charade, just like the half-reverent, almost worshipping kiss he had given her just outside the church doors. Sighing, Sapphire hung up her clothes. She would wear the plain black wool dress she had brought; it was a perfect foil for her colouring and a perfect accompaniment for her mood; Alan had always liked her in it.

Alan! She hadn't told him yet about Blake. She gnawed on her lip uncertain as to whether to ring him, or wait until he came up. She was sure he would understand; Alan was always logical and reasonable. For the first time it struck her just what she had committed herself to. She would have to give up her job; her flat; her London life; everything she had fought so hard for when she left Blake. But surely it was a small price to pay for her father's peace of mind? But say Alan did not accept her decision. She would not only have lost her job, she would have lost a good friend and potential lover as well. She couldn't understand why the knowledge should cause her so little pain. Perhaps the agony of meeting Blake again; of being forced to remember how much he had hurt her had anaesthetised her against other, lesser hurts. Sighing she finished unpacking and went downstairs. One thing she did remember about farm life was that there was always work to be done and work, as she had learned in London, was a very effective panacea.

'I'm just going down to the village to do some shopping and pick up your father's prescription,' Mary told her when Sapphire asked if there was anything she could do. 'Want to come with me?'

'No, I'll stay here if you don't mind.' Sapphire frowned. 'I would have thought the doctor would call every day, in view of Dad's illness.'

Mary eyed her sympathetically. 'There's really no point now,' she said gently. 'Are you sure you won't come with me?'

'No . . . no thanks.'

'Well I'll be on my way then. I want to call at the butchers, your father loves shepherd's pie and I thought I'd make one for him tonight.'

How could Mary be so matter of fact, Sapphire wondered, watching the other woman driving away, but then as a nurse she would be used to death; she would have learned to accept the inevitable. As *she* had not, Sapphire acknowledged, but then she had had so little time to come to terms with the reality of her father's condition. Blake had broken the news to her almost brutally. The way he did everything. Unable to settle to anything she went up to her father's room, but he was asleep. Not wanting to disturb his rest she left again. What on earth could she do with herself? Perhaps she ought to have gone with Mary. She wandered aimlessly into the yard, bending to pet the sheepdog that suddenly emerged from the field. Tam, the shepherd followed close behind, a smile splitting his weather-seamed face as he recognised her. Tam had been her father's shepherd for as long as she could remember. He had seemed old to her when she was a child, and she wondered how old he was. He was one of a dying breed; a man who preferred the solitude of the hills, spending most of the summer in his small cottage watching over his flocks. The rich acres of farmland in the valley were given over to crops now, but her father still maintained his flock of sheep on his hill pastures.

'Weather's going to turn bad,' Tam told her laconically, 'Ought to get the sheep down off the hills, especially the ewes. Suppose I'd better get over to Sefton and see Blake,' he added morosely, whistling to his dog.

Watching them go Sapphire realised the extent of Blake's influence on Flaws Farm. No wonder he didn't want to lose the land. He probably looked on it as his own already. She had wanted to protest to Tam that her father was the one to ask about the sheep, but instinctively she had known that Tam wouldn't have understood. What she considered to be Blake's interference would be taken as good neighbourliness by the old shepherd.

As she walked back into the kitchen the 'phone was ringing, and she answered it automatically.

'Sapphire, is that you?'

'Yes, Blake.'

'I forgot to mention it this morning, but I'll be round about seven-thirty tonight to take you out to dinner, and before you say anything, I didn't plan it. It was your father who mentioned it; he seemed to think some sort of celebration was in order, and I think he's probably right. If we're seen dining together, it won't come as too much of a surprise to people when they know we're back together.'

'Surprise? Don't you mean shock?' Sapphire gritted into the receiver. 'Especially where your female friends are concerned Blake.'

'If I didn't know better I might almost believe that you're jealous.'

'Funny,' Sapphire snapped back. 'I never realised you had such a powerful imagination. I must go now Blake,' she lied, 'Dad's calling me.'

'See you tonight.'

She hung up quickly leaving her staring at the black receiver. How could her life have changed so radically and so fast. One moment she had been looking forward to her holiday with Alan; to their relationship perhaps deepening from friendship into marriage, convinced that she had laid the ghosts in her past, and now, so swiftly that she could scarcely comprehend even now how it had happened, her life had somehow become entangled with Blake's again, but this time she was older and wiser. She had been burned once—so badly that there was no way she was ever going to approach the fire again.

But fire has a way of luring its victims, she acknowledged, bitterly, just like love.

# CHAPTER FOUR

SHE was ready when Blake arrived. He gave her black-clad body a cursory examination as he stepped into the kitchen and then drawled, 'Mourning, Sapphire?'

'It was the only dress I had with me.'

Again those golden eyes studied her body, but this time there was no mocking warmth to light their amber depths as Blake said coolly, 'You should have told me, I've still got a wardrobe-full of your things up at the house, and by the looks of you you could still get into them.'

He made it sound more of an insult than a compliment, and Sapphire turned away so that he wouldn't see the quick flush of colour warming her skin. Why was it that Blake seemed to possess this ability to put her in the wrong, even when she wasn't?

'If you're ready I think we'd better be on our way. I've booked our table for eight.' He glanced at his watch, the brief glimpse she had of his dark sinewy wrist doing strange things to Sapphire's stomach. She recognised the sensation immediately, and it gave her a sickening jolt. She had thought she was long past the stage of experiencing sexual appreciation of something as mundane as a male arm. As a teenager, the merest glimpse of Blake in the distance had been enough to start her stomach churning with excitement but that was all behind her now. Shrugging aside her feelings as an

63

echo of the past she picked up her coat and
followed Blake to the door.

To her surprise he hadn't brought the
Land Rover but was driving a sleek black BMW.
Some of her surprise must have communicated
itself to Blake because he glanced at her
sardonically, his eyebrows raised as he waited for
her to join him, opening the door for her as she
reached the car. But then he always had had that
air of masculine sophistication, a rare commodity
in the Borders where most of the boys she had
grown up with thought only of their land and
their stock. But she had lived in London for
long enough not to be overawed by Blake any
longer, surely? Alan was always meticulous about
handing her into his car, but his fingers beneath
her elbow didn't provoke the same jolting,
lightning bolt of sensation that Blake's did, her
senses told her treacherously.

Ridiculous to feel so affected by such casual
contact—no doubt she was over-reacting. She had
had to guard herself against thinking about Blake
for so long that she was almost hyper-sensitive to
him. Yes, that must be the explanation Sapphire
decided as Blake set the car in motion. Of course
she was wound-up and tense, who wouldn't be-
after learning that their father was close to death
and that the one thing he wanted in life was the
one thing she least desired. Marriage to Blake! She
glanced covertly at his profile. He was concentrating on the road, his lips set in a hard line. Reaction
suddenly shivered through her. What had she
committed herself to? Despite the warmth from
the car's heaters she felt chilled, and yet her face
seemed to be burning. She *couldn't* go through

with it. Her father would understand. She must talk to Blake, she. . .

'If you're having second thoughts, forget them, I'm not letting you back out now Sapphire.' The coldly harsh words cut through her anguished thoughts like a whiplash. How had he known what she was thinking? He was right about one thing though, it was too late to back out now. Her father wanted their reconciliation too desperately.

'Where are we going?' She asked the question more to dispel the tense atmosphere inside the car than because she really wanted to know.

'Haroldgate,' Blake told her briefly.

She only just managed to catch back her protest. Haroldgate was a small village nestling in one of the valleys and as far as she knew it possessed only one restaurant. Blake had taken her there the evening he had proposed to her. She had been so thrilled by his invitation. 'The Barn' at Haroldgate was the most sophisticated eating place in the area and she had never been before. She could vividly recall how impressed she had been by her surroundings, and how tense. Shaking herself mentally she tried to appear unconcerned. 'The Barn' might have seemed the very zenith of sophistication to an awkward seventeen-year-old who had never been anywhere, but it could hardly compare with some of the restaurants Alan had taken her to. Alan was something of a gourmet and discovering new eating places was one of his hobbies. He also liked to be seen in the right places, unlike Blake who had little concern for appearances or being seen to do the 'right thing', Sapphire acknowledged. Neither did Blake make a sacred ritual out of eating as Alan did. Frowning

Sapphire tried to dispel the vague feeling that somehow she was being disloyal to Alan by comparing him with Blake. They were two completely different men who could not be compared, and of the two. . .

'We're here.'

The curt comment broke across her thoughts. Blake stopped the car and in the darkness Sapphire felt him studying her. Her muscles tensed automatically and defensively, although she couldn't have said why.

'I won't have you thinking about him while you're with me,' he told her tersely. 'I won't have it Sapphire, do you understand?'

She was far too taken aback by the tone of his voice to make any immediate comment. How had Blake known she was thinking about Alan? And why should he object? His attitude fanned the embers of resentment that had been burning in her all day.

'You don't own my thoughts Blake,' she told him mockingly, 'and if I choose to think about the man I love that's my affair. You can't stop me.'

'You think not?'

The headlights from another car turning into the carpark illuminated the interior of the BMW briefly and Sapphire was struck by the white tension of Blake's face. Did getting her father's land mean so very much to him? Fear feathered lightly along her spine.

'Don't push me too hard Sapphire,' he warned, as he unfastened his seat belt. 'I *am* only human.'

'You could have fooled me.' She muttered the words flippantly beneath her breath, but he caught them, leaning across to grasp her forearms while she was still fastened into her seat.

'Could I? Then perhaps this will convince you just how human I can be, and not to rely too heavily on your own judgment.' The words carried a thread of bitterness Sapphire couldn't decipher but there was nothing cryptic about the pressure of Blake's mouth against her own, hard and determined as his hands pressed her back into her seat.

It was a kiss of anger and bitterness, even she could recognise that, and yet it called out to something deep inside her; some shadowing of pain she hadn't known still existed and which suddenly became a fierce ache, leaping to meet and respond to the anger she could feel inside Blake.

The result was a devastation of her senses; a complete reversal of everything she had ever thought about herself and her own sexuality; her physical response to Blake so intense and overwhelming that it succeeded in blocking everything else out.

Without her being aware of how it had happened her arms were round his neck, her fingers stroking the thick softness of his hair, and yet it was pain she wanted him to feel—not pleasure, and it was anger she wanted to show him as she returned the fierce intensity of his kiss, and not love.

'You want me.' It was Blake's thick utterance of the words that brought her back to reality. That, and her own bitter mental acknowledgment that somehow he had aroused her, had touched a deep core of need inside her that none of Alan's gentle caresses had ever revealed.

'I *want* Alan,' she lied curtly, 'but since he's not here. . .'

Blake withdrew from her immediately as she had known he would. His pride would never allow him to be a substitute for someone else, but what did surprise Sapphire was that he believed her. But then he could not, as she could, compare her reaction to him with her reaction to Alan. She did love Alan. What she had just experienced in Blake's arms; that bitter tension that had made her body ache and her eyes sting with suppressed tears was just something left over from the past, that was all.

'Are we going to eat, or do you want to spend the rest of the evening in the car?'

The harsh words rasped over too-sensitive nerves. Sapphire pushed Blake's hand away as he reached out to help her with her seat belt, and knew by the tension in his body that she had annoyed him. How on earth were they supposed to live together, supposedly as man and wife, preserving the fiction that they had been reconciled when they reacted so explosively to one another? If only she hadn't made that stupid comment to her father, but he had looked so ill . . . and he had been so pleased, almost as though she had given him a reason to go on fighting to live. And so she had.

The restaurant was just as attractive as she remembered. The old barn had been sensitively restored, and while the atmosphere was not one of luxurious glamour there was something about it that Sapphire found more appealing than any of Alan's favourite haunts.

The Head Waiter recognised Blake immediately and they were swiftly shown to a table for two.

The restaurant wasn't a large one, the proprietors preferring not to expand and risk losing their excellent reputation. As they studied their menus, Sapphire glanced covertly round the room, wondering if she would recognise any of their fellow diners. A couple sat at one table talking and Sapphire stiffened as she recognised Miranda.

Four years ago this woman had been her husband's mistress, and she was still as beautiful as ever Sapphire recognised, and still obviously bemusing the opposite sex if her table companion's expression was anything to go by. Just as Sapphire was about to look away, she raised her head, her eyes narrowing as they met Sapphire's. Conscious that she was staring Sapphire tried to look away and found that she could not. A familiar nausea started to well up inside her, and she fought it down. She was over all that now. She wasn't going to let it happen again, and yet against her will her mind kept on relaying to her mental images of Blake and Miranda together, of Blake's long-legged, narrow-hipped body making love to Miranda's, in all the ways it had never made love to hers. The menu dropped from her fingers as she tried to stem the flood of images. She was over this; she had been over it for years. . . She knew now that most of her anguish sprang not from the fact that Blake and Miranda had been lovers, but rather from the knowledge that he had desired Miranda as intensely as he had not desired her. If Blake had made love to her she would not have suffered this torment; she and Miranda would have met as equals; as women, not as adult and child.

'Sapphire?'

She realised that Blake was talking to her; watching her, and her face closed up. How much had she already given away? She glanced desperately at him but he was looking at Miranda.

Sapphire followed his look, tensing as she saw the other couple stand up and head towards them.

'Blake.' Miranda's companion held out his hand to Blake, who rose to shake it, but it was at Sapphire that he looked.

'Sapphire.' Miranda's greeting to her was coolly mocking. 'You've barely changed.'

The words were designed to hurt, but Sapphire chose to turn the barb back on its sender. 'In four years?' she murmured, 'How flattering. I must confess I barely recognised you.'

A blatant lie, but she could always use it to explain away her too lengthy scrutiny of the other woman. And she *had* aged, Sapphire noted now. Although she was still very beautiful, she was now more obviously a woman well into her thirties. She must be a year or two older than Blake. Her companion was in his forties, and although he looked pleasant enough, physically he could not compare with Blake.

'Sapphire, let me introduce you to Miranda's husband.' Blake's words were a shock. Her husband? Her eyes went automatically to Miranda's ring hand where a huge diamond solitaire nestled against an obviously new wedding ring.

'Jim is the Senior Registrar at Hexham General.' Blake told her. 'He and Miranda got married a couple of months ago.'

'What brings you back up here Sapphire?' Miranda questioned her.

She started to reply but Blake beat her to it, drawing her hand through his arm, pulling her into the warmth of his side as he said calmly, 'We've decided to give our marriage another try.'

'A rather sudden decision surely?' Icy blue eyes swept over Sapphire, Miranda's tone intimating disbelief.

'Not really.' Blake's voice was as smooth as silk and for the first time, Sapphire was grateful for his ability to conceal the truth. 'It's been on the cards for some time. Sapphire just took a bit of convincing that's all.' His possessive smile was meant to indicate that he considered himself lucky to get her back, but Sapphire wasn't deceived for one moment. There was a subtle tension between Blake and Miranda which suggested to Sapphire that getting her father's land wasn't the sole reason Blake wanted a 'reconciliation'. Had Miranda married to spite Blake? To prove to him that if he didn't want marriage then other men did, and was he now retaliating by announcing their reconciliation? Even worse, had he known that Miranda and Jim would be here tonight?

'Well congratulations to you both.' Jim smiled warmly at them, and took Miranda's arm.

'Yes indeed, better luck this time.' The words were innocuous enough but Sapphire wasn't deceived. She read the venom behind them, and knew that Blake had too.

When the other couple had gone she sat down and picked up her menu. Eating was the last thing she felt like but she was determined not to let Blake see how much seeing Miranda again had disturbed her.

'I'm sorry about that.' His terse apology

stunned her and Sapphire looked up at him. There were deep grooves of tension running from his nose to his mouth. 'I didn't know they'd be here.'

Sapphire shrugged dismissively, 'It doesn't matter. I didn't realise Miranda was married.'

'Why should you?' Blake was curt and abrupt, 'I didn't realise that. . .' He broke off, his mouth grim. 'Look I don't think coming out tonight was such a good idea. Let's leave shall we? I don't think either of us is in the mood for the type of celebration your father had in mind.'

'But what about Miranda?' Sapphire objected. 'If we leave now, she'll never believe what you said about us being reconciled.'

Blake shrugged, standing up to come round and hold her chair as she got to her feet. 'Does it matter what she thinks?' He sounded tense. 'As a matter of fact, what she probably will think is that we've decided we'd rather be making love than eating.'

'Because that's what you'd be doing if you were with her?' The words were out before Sapphire could stop them. 'Aren't you forgetting something,' she added bitterly. 'Miranda knows exactly how undesirable you find me. You told her—remember?'

'I told her nothing,' Blake grated back. 'She tricked that admission out of you, but if it worries you so much I can take you back to Sefton House right now and make you my wife in every sense of the word.'

'Thanks, but no thanks.' Somehow she managed to inject just the right amount of scathing indifference into her voice, but it was hard not to react to his words; not to shiver beneath the rough velvet urgency of his voice, nor to turn to him in blind acceptance of the pleasure it promised, but instead to simply precede him and walk out of the restaurant as calmly as though she were completely unaffected by his words.

Were he and Miranda still lovers? Somehow Sapphire didn't think so; there hadn't been the complicity between them she would have expected had they been. Instead there had been something almost approaching antagonism.

They drove back along the road they had come in a silence which remained unbroken until Sapphire realised that Blake had taken the turning for his own house instead of carrying on to her father's farm.

'Don't worry, I'm not kidnapping you,' he told her sardonically as she turned to him in protest. 'It's barely ten o'clock. If I take you home now your father will think there's something wrong.'

'And he'd be right.' Sapphire muttered the words under her breath but Blake heard them.

'This isn't easy for me either you know,' he told her grittily, 'but why should I expect you to realise that? You were never any good at seeing the other person's point of view.'

'Meaning what exactly?' The anger that had been burning inside her all evening burst into destructive flames. 'That I should have played the "understanding" wife and turned a blind eye to your affair?'

Light spilled out into the cobbled courtyard as Blake pulled up outside his house. He stopped the engine and Sapphire saw him tense almost as though he were bracing himself to do something.

'Sapphire, look, my "affair" as you call it never. . .'

'I don't want to hear about it.' She cut across him quickly. She didn't want to exhume the past; it was far too painful. Talking about his relationship with Miranda forced her to remember how intensely she had once longed to have those brown hands touching her body, exploring its contours, giving her the pleasure her feverishly infatuated senses had told her she could find in his arms. 'It's over Blake,' she reminded him determinedly. 'We're two different people now.'

'If you say so.' He unfastened his seat belt and opened his door. 'Hungry?'

Sapphire shook her head.

'Come inside and have a cup of coffee then, I've got a mare waiting to foal in the barn, I'll check up on her and then I'll take you home.'

He didn't invite her to go with him, and Sapphire stood forlornly in the immaculate kitchen of Sefton House listening to the sound of his footsteps dying away as he crossed the yard and entered the large barn.

Once she had been part of this world, and he would have thought nothing of inviting her to join him. Together they had shared the miracle of birth on many occasions in the past, but now she was deliberately being excluded. It baffled Sapphire that the anger she sensed churning inside him should be directed against her. Blake had no rational reason for being angry with her: had someone asked her she would have said he was incapable of feeling any emotional response towards her whatsoever.

More to keep herself occupied than because she wanted any she started to make some coffee. The kitchen was immaculate, but somehow impersonal. Presumably he had his own reasons for not replacing his aunt with a housekeeper. At least that was one complication she wouldn't have to face this time. Sarah Sefton had never made any secret of the fact that she considered her far too young for Blake. She had disapproved of her right from the very start, Sapphire mused, watching the aromatic dark-brown liquid filter down into the jug, and breathing in the heavenly smell.

'That smells good.' She hadn't heard Blake return, and she swung round tensely, trying to mask her automatic reaction to him by asking after the mare.

'She's fine. This will be her third foal, and we don't anticipate any problems, but like any other female she needs the reassurance of knowing someone cares.'

He said the words carelessly but the look in his eyes was far from casual as he added softly, 'Does Alan let you know he cares Sapphire?'

'All the time.' She managed a cool smile, 'I've made us some coffee, I hope your "help" won't mind my rummaging in her cupboards.'

'I'm sure she won't,' Blake responded equally blandly, 'but when my aunt retired I decided I preferred having the place to myself. A woman comes up from the village to clean; apart from that I'm self-sufficient.' He saw the assessing glance Sapphire slid over the immaculate kitchen, and said softly, 'I don't spend enough time here to make it untidy. In fact recently I've been eating as many meals at Flaws as I have here.'

'Yes, I haven't thanked you yet for taking on the responsibility for the farm.'

He smiled sardonically at her, as though he knew just how hard she had found it to mutter the words.

'That's what neighbours are for. Your father would have done the same thing for me had our positions been reversed.' He pulled off his jacket, dropping it carelessly on to the table, and then checking and picking it up again. 'One special licence,' he told her withdrawing a piece of paper from an inner pocket. 'Special dispensation from the Bishop of Hawick. I went to see him today.'

'So we'll be married. . .'

'The day after tomorrow,' Blake told her. 'In Hexham, everything's arranged, the vicar. . .'

'A Church wedding?' Sapphire's head came up, her forehead creased in a frown. Somehow she had expected the ceremony to be conducted in the more mundane surroundings of a registry office.

'It seemed less public,' Blake told her carelessly. 'Have you told your boyfriend yet?'

Sapphire shook her head. 'No, but he's coming up for his car, I'll tell him then, it isn't the sort of news I could break over the 'phone.'

'He's going to get quite a shock.'

Why should she think she heard satisfaction beneath the cool words? 'It's only for a few months, once I've explained the situation to him. . .'

'He'll wait for you?' Blake supplied sardonically, 'Get your coat on and I'll take you back to Flaws, I've got to be up early in the morning. We've got to get the sheep down off the high pastures, the weather's about to change.'

They didn't speak again until Blake stopped his car outside the back door to Flaws Farm. For a moment as she unfastened her seat belt Sapphire panicked. What if he should try to kiss her again?

But apart from opening her door for her Blake didn't attempt to touch her. He walked with her across the cobbled yard, both of them stopping by the door.

'I won't see you tomorrow,' he told her, 'but I'll be round the morning after. Our appointment with the Vicar is for eleven o'clock, so I'll pick you up at ten.' Giving her a brief nod he turned away and walked back to the car. He had reversed out of the yard before Sapphire had managed to pull herself together sufficiently to open the back door.

What was the matter with her, she chided herself as she prepared for bed. Surely she hadn't wanted him to kiss her? Of course she hadn't. So why this curiously flat feeling; this niggly ache in her body that was all too dangerously familiar? Stop it, she cautioned herself as she slid into the cold bed. Stop thinking about him.

It was easier said than done, especially with twenty-four empty hours stretching ahead of her with nothing to fill them other than doubts about the wisdom of marrying Blake for a second time, no matter how altruistic the reasons.

She helped Mary with her chores, and spent the afternoon outdoors, but although she kept her hands busy she couldn't occupy her mind. Her father noticed her tension when she went to sit with him.

'Worrying about tomorrow?' he asked sympathetically, closing the book he had been reading.

'Blake is a fine man Sapphire,' he told her gently, 'I've always thought so. In fact in many ways I blame myself for the break-up of your marriage.'

When she started to protest he lifted his hand. 'I wanted you to marry Blake, even though he thought you were too young. He wanted to wait, but. . .'

'But you dangled the bait of this farm,' Sapphire interrupted briefly, 'and he couldn't resist it.' She bit her lip as she realised how cold and unloverlike her voice sounded. Deliberately trying to soften it, she added, 'But that's all over now, we're making a completely fresh start. We're both older and wiser.'

She couldn't bear to look at her father. His fragility still had the power to shock her, but even so her mind refused to accept that soon he would be gone from her.

Downstairs she found Mary busily baking. 'Blake just rang to confirm that he'll pick you up at ten tomorrow,' she said cheerfully. 'Having a day out?'

Her curiosity was only natural and Sapphire forced a smile. 'Yes . . . In fact you might as well know Mary, that Blake and I are going to give our marriage another try.' She couldn't look at the other woman. 'I suppose it took something like my father's . . . illness to show us both how we really felt.' That at least was true, even if Mary was hardly likely to interpret her words correctly. The other woman's face softened.

'Yes I know what you mean,' she agreed. 'So you'll be moving to Sefton House.'

'Yes.' Sapphire swallowed nervously. So far she hadn't let herself think about the intimacy of living in such close proximity to Blake. No matter how non-sexual their relationship was going to be; the thought made her stomach tense and knot in anxious apprehension. What was she frightened of for goodness sake? Not Blake. She already knew that he felt absolutely no desire for her, but last night he had talked about taking her home with him and making her truly his wife. Sapphire shivered. Those had been words; nothing more; words designed to keep her tense and apprehensive; and in her place. No, she had nothing to fear from Blake. Or from herself? Of course not. She had suffered the agony of loving him once, it was hardly likely to happen again.

# CHAPTER FIVE

SHE and Blake were husband and wife again; Sapphire could hardly believe it. She glanced down at the gold band encircling her finger. It was the same ring that Blake had given her once before. She had been stunned when she saw it. Somehow she had never imagined Blake keeping it, never mind giving it back to her.

'It saved the bother of buying a new one,' he told her sardonically correctly following her chain of thought. He glanced at his watch flicking back his cuff in a manner that was achingly familiar. It shocked her that her mind should have stored and retained so many minute details about him. 'We'd better get back. I take it you don't want to go out and celebrate our reunion?'

'Can you think of any reason why I should?' Her voice was as cool as his, her eyes locking with the gold blaze that glittered over her too pale face. 'I've married you for one reason and one reason only Blake—my father's peace of mind, and just as soon as . . .' she gulped back the stinging tears that suddenly formed, '. . . just as soon as that reason no longer exists our marriage will be over.'

The silence that filled the car on the way back to the valley was not a comfortable one. Sapphire sat back in her seat, her head on the headrest, her face turned dismissively towards the window, and yet despite her determination to ignore Blake, she was acutely aware of him. Every time she closed her

eyes she saw his face; pictured the lean strength of
his hands on the steering wheel. For a moment,
unnervingly she even pictured those hands against
her skin, touching; stroking... Stop it, she
warned herself. Dear God what was happening to
her? Blake no longer possessed the power to affect
her in that way. She was completely over him and
the childish infatuation she had once had for him.

'We'll drive to Flaws Farm and pick up your
things first.' His cool voice broke into her
thoughts. 'I've got the vet coming out this
afternoon to look at the mare, so we won't linger.'

'The fact that we're married doesn't mean we
have to do everything together,' Sapphire pointed
out tartly, not liking the way he was taking
control. 'I can easily drive myself over to Flaws. In
fact,' she turned in her seat to look determinedly
at Blake, 'in view of my father's illness and the fact
that no-one knows that we've been divorced, I
think it would be quite acceptable for me to
remain at Flaws...'

'Maybe it would,' Blake agreed sardonically, 'if
your daughterly devotion wasn't a bit late in
coming, and I was prepared to agree. Oh no,
Sapphire,' he told her softly, 'I want you where I
can keep an eye on you. You're not running out
on me twice. Besides,' he added, 'if you don't come
back to Sefton House with me, your father's going
to get suspicious.'

His last words were undeniably true. Biting
down hard on her lip to prevent her vexation from
showing Sapphire turned back to stare out of her
window, relieved when she saw the familiar turn-
off for Flaws Valley. This tension between herself
and Blake wasn't something she remembered from

the past. Of course, she had always been aware of him; but surely never like this, with a nerve-rasping intensity that made her muscles ache from the strain she was imposing on them.

'You're back early.' Mary greeted them without any surprise, but of course as far as she was concerned she and Blake had merely had a morning out together. 'Are you staying for lunch?' Her question was addressed to Blake, but his arm tethered Sapphire to his side when she would have slipped out of the room. 'We haven't got time, I've got the vet coming this afternoon.' He released Sapphire to smile down at her, his eyes so warm and golden that his glance was like basking in the heat of the sun. 'I'll go up and see your father while you pack.'

He was gone before Sapphire could speak, leaving her to face Mary's raised eyebrows and expectant expression. Sapphire couldn't face her. 'I . . . I'm going back with Blake,' she said hesitantly, 'I . . . we. . . .'

'Your father will be pleased,' Mary assured her coming to her rescue. 'Look,' she added, 'why don't I make some coffee and then come upstairs and give you a hand with your packing. Not that you brought a lot with you.'

Sensing the speculation behind her words Sapphire said shakily. 'N . . . I had no idea then that Blake. . .'

'Still loved you?'

The words surprised her into a tense stillness, but mercifully Mary was too busily engaged in making the coffee to notice her startled response. It had been on the tip of her tongue to blurt out that Blake had never loved her, but fortunately she had caught the words back just in time.

It was over an hour before they were finally able to leave. Her father had been so pleased by their news. Sighing Sapphire tried to settle herself in the car, telling herself that her sacrifice must surely have been made worthwhile by her father's pleasure.

'I'm going to have to leave you to find your own way about,' Blake told her tensely when he stopped the car in his own farmyard. 'I want to have a word with the shepherd before the vet arrives. You'll have to make yourself up a bed I'm afraid—unless of course you prefer to share mine.' The last words were accompanied by a cynical smile.

'Hardly,' Sapphire told him crisply, 'I'm no masochist, Blake; nor am I a naive seventeen-year-old any longer.'

'No,' he agreed bitterly, and for a moment Sapphire wondered at the deeply intense timbre of his voice and the drawn expression tensing his face, before dismissing her impressions as false ones and berating herself for allowing her imagination to work overtime. Blake had no reason to feel bitter—unlike her.

As she let herself into the kitchen she was struck by the fact that despite, or perhaps because of its gleaming appearance the room seemed oddly sterile; not like a home at all. The mellow wooden cabinets which should have imparted a warm glow, looked too much like a glossy, cold advertisement; there were no warm, baking smells to tantalise or tempt. Blake's aunt had made her own bread, she remembered with unexpected nostalgia, and she remembered this kitchen best filled with its warmly fragrant scent. Of course if the smell of freshly baked bread was all it took to bring the place alive, she was more than capable of supplying that herself. Her culinary efforts so much despised by Blake's aunt had improved rapidly in the security of her own small home. Alan often asked her to cook for important clients and among their circle of friends she had quite a reputation as a first-rate hostess. Alan approved of her domestic talents; Alan! Her body tensed. What was he going to say when he heard about all this? She could well lose him. Why was she not more concerned at the prospect; after all she had been planning to marry him? Pushing aside the thought she opened the kitchen door and stepped into the square parquet-floored hall.

On the plate rack encircling the hall were the plates she remembered from the early days of her marriage, the smooth cream walls otherwise clean and bare. The parquet floor glistened in the bright March sunshine, but the table was empty of its customary bowl of flowers and she found she missed their bright splash of colour. Whatever her other faults Blake's aunt had been a first rate housewife, and she had obviously learned something from her Sapphire thought wryly, noticing the thin film of dust beginning to form on the hall table. The rich reds and blues of the traditional stair carpet carried her eye upwards. The house had six bedrooms and two bathrooms; a more than adequate supply for two people. Did Blake still occupy the master bedroom? It had been redecorated especially for them before their marriage she remembered, in soft peaches and blues that Blake had told her he had chosen with her eyes in mind. Her mouth curled into a sardonic smile. And to think she had been fool enough to believe him. The door handle turned easily under her fingers, but she stood still once it was opened. Everything was just as she remembered it; everything was clean and neat, but the room gave the impression of being unused.

'Re-living old memories?' Blake's voice was harshly discordant making her whirl round in shock.

She said the first thing that came into her mind. 'It doesn't look used.'

'It isn't.' His voice was still harsh, his eyes fiercely golden as they all but pinned her where she stood. 'Let's face it,' he added cynically, 'the memories it holds aren't precisely those I want to take to bed with me every night. I sleep in my old room, but you can have this one if you wish.'

His old room. Unwillingly her eyes were drawn along the corridor to the room she knew he meant. She had only been in it once. She had come with a message from her father and finding the kitchen empty and hearing Blake's voice had hurried upstairs. He had emerged from his room just as she reached it, a towel wrapped round lean hips, his body still damp from his shower. She hadn't been able to take her eyes off him, she remembered sardonically; and neither had she been able to speak. Blake had drawn her inside the room closing the door. 'What is it little girl,' he had asked tauntingly, 'haven't you ever seen a man before?' She had turned to flee but he had caught her, kissing her with what she had interpreted as fierce passion but which in reality could only have been play-acting. . .

'Sapphire, are you all right?' His voice dragged her back to the present.

'Fine,' she told him in a clipped voice. 'I might as well use this room. The woman who comes up from the village, when. . .'

'Three days a week, if you feel you need her more then arrange it. Don't worry,' he added sardonically, watching her, 'I don't expect you to soil your ladylike hands with housework, or cooking.' If anything his mouth curled even more cynically. 'I have too much respect for my stomach for that. I came up to tell you that I've brought your cases in. Once the vet's been, I've got to go out and check one of the fences, some of the sheep were found on the road. . .'

He disappeared, leaving Sapphire standing by the open door, her face still scarlet from his insults about her cooking. So he thought she was still the same useless, timid child he had first married, did he? Well she would show him.

Returning upstairs, Sapphire quickly changed into her jeans and an old tee-shirt. A thorough inspection of the kitchen cupboards revealed the fact that they were surprisingly well stocked and within an hour of Blake's exit she had a large bowl of dough rising in the warmth of the upstairs airing cupboard—a trick she had learned in her London flat which lacked the large warming compartment of the old-fashioned stove at home.

She heard the vet arrive while she was making the pastry for Beef Wellington, but continued with her self-imposed task. Blake would soon discover that she was not the timid child she had once been, and she wouldn't have been human, she told herself, if she didn't take pleasure from imagining his surprise at the discovery.

She had half-expected Blake to bring the vet in for a cup of tea after he had inspected that mare—it was a cold day, and she was sure the older man would have welcomed a warming drink, but instead when they emerged from the barn Blake walked with him to his Range Rover. The two men stood talking for a few minutes and then the vet climbed into his vehicle and Blake turned back towards the stable, disappearing inside.

Sapphire had just put her loaves in the oven when the 'phone rang. Wiping her floury hands on a towel she picked up the receiver, recognising Miranda's slightly shrill voice the moment she heard it.

'Is Blake there?' the other woman demanded imperiously. 'I want to speak to him—urgently.'

'He's in the barn at the moment,' Sapphire responded coolly, suppressing the urge to slam the receiver down. 'If you'd like to hold on for a moment I'll go and get him.'

The interior of the barn, so dark after the bright sunlit afternoon was temporarily blinding. Sapphire was peripherally aware of the familiar barn sounds; the mare shuffling restlessly in her stall, the scent of hay, the rustling sound it made. As her eyes grew accustomed to the gloom she stepped forward calling Blake's name.

'Up here,' he called back, making her start tensely and peer upwards into the dimness of the upper hayloft.

'There's a 'phone call for you,' Sapphire told him curtly, not wanting to think she had come looking for him on her own account. 'Miranda.'

'I'll have to ring her back.' Blake was frowning as he turned back into the interior of the loft, and although she knew she was being foolish Sapphire couldn't quite control the sudden leap of her senses as she caught a glimpse of the tawny skin of his chest where his shirt had come unfastened. Enough, she berated herself, as she walked blindly towards the door. 'You don't even like the man—you loathe him, so how can you possibly . . . feel desire for him?' Somehow the words insinuated themselves into her mind and wouldn't go away, making her face up to the truth. Blake still had the power to disturb her; still held a sexual appeal for her, which although it had nothing to do with love, or indeed any genuine worthwhile emotion, did, nonetheless, hold a dangerously potent allure.

Deep in thought Sapphire recoiled with pain as she cannoned into one of the posts supporting the upper floor, the intensity of the unexpected pain almost robbing her of breath as she stumbled backwards.

She was aware of sounds behind her, of Blake's peremptory command and then the firm strength of his arm supporting her against his body as she slowly crumpled.

'Sapphire, are you all right?'

His voice was a roughly urgent mutter somewhere above her left ear; the heat of his body against her back drowning out her earlier pain and replacing it with a dangerous languor that reinforced every one of her earlier thoughts.

'Sapphire?'

This time the urgency in Blake's voice compelled her to make some response. 'I'm fine,' she told him shakily, 'it was just the shock... It took my breath away.'

'I know the feeling.' She could feel the reverberations of his words rumbling in his chest, but the dry tone in which they were uttered made her lift her head and turn round the better to study his face.

'Can't you feel what having you in my arms does to me?' he murmured rawly. 'I'd almost forgotten it was possible to feel like this.'

Sapphire didn't need to ask 'to feel like what?' Her own treacherous body was already reacting shamelessly to Blake's proximity. You fool, she protested inwardly, he doesn't care any more about you than he did before; it's just another act, another scene of the charade he insists we play. He doesn't want you.

But Blake's body was telling her otherwise. More experienced now than she had been at seventeen, she could clearly read the tell-tale signs; in the dim light of the barn his eyes glittered dark gold, searching her face as he cupped her jaw with one hand and turned her round to face him. There was a tension in his body that was betrayed by the fine tremor of his muscles and the harsh control he exercised over his breathing.

The knowledge that she had aroused him was infinitely exciting; dangerously intoxicating, so much so that she was drunk on it. There could be no other explanation for the suicidal desire she suddenly experienced to trace the deep vee of Blake's open shirt with the tip of one finger, nor for giving into it.

Apart from one deep inhaled breath Blake kept absolutely still. His skin felt warm and surprisingly vulnerable, the difference in texture between his skin and the crispness of his dark chest hair deeply erotic. She had never touched him like this in the past; had never dared to initiate any intimacy between them. A pulse thudded at the base of his throat, his fingers tensing into her waist as he looked down at her.

'Sapphire!'

Her name seemed to well up from the very depths of his soul, spilling into the silence of the barn as a tormented groan. Her shocked senses barely had time to register it before the hard fingers cupping her jaw were tilting her face up and his mouth was consuming hers, burning it with a kiss of such fierce intensity that her senses took fire from it, liquid heat running moltenly through her veins, making her melt into him with a feverish need to meld with him and become part of him.

When his tongue stroked her lips, coaxing them apart Sapphire surrendered willingly, an ache that was partly desire and partly pain flowering to life inside her. Never once had he kissed her like this before; like a man who had hungered desperately for the feel of her mouth beneath his; who burned with a totally male desire to conquer and possess.

His free hand stroked down her body, finding the soft curve of her breast his thumb finding the newly burgeoning peak and caressing it with a feverish intensity that was echoed in the taut tension of his body.

Everything in her that was feminine yielded beneath the force of such a rawly masculine need and as though his body sensed the responsiveness of hers, Blake slid his hand beneath her tee-shirt, searching for and finding the aroused swell of her breast.

Which of them made the small murmur of satisfaction Sapphire didn't know, all she did know was that by the time Blake's mouth left hers, to investigate the creamy curve of her throat, she was totally acquiescent; mutely encouraging the exploration of warm male lips and slightly calloused male hands.

'Sapphire if you don't stop me now, I'm going to end up making love to you where we stand.'

Blake groaned the words into her skin, using his superior strength to urge her against the hard arousal of his body, muttering thick words of pleasure as his hands slid down to her hips, moulding her against him, but his words had penetrated through the dizzying heat of desire welling up inside her and Sapphire pulled away. He released her almost immediately, the desire she had seen so recently in his face draining away to be replaced by sardonic comprehension.

'You forgot who I was, is that it?' he taunted, watching the emotions chase one another across her mobile face. 'You forgot that I wasn't your precious boyfriend, is that what you're going to tell me? Well I'll save you the trouble,' he told her. 'That was *me* you responded to Sapphire, *me* who set you on fire; *me* who you wanted to make love to.'

'Oh yes you did,' he insisted when she tried to speak. 'You wanted me Sapphire, whether you're honest to admit it or not.'

'Whatever there once was between us is gone,' Sapphire protested, bitterly aware that he was right; she *had* wanted him and with an intensity that, now that she had herself under control again, shocked her.

'But you can't deny that you responded to me,' Blake pressed softly, watching her, making her feel trapped and tormented.

'I can't deny that I responded to your *masculinity*,' Sapphire agreed in a face-saving bid... 'I'm a woman now Blake, with all the desires and needs that that implies.' Heavens was this really her saying this? Inwardly she was trembling, praying that he wouldn't see through her pitiful attempt to deny the effect he had on her.

'Meaning that you would have responded to any man in the same way?' Blake asked her sardonically. 'I don't think so, Sapphire. In fact, judging by your response to me, there must be something lacking in your boyfriend's lovemaking. You responded to me as though you were starving for...'

'Stop it,' Sapphire interrupted his cruel speech. 'I won't listen to this, Blake.' She hurried to the barn door, wanting only to escape from him and the turbulence of her own emotions, completely forgetting the original purpose of her journey to the barn, until she got back to the kitchen and found the receiver still on the table. There was no-one at the other end and so she replaced it, busying herself in the kitchen, trying to find some balm to her disordered senses in the warm scent of baking bread that filled the room, but instead only able to remember the rough sensuality of Blake's mouth on hers; the urgent caress of his hands on her body; the unashamed arousal of his as he kissed and caressed her, but no, she mustn't think of these things. She must concentrate instead of remembering why she was here; how Blake had trapped her.

She was busily clearing away the remnants of pastry from the table when Blake walked in, checking on the threshold, frowning slightly as the warmly rich scent of her baking filled his nostrils. She ought to have been pleased by the startled expression on his face, but instead all she could think of was the way his mouth had felt against her own, and it took an almost physical effort to draw her gaze away from the slightly moist fullness of his lower lip.

'Bread?' he quizzed her, obviously surprised.

'Alan liked me to bake it for him,' Sapphire responded, knowing that she was deliberately invoking Alan's name as though it were a charm which had the ability to destroy Blake's powerful pull on her senses. Blake's face hardened immediately, as he strode across the kitchen and picked up the 'phone. Watching him punch in a series of numbers, so quickly that he must know them by heart, Sapphire was pierced by a feeling of desolation so acute that it terrified her. She mustn't become emotionally involved with Blake again. She had travelled that road once and knew all too well where it led; she wasn't going to travel it again.

Her desolation turned to sick pain as she heard him say Miranda's name. The other woman must have said something because Blake laughed, a deeply sensual sound that stirred up the tiny hairs on the back of Sapphire's nape, making her spine tingle.

'No, she must have forgotten to give me the

message,' Sapphire heard him say, his eyes hard, his gaze unwavering splintering her with pain as she turned to face him. 'Umm . . . well how about dinner tonight? Yes I'll pick you up.'

Sapphire turned away, Blake was taking Miranda out to dinner? She glanced at the 'fridge where the pastry and fillet steak she had prepared for their evening meal lay, and her mouth compressed in a bitter line. Hadn't she already learned her lesson?

By the time Blake had replaced the receiver she had decided what she would do. Let Blake take his . . . mistress out to dinner if he wished, but she wasn't going to sit at home, moping, waiting for him. She would go over to Flaws and spend the evening with Mary and her father.

It wasn't until she heard the door close behind Blake that she realised that she had been holding her breath. Her lungs ached with the strain she was imposing on them, her body so tense that her muscles were almost locked.

Why on earth had she allowed Blake to kiss and touch her as he had? And why had she responded to him so . . . so ardently. She didn't love him any longer; but she still desired him; part of her still felt the old attraction; *that* must be the explanation. Like an amputee suffering pain from a limb that no longer existed she was still experiencing the pangs of her youthful love for Blake even though that love had long ago died.

Sapphire was in her room when Blake went out; she had gone there, deliberately avoiding him, and only emerged once she had heard his car engine die away.

Despite the fact that the heating was on the house felt slightly chilly—a sure sign that the threat of bad weather hadn't gone. In the living room a basket of logs stood on the hearth of the open fire, and Sapphire glanced longingly at them, acknowledging that it was pointless lighting a fire just for herself, especially when she didn't intend staying in. Why, when she knew where Blake had gone; when she knew how he had manipulated her, did her imagination insist on filling her mind with pictures of Blake as she had always wanted him to be rather than as he was; of herself at his side; their children upstairs asleep while they sat side by side by the warm glow of the fire; happy and content. Suppressing a sigh Sapphire walked into the kitchen, still redolent with the fragrance of her newly baked bread. On the table one of her loaves stood on the breadboard surrounded by crumbs. Blake had obviously cut himself a slice, and probably given himself indigestion she thought wryly, touching the still warm loaf.

Knowing that if she remained alone any longer in the house she would only brood, Sapphire picked up her jacket and headed for the Land Rover. Spending the evening with her father would stop her thinking about the past; about useless might-have-beens, she decided firmly, as she swung herself up into the utilitarian vehicle. She was just about to start the motor when a sound from the barn stopped her. Tensing she listened, wondering if she was imagining things, and then she heard it again; the shrill, unmistakable whinny of a horse in pain.

Blake's mare! But he had told her that the vet had said she probably wouldn't start to foal for at least twenty-four hours. Frowning Sapphire glanced towards the barn door, her conscience prodding her to get out of the Land Rover and go and investigate. She wasn't a stranger to animal birth; and as she hurried into the barn, snapping on the light, her experienced eye quickly took in the mare's distressed state and knew that the vet had been wrong. By the looks of her the mare was already in labour.

Despite her long years in London old habits reasserted themselves. Soothing the mare as best she could, Sapphire left her to race back to the house. To her relief the vet's wife answered the 'phone almost immediately. Quickly Sapphire explained the position.

'The vet isn't here,' she told Sapphire, 'but I know where he is. I'll 'phone him and let him know the position. I know he'll be with you just as soon as he can. Are you able to get in touch with Blake?' she asked worriedly, 'I know how much he thinks of that mare. . .'

It wasn't hard for Sapphire to find Miranda's telephone number, but she hesitated before dialling it. As she had half-expected, there was no answer. She ought to have felt a savage satisfaction that Blake was being repaid for his duplicity, but all she could feel was a growing concern for the mare, and concern at her own ability to handle the situation. The shepherd who might have been able to help was out on the hills with his flock; her father was far too ill to help and Mary. . . Mary was a trained nurse, Sapphire remembered excitedly, picking up the phone again and punching in the numbers quickly.

Mary listened while she explained the situation.

'I'll be right over,' she assured Sapphire. 'The vet may not be long, but it's better to be safe than sorry. This won't be the first birth I've attended bya long chalk.'

While she was waiting, more to keep herself busy than anything else Sapphire boiled water and scalded the buckets, finding carbolic soap, and a pack of clean, unused rope. If for some reason the foal was turned the wrong way they might need the rope. Hurriedly she tried to think of anything else they might need, rushing out into the yard when she heard the sound of a vehicle. To her disappointment it was Mary and not the vet who alighted from the Range Rover.

'You've done well,' she approved as she followed Sapphire into the barn. 'But where's Blake?'

'He had to go out,' Sapphire avoided her eyes. 'I haven't been able to reach him.'

Fortunately Mary was too busy examining the mare to hear the slight hesitation in her voice.

'The foal's turned into the breech position,' Mary explained, fulfilling Sapphire's own fears. 'I'll try and turn it, can you hold the mare's head, try and soothe her?'

Her father had once told Sapphire that she had a way with animals, and Sapphire prayed that he might be right as she softly coaxed the nervous mare, talking to her in soothing whispers.

'This isn't her first foal,' Mary commented, 'but she's very nervous.'

'Missing Blake, I expect,' Sapphire murmured absently. 'Are you going to be able to turn it?'

'I think so.' Mary's face was strained with the effort of concentrating on her task, and Sapphire felt herself willing her to succeed.

'There . . . I think that's done it. Good girl,' she soothed the mare, adding to Sapphire, 'I think we can let nature take its course now, although I hope the birth won't be too protracted, she's already suffered a lot of pain.'

As the birth pangs rippled through the mare's swollen belly Sapphire found herself tensing in sympathy with her, and yet the mare did seem more relaxed as though she knew that they were there to help her.

'Quick, Sapphire, look.' Mary's voice was exultant as she pointed to the foal's head as it emerged from its mother's body. Deftly she moved to assist the mare, Sapphire immediately moving to help, remembering how she had assisted her father in the past.

The foal was a tiny bundle of stick-like limbs on the straw at its mother's feet when they heard the sound of a vehicle outside.

A door slammed and the vet came hurrying in bringing a gust of cold air with him, his anxious frown relaxing into a smile as he saw the foal. 'Well, well what have we here?' he asked gently, quickly examining the mare, nodding with approval as he inspected the foal.

'I'm sorry I couldn't get here before—an emergency at Low Head farm, but you seem to have managed well enough without me.' His smile was for Sapphire, but she shook her head, directing his attention to Mary. 'Without Mary's help I couldn't have done it.'

'The foal had turned,' Mary explained, 'but fortunately he was small enough for me to turn back.'

'Umm, quick thinking on your part to send for

Mary,' the vet praised Sapphire, 'but where's Blake?'

'He had to go out.' Sapphire repeated the explanation she had given Mary.

'Lucky for him and the mare that you were here.' His eyes were curious as he inspected her, and Sapphire wondered if he knew that she was Blake's wife, and that they were back together again.

It was another two hours before Sapphire could crawl into bed. She had made supper for Mary and the vet, who had pronounced both mother and foal to be in perfect health, and by the time they had gone she had been almost too tired to sink into the hot bath she had run for herself. As she pulled the quilt up round her ears she glanced at her watch. One o'clock, and Blake still wasn't back. A bitter pain invaded her body. Was he at this very moment making love to Miranda, kissing her with the barely restrained passion he had shown her earlier in the day? They had not been lovers he had said to her, and for a moment she had believed him, but surely his actions tonight proved that he had lied?

She closed her eyes, willing herself to sleep. She *wasn't* going to lie here awake, wondering where he was, waiting for him to return as she had done so often in the past.

# CHAPTER SIX

A SURPRISE awaited Sapphire when she opened her eyes the following morning. It was the clarity of the light in her bedroom that first alerted her, and padding across the room on bare feet she flung back the curtains, bemused to see the white blanket of snow that must have fallen during the night. Everything was so quiet; the air so crystal clear it was almost like wine. She frowned; where was Blake? Had he even returned? She padded back to bed, picking up her watch and nearly dropping it as she realised how long she had overslept. It was gone ten o'clock!

Showering quickly she ran downstairs and opened the kitchen door. The room was empty but there was evidence that Blake had had some breakfast. The aroma of coffee hung tantalisingly in the air making her aware of her thirst. Deftly she moved about the kitchen going to stand by the window as she waited for the coffee to filter into the jug. The snow lay surprisingly deep in the yard, criss-crossed with footmarks plus those of a dog. Of course, the sheep! Sapphire gnawed at her bottom lip. Attractive as though the snow was to look at it could spell disaster for any unwary farmer. She remembered her father's shepherd telling her that he had expected this weather. Had Blake got the ewes down to the lower pastures? If not there was every danger that the new lambs would be lost beneath the huge drifts Sapphire knew could form on the bleak mountain tops. Without consciously making any decision she found herself searching in the porch for a pair of suitable wellingtons, mentally ticking off all that she would need if she was to be any help to the men. She could follow their tracks through the snow without any difficulty. Perhaps if she took them hot coffee and tea . . .

Fifteen minutes later Sapphire tramped through the farmyard, following the clearly defined footprints upwards. The snow had frozen to a crisp crust, her laboured breath made white plumes in the sharp morning air. At another time she would have found the atmosphere invigorating, but right now she was too concerned about the sheep to really enjoy the delights of the morning.

The baaing of the sheep and the sharp yelps of the dogs reached her first, carrying easily on the clear air, and she expelled her breath on a faint sigh of relief. Obviously some of the sheep at least had been brought down to the lower meadows. As she followed the footprints along a dry-stone wall Sapphire caught her first glimpse of her quarry, a rough shelter had been constructed in one of the fields, and men were busy unbaling hay from a tractor. The field sloped away slightly offering some protection from the wind and drifts, and as she got nearer Sapphire recognised her father's shepherd, busily at work. The other men she also vaguely recognised as general farmhands attached to Blake's farm whom he had no doubt taken from their other tasks to help with the all-important job of saving the sheep.

Tam recognised her face, a weary grin splitting his weathered face as he hailed her.

'I've brought you something hot to drink,' Sapphire called out as soon as she was close enough, adding anxiously, 'How's it going? The ewes. . .'

'Brought most of them down yesterday,' Tam informed her. 'Blake's gone looking for the rest of the flock. Shouldn't have too much of a problem with my Laddie to help him. Fine sheepdog.'

'Anything I can do to help?' Sapphire asked, handing out the thermos flasks and cups.

'No. I reckon everything's under control. Luckily Blake was running your dad's flock with his own, so we shouldn't have too many casualties. If this weather had come another two weeks on we could have been in trouble—the first ewes are due to start lambing then.'

'You don't think it will last then?' Sapphire asked, studying the snow-covered landscape.

Tam shook his head. 'Not more than three or four days, and we were prepared for it.' He nodded in the direction of the new shelter and the bales of hay. 'Blake knows what he's doing all right.' There was approval in his voice and Sapphire turned away, not wanting the shepherd to see her own bitter resentment. What time had Blake come home last night? He could have had precious little sleep she thought revengefully. Had he arrived before the snow came or had the fact that she had not heard him been due to the fact that it had muffled his return?

What did it matter? It was no business of hers how he spent his time, or whose bed he shared.

She waited until the men had finished their drinks before gathering up the empty flasks.

'I'll keep this one for Blake,' Tam offered taking

a half-full one from her and screwing on the top. 'He'll be fair frozen by the time he gets back.'

'Is he up there alone?' Sapphire frowned when the shepherd nodded. 'Is that wise?'

'Blake knows what he's doing.'

Tam had been right, Sapphire reflected several hours later when a noise in the yard alerted her to Blake's return. Snow clung to his thick protective jacket and the cuffs of his boots, his skin burned by the icy cold wind. She hadn't known whether to prepare a meal or not—there was still the Beef Wellington to cook from last night, and she had spent what was left of the morning making a nourishing hot soup, thinking that if Blake didn't return she could take it out to the men in flasks.

She had also been in to inspect the new foal, now standing proudly on all four spindly legs while his mother looked on in benign approval.

As Blake crossed the yard the 'phone rang. It was her father calling to enquire about the sheep. 'Everything's under control, Dad,' she assured him. 'Blake had already got the ewes down to the lower pastures and he's been up to the top to bring the rest down.'

'Yes, Mary told me I didn't need to worry, but old habits die hard.'

The kitchen door opened as she replied, and she could hear the sound of Blake tugging off his boots. 'Blake's back now,' she told her father, 'would you like to speak to him?'

'No, I know myself what it's like. He'll be frozen to the marrow and tired out—the last thing he'll feel like is talking to me. I'll speak to him later when he's thawed out.'

'Who was that?'

She hadn't heard Blake cross the floor in his stockinged feet and whirled round apprehensively. Exhaustion tautened the bone structure of his face, dimming the gold of his eyes to tawny brown. White flecks of snow clung to his hair and jumper.

'My father. Is it snowing again?'

'Trying to. God I'm tired. Is there any hot water?'

'Plenty. Would you like something to eat?' She saw his eyebrows lift and mockery invade his eyes. 'Quite the devoted wife today aren't we? What brought about this metamorphosis?'

'Nothing . . . there hasn't been one.' Sapphire retorted flatly cursing herself for her momentary weakness. 'I just thought. . .'

'Yes, I'm sorry.' Strong dark fingers raked through his already tousled hair. 'That was uncalled for—put it down to sheer male. . .' His glance studied her slim body in its covering of jeans and sweater and he grimaced faintly before adding bluntly, 'frustration. . . Deprivation of physical satisfaction does tend to make me behave like a churlish brute, and I haven't even thanked you for your midwifery last night. . .'

'Mary's the one you should thank,' Sapphire told him, turning away and busying herself filling the kettle. She wanted to scream at him that she didn't want to know the details about his relationship with Miranda or about his physical hunger for her. Was that why he had made love to *her* so intensely yesterday? In anticipation of holding Miranda in his arms? The thought made her feel physically sick, but what was even more shocking was the knowledge that she could feel so strongly and primitively about a man for whom she had already told herself she felt only the echoes of an old physical desire.

'Is something wrong?'

She could feel him approaching and tensed. 'No, nothing.' She couldn't bear him to come anywhere near her right now, not when her far too active mind was picturing him with Miranda, kissing and caressing her. The handle of the mug she had been holding in her hand snapped under the intensity of her grip, the mug falling to the floor where it shattered into fragments.

'No . . . don't. Leave it.' Her voice was sharper than she had intended, almost shrill in its intensity and she prayed that Blake wouldn't recognise the near hysteria edging up under it. 'You haven't got anything on your feet,' she added weakly. 'You go and have your bath and I'll clean it up. Are you hungry now, or can you wait an hour or so?'

'I can wait.' He too sounded clipped and terse, but Sapphire couldn't look at him to read the reason in his expression. Instead she waited until she heard the door close behind him and then carefully skirting the broken china went to get a brush and pan to clear up the mess.

She was putting the Beef Wellington into the oven when she heard Blake call out something from upstairs. Reacting without thinking Sapphire hurried up them, coming to an abrupt halt outside his bedroom door, wondering whether to knock or simply walk in. The dilemma was solved for her as Blake pulled the door open. He had taken off his sweater and shirt, and his skin gleamed silky bronze beneath the electric light. Her breathing which hadn't been in the slightest affected by her dash upstairs, now suddenly constricted, her heart thudding heavily its beats reverberating through her body.

'I've scraped my back against a wall. I think the skin's broken.' Blake turned his back to her as he spoke and Sapphire saw the patch of broken skin, slightly swollen and discoloured with dried blood.

Farm accidents no matter how minor always had to be properly attended to; that was one of the first rules Sapphire had ever learned and she knew better than to accuse Blake of being too fussy in wanting the graze attended to. Neither would he be able to deal with it himself, positioned as it was just below his shoulder blade.

'I'll go and get some antiseptic and cotton wool. Your tetanus shots are up to date I hope?'

'Do you?' Blake grimaced sardonically, flexing his shoulder as he moved away from her, as though the muscles pained him. 'Funny, I had the distinct impression you'd like nothing better than to see me suffer.'

'Don't.' Sapphire whispered the protest, her face paper white, remembering the stories Tam had told her as a child about farm workers who had died from the dreaded 'lockjaw'. Fortunately, with his back to her Blake couldn't see her betraying expression, nor question her as to why she should feel such concern for someone she purportedly hated.

Why did she? She was forced to ask herself the question as she hurried into the bathroom for antiseptic and cotton-wool. There was nothing personal in her concern, she assured herself, she would have reacted the same way no matter who was involved. But she would not have reacted so intensely to the sight of anyone else's half-naked body; she would not have wanted to stretch out and touch the bronze skin and hard muscles, excitement gripping her by the throat as she visualised that same body... No ... she was over all that. She no longer loved Blake, but for some reason her senses were playing cruel tricks on her, tormenting her with mental images of herself in Blake's arms; of Blake making love to her with all the fierce passion she suspected lay beneath his sardonic exterior.

Fool, fool, she berated herself as she hurried back to the stark, functional bedroom Blake had chosen for his own occupation. As she walked in she noticed that the bed looked untidy and rumpled. When she had dealt with Blake's wound she would change the sheets and tidy up a bit. *Very wifely*, the inner cynical voice she had come to dread mocked her, *but it won't make him want you*. I don't want him to want me. The denial seemed to reverberate inside her skull, and then as though it knew how paper-frail it was that other voice taunted softly, *Liar*.

'Sapphire?' Blake's curt voice cut across her thoughts. 'Are you all right?' He was frowning, his eyes sharpening to vivid gold as they searched her face.

'I'm not going to faint at the sight of a drop of your precious blood if that's what you think,' Sapphire responded tartly, adding with a calm she was far from feeling. 'While you're having your bath I'll change the bed for you. You'd better sit down on it, otherwise I'll never be able to reach the graze.'

'If you just clean it up for now,' Blake suggested, 'that should do the trick.'

'It will need a dressing on it,' Sapphire protested.

'Which will get soaked through the moment I get in the bath.'

'Then I'll put it on when you've finished,' Sapphire told him tartly, complaining, 'Honestly Blake, I never thought you of all people would be so irresponsible.'

'Perhaps I'm just testing to see exactly how deep your hatred of me really is,' Blake taunted back.

Sapphire compressed her lips. 'I'm not a child any more, Blake,' she reminded him. 'No matter what my personal feelings for you are, I wouldn't want to see you take the risk of getting a bad infection through a neglected skin wound.'

'Which doesn't really answer my question does it?'

'Sit down,' Sapphire instructed, ignoring his probing comment. 'This will sting,' she warned him as he sat down on the edge of the bed with his back to her. His skin looked so warm and inviting that it took all the self-control she possessed not to reach out and caress it.

'And won't you just enjoy it,' Blake muttered under his breath, tensing slightly as Sapphire applied the antiseptic soaked pad to his skin, gently cleaning the graze, until the blood flowed cleanly from it.

She let it flow for a few seconds, and then quickly stemmed it with fresh antiseptic, hiding a faint smile as Blake winced.

'Give me a shout when you're ready,' she told him when she had finished, 'and I'll come up and put a dressing on it for you. It should start to heal by morning.'

'Yes, nurse,' Blake mocked, getting up off the bed and momentarily making her feel at a distinct disadvantage as he towered over her. 'Taking a risk aren't you?' he drawled, watching her. For a moment Sapphire thought he meant the temptation she had exposed herself to in being so close to him, and her face flamed until he added softly, 'Isn't it a well known fact that patients always fall for their nurses?'

'In that case I think I'm pretty safe,' Sapphire responded, struggling to appear calmly unconcerned. 'After all I already know how you feel about me, don't I?'

Blake walked out without responding, and when she heard the bathroom door close behind him Sapphire got up and went to the large, old-fashioned airing cupboard situated on the landing to get clean sheets for his bed.

She worked methodically, changing the sheets, tidying up automatically, filling the laundry basket with the items of discarded clothing she found scattered round the room. Blake was basically a tidy man and there was nothing really in the starkly furnished room apart from his clothes that had his stamp of possession on it. If anything the room was rather bleak, she thought, studying it, almost monk-like. Mocking herself for her thoughts Sapphire carried the laundry out on to the landing. Blake was no monk, as she had seen last night.

She had just finished preparing the table when Blake called. Guessing that he would probably be tired she had decided that they might as well eat in the kitchen. It was warm and cosy enough and the table was large enough to seat an entire family, never mind merely two adults.

This time she walked into Blake's room without thinking, coming to an abrupt halt as she realised that he was nude. Of the two of them she was the one to be embarrassed she recognised angrily, as Blake merely grinned mockingly at her, taking his time in reaching for the towel that lay discarded on the bed.

'Why the outraged expression?' he demanded calmly. 'I can't be the first naked man you've seen.'

He was the only one, but Sapphire wasn't going to tell him that. 'Hardly,' she lied, shrugging aside the frisson of awareness the sight of his naked body had given her.

'And we are married. . .'

'Maybe, but it isn't the sort of marriage that involves parading around naked in front of one another.'

'What a pity.' Genuine amusement glinted in Blake's eyes as he teased her, and Sapphire had to fight against responding, against remembering how much joy there had been in loving him before she discovered the bitter truth. Blake had always been able to make her laugh, and even now she could feel the corners of her mouth twitching in response to his droll expression. The towel was firmly in place around his hips now, but to her chagrin that didn't stop Sapphire from visualising the taut shape of masculine buttocks and long hard thighs.

'Something smells good.' Blake's voice jerked her out of her reverie, and Sapphire bent her head to hide her guilty flush of colour. What on earth would he think if he knew what had been in her mind?

Fortunately he didn't, she assured herself as she gestured to the bed and suggested that he sit on it. This time she didn't allow herself to dwell on the supple texture of his skin or the masculine formation of muscle and bone that lay beneath it, finishing her self-imposed task with a haste she was surprised Blake didn't pick up on.

When the dressing was in place, she stepped away from him, tensing nervously as his fingers curled round her arm, preventing her from moving.

'Blake, let me go.' Her voice sounded sharp and nervous even to her own ears, and her anxiety increased when Blake refused to accede to her demand.

'I haven't rewarded you yet,' he told her softly, the hard grip of his fingers pulling her inexorably closer to him. 'All ministering angels deserve a reward, don't you agree?'

Whatever she might have said was lost as she felt the warm heat of Blake's body. She put out a hand to push him away, but the sensation of warm, sensuously silken male skin beneath her fingertips was so intoxicating that her resistance melted.

Dimly she was aware of Blake pulling her down on to his lap, and of the single bed creaking protestingly under their double weight.

She struggled to pull away out of his constraining arms, but Blake simply toppled her over on to the bed, imprisoning her against it with the superior weight of his body. His thighs pinned her lower body to the mattress, his chest hard against the softness of her breasts.

Sapphire felt vulnerable and helpless and yet the

sensations coursing through her veins and along
her nerve endings whispered sensuously of pleasurable excitement rather than fear. Even so, she felt
moved to protest shakily, 'Blake, let me get up, the
dinner. . .'

Soft laughter brushed against her skin. 'Right
now I'm hungry for more than just food.'

'Then perhaps you ought to give Miranda a
ring,' Sapphire suggested tartly, struggling to push
him away. She was glad she had said that, until
that moment she had been dangerously close to
giving way to the insidious pull of her too
vulnerable senses.

'Why should I need another man's wife, when
I've got one of my own?' Blake countered
outrageously, following her squirming movements
and refusing to let her escape. His towel, Sapphire
realised, had become dislodged, and weakening
darts of pleasure relaxed her muscles into a
sensuous lethargy as she felt her body reacting to
the male provocation of Blake's body.

'Kiss me, Sapphire.'

She looked at him with desire-hazed eyes, barely
comprehending the softly whispered command as
she fought to subdue the treacherous impulses of
her body.

'No.' She mumbled the denial huskily, knowing
that it was far more than a kiss that Blake wanted
from her. She wouldn't, she couldn't play
substitute for Miranda.

'Yes.' The silky affirmation was whispered
against her lips, the warmth of Blake's breath
stirring to life a thousand tiny drumming pulses.
Against her will Sapphire felt her mouth soften,
her breathing suddenly ragged as Blake touched its

soft contours with the tip of his tongue, expertly teasing light kisses into the corners, tormentingly stroking her sensitised skin, until she reacted with a feverish protest, lifting her arms, and locking her fingers behind his neck, her body arching instinctively into the hard heat of his, as her mouth opened to capture the marauding torment of his tongue. The sudden fierce pressure of his mouth, searing into her skin, took Sapphire by surprise, making her realise the extent of Blake's self-control. The kisses he had given her before had been so lightly teasing that she had been lulled into a false sense of security, and yet there was a wild elemental pleasure in responding to Blake's hunger; a knowledge that they were meeting as equals, not child and adult.

When he eventually released her mouth it felt bruised and slightly swollen, and yet the sensation was a pleasurable one, her lips acutely sensitive to the light kisses he caressed them with as he murmured softly, 'Let me take this tee-shirt off, I want to feel you against me, Sapphire.'

His hands were already gripping the edge of her tee-shirt, and to her shame Sapphire knew a wild impulse to help him. Once she had fantasised about seeing their bodies intimately enmeshed; the paleness of her fair skin against the gold-bronze of his and now, treacherously, that memory resurfaced making her protest only a token one as Blake tugged the stretchy fabric up over her body.

Her figure had changed in the intervening years, she knew; her shape no longer that of a young girl. Her waist had narrowed, but her breasts were fuller, more mature, crowned with deep pink nipples, at the moment veiled from Blake's intense scrutiny by the lacy fabric of her bra.

'Beautiful,' he murmured huskily, his thumb stroking caressingly along the edge of the dainty lace and down into the hollow between her breasts.

Desire seemed to explode like fireworks deep inside her, stunning Sapphire with its intensity. She had desired Blake before, but surely never with this consuming, all-important depth, that pushed aside every other emotion as trivial and not to be considered. She wanted to respond to him with every feminine nerve ending; she wanted to feel his hands and mouth against every inch of her skin; and she wanted the freedom to caress and know him in exactly the same way. The knowledge that she could feel like this was shocking and yet exciting; freeing her suddenly from the fear she had always had that somehow she was not quite 100 per cent feminine; that the deep inner core of her was cold and unfunctioning. No other man had made her feel like this, certainly not Alan.

Alan! She tensed, suddenly shocked back to reality. Blake's fingers were curled round the lacy cup of her bra, his eyes so brilliantly gold as he stared down at her that she found herself blinking, half-dazzled by their glitter.

'Blake, I don't want. . .' She shivered as he cut off her protest by bending his head and brushing his lips provocatively along the delicate skin exposed above the white lace.

A tumult of sensations poured moltenly through Sapphire's veins. She made a small sound, meant to be a protest, but which emerged as a soft cry of pleasure as Blake's fingers eased back the lace and

his lips followed the path they made until they
found the aching centre of her breast, being teased
into wanton erectness by the caressing movement
of his fingers.

Awash with pleasure Sapphire was barely aware
of Blake unsnapping her bra, and exposing her
other breast until he repeated his tormenting
caresses on it with a nerve-racking delicacy that
left Sapphire shivering and aching beneath an
onslaught of pleasure she hadn't believed could
exist.

'You respond to me as though no-one's ever
touched you like 'that before,' Blake muttered
rawly, cupping her breasts possessively as he
looked up at her. 'I expected you to be more
blasé.'

As she shuddered in reaction, he moaned
thickly, 'Don't do that, you make me go up in
flames, just thinking about...' His sudden
tension alerted Sapphire to the sound of a vehicle
arriving in the yard.

'Damn,' Blake swore softly. 'The last thing I feel
like right now is leaving this bed.'

His words brought Sapphire back down to
earth, making her shrink in self-disgust from her
own behaviour. How could she have behaved so
foolishly? She was lucky that Blake didn't appear
to have guessed how much she still cared about
him... Stunned, Sapphire stopped what she was
doing. That wasn't true, she didn't care about
Blake at all... But if that was true, why had she
reacted so intensely to him ... why had her body
welcomed him as its lover? She *didn't* still love
him; she *couldn't* ... but deep inside Sapphire
knew that she was only deceiving herself. If sex

was really her only motivation she could have
found that with anyone of a dozen or more
attractive men whom she had dated since leaving
Blake, but she hadn't wanted to. She had remained
sexually cold to them. She still loved Blake all
right, and deep down inside her she must have
known it all along, even though she had tried to
hide from the truth.

Sick at heart, too numb almost to pull on her
tee-shirt, she heard someone knocking on the back
door, and hurriedly completed her task.

'I'll get it,' she told Blake, too disturbed to turn
and look at him.

The rich smell of their evening meal filled the
warm kitchen as Sapphire hurried across it, her
hair was uncombed and her face free of makeup,
her lips no doubt still swollen from Blake's kisses.
A flush of embarrassment stained her skin as she
pulled open the door, and then came to an abrupt
halt, stunned by the sight of the very last person
she had expected to see standing there.

'Alan,' she managed weakly, staring at him,
thinking how out of place his dark business suit
and obviously new sheepskin jacket looked—and
how alien he seemed to her. She had only been
away from London for a few days, but already it
seemed like another life-time.

'Your father told me you were here,' Alan
frowned. 'I've been to make arrangements to get
the car back. You really should have been more
careful, Sapphire, and what are you doing here?'
he demanded waspishly. 'I expected to find you
with your father, instead he directed me here ...
or rather his housekeeper did. Not a very
forthcoming woman, but then I suppose it's only

to be expected from these country types. Aren't you going to let me in?' he asked her querulously. 'It's freezing out here, and what on earth are you wearing?' He surveyed her jean-clad figure with open disapproval. 'Sapphire, what's going on, I. . .'

'Why don't you tell him, darling?'

Blake's voice from the other side of the kitchen made Sapphire wrench her head round in open-mouthed disbelief. Clad only in a towelling robe, Blake stood by the door, arms folded, hair tousled, the sight of his bare chest and long lean legs making Sapphire go weak at the knees, treacherous, reactionary sensations warming the pit of her stomach.

'Sapphire, who is this?' Alan demanded.

'Blake,' Blake offered, answering for her, and walking towards Alan, proferring his hand, 'Sapphire's husband.'

'Husband!' Alan practically goggled, and watching him Sapphire knew that no matter how she might have chosen to deceive herself, when it came to it, she would never have married Alan. The emotions she felt for him were lukewarm nonentities when compared with the fierce, tumultuous feelings she had for Blake.

'Yes, Sapphire and I have decided to give our marriage another try,' Blake told him calmly.

'Marriage. You told me you were divorced,' Alan accused Sapphire. 'When did all this happen? Why didn't you say something when I rang?'

'I wanted to tell you, Alan, but. . .'

'I was hoping your father would put me up for the night. It's too late to drive back to London now, and there isn't a decent hotel in miles.'

'You can stay here,' Blake offered, stunning Sapphire with his offer. 'There's plenty of room. If you bring in your case I'll take it upstairs for you—it will give you and Sapphire a chance to talk.'

Sapphire had expected Alan to refuse, but instead he walked out to his hired car and returned with an overnight case. When Blake took it upstairs Alan demanded, 'What's going on? When you left London you were going to marry me, now. . .'

'I'm sorry, Alan, but I didn't want to tell you over the phone. I thought you'd ring again before coming up here, and everything's happened so quickly that. . .'

'By everything I suppose you mean going to bed with your supposed "ex",' Alan interrupted crudely. 'He's obviously got something I don't have. . . . Oh, come on Sapphire,' he added angrily when she tried to protest, 'it's written all over the pair of you. Well I'm beginning to think he's welcome to you. You aren't the woman I thought, that's obvious,' he added in disgust, 'and if it wasn't for necessity, there's no way I'd stay here tonight. My sister was right it seems. She warned me not to get too involved with you.'

Alan's sister was a domineering possessive woman whom Sapphire had never liked and she sighed faintly.

'I've put your case in your room. The door on the right,' Blake announced, coming back into the kitchen. 'How long until we eat?' he asked Sapphire, 'I want to check on the mare and foal. Sapphire told you about her midwifery skills yet?' he asked Alan. 'She's practically delivered him all by herself. Messy business too—breech birth. . .'

Alan had gone green and Sapphire suppressed a momentary flash of irritation against him. Poor Alan, he couldn't help being so squeamish. If she didn't know better she would have thought that Blake was deliberately trying to show him in a bad light. She frowned suddenly, remembering which room Blake had given Alan. That was Blake's own room. Perhaps he had put Alan's case there because he knew the bed was freshly made up, and after all there were plenty of other rooms for him to sleep in.

'We'll be eating in half an hour,' she told him. 'Alan, the bathroom's first on the left if you want to use it.'

# CHAPTER SEVEN

IT was definitely one of the worst meals Sapphire
had ever endured. Alan had lapsed into a sulky
silence, punctuated by petulant little-boy responses
to her questions, designed to reinforce her guilt,
but what was even harder to cope with was the
proprietorial, and very obviously male-in-posses-
sion, stance adopted by Blake, who remained
sublimely indifferent to the killing looks she gave
him, taking every opportunity he could to touch
her, or to look at her with such blatant sexuality
that if she hadn't known exactly why he was doing
it, she would have been in serious danger of
succumbing to them.

Afterwards both men accepted coffee, and the
tense silence pervading the sitting room as they all
sat drinking it made Sapphire heave a sigh of relief
when Blake announced that he ought to go and do
his final rounds.

'We go to bed early in these parts,' he told Alan
blandly.

'Yes, I'm sure with the livestock and. . .'

'Oh that isn't the only reason,' Blake interrupted
softly, watching Sapphire.

'I thought you told me you hated him,' Alan
said stiffly the moment they were alone, 'and yet
now, apparently you're reconciled.'

For a moment Sapphire was tempted to tell him
the truth, as she had been planning to, but what
was the point now? It was kinder in the long run

to let Alan have the pride-saving cleansing of genuine anger to sustain him, and it would be selfish of her to tell him the truth now, knowing that she could never marry him.

'I made a mistake,' she told him quietly.

'But not as big a one as I made,' Alan told her through his teeth. 'I thought . . . oh what's the use? I might as well try and get what sleep I can. I'm leaving here in the morning. I'll have your office cleared out and your things sent on.'

'Thank you.' How stilted and formal they were with one another. Sapphire sighed. She wished they could have remained friends, but sensed that Alan's sister would prevent that!

When she had finished clearing away from their meal Sapphire went upstairs herself. Blake was still outside, and a thin line of light showed under the door of the room he had given Alan, the bathroom door open.

After showering in the privacy of her own en suite bathroom Sapphire towelled herself dry, clicking her tongue impatiently as she realised she had left her nightdress on the bed. Thank heavens for central heating, she reflected self-indulgently, as she dropped her damp towel and walked through into the other room. The lamps on either side of the half tester bed threw a soft haze of peach light across the room, emphasising the subtle blues of the decor, her progress silent as she wriggled her toes luxuriously in the thick blue pile of the carpet.

She was just picking up her nightdress when she froze in disbelief as the handle of her bedroom door turned. Clutching the thin silk to herself she stared as the door opened inwards and Blake walked casually in.

'Blake!' Her astonishment showed in her voice. 'What are you doing in here?'

'I am your husband,' he reminded her tauntingly, 'or is the maidenly shock because you were expecting someone else—your lover, perhaps? Sorry to disappoint you, but unless he wants to share your bed with me as well as with you, he'll have to sleep alone tonight,' Blake told her crudely.

Sapphire was too stunned to be embarrassed about her nudity, anger heating her blood to boiling point as she stared at him. 'Alan would never . . .' she began, only to be interrupted by Blake who drawled insultingly, 'Oh surely that can't be true, Sapphire? He must have wanted you once at least for you to be lovers, but not under my roof, and not while you're wearing my ring, and just to make sure he doesn't, I'll be sleeping in here with you tonight.'

'You can't.' The protest was out before she could stop it, her eyes widening with shock. 'Blake, there are half-a-dozen bedrooms for you to choose from. . .'

'But I've chosen this one,' he told her grimly, adding, 'Oh come on, Sapphire, I wasn't born yesterday, you really didn't think I was going to make it easy for you do you? You alone in one room, him virtually next door? When did you arrange for him to come here?'

He was across the room in four strides, gripping her upper arm with fingers that bit into the soft flesh, surprising a gasp of pain from her lips.

'Blake, I didn't arrange anything. I was as surprised as you to see him. Oh I knew he was coming to collect his car. . .' Anger fired her eyes to deep blue-black as she added bitterly, 'Why should I defend my actions to you? There's no reason why I should be faithful to you, Blake, no reason at all.'

'No?' His face was white with anger. 'Then perhaps I'd better give you one. Why didn't you tell him you were coming back to me, Sapphire? Were you afraid he wouldn't wait for you, is that it?'

'I wanted to tell him in person, not over the telephone. Alan fully understands the situation,' she lied, urged to utter the falsehood by some only dimly conceived knowledge that if Blake thought she still loved Alan, it would in some way protect her from him. This afternoon she had come dangerously close to succumbing to the raw masculinity of him; of succumbing to her own reluctantly admitted love for him, she told herself. If Blake discovered how she really felt she had no guarantee that he wouldn't somehow manipulate her vulnerable emotions and her, using them to his own best advantage. She shivered suddenly, wishing she had not as her shudder drew Blake's attention to her nude body.

In the lamplight her skin glowed pearly cream, her hair curling wildly round her shoulders, still damp from her shower, her face completely free of makeup.

'How many times has he seen you like this?' Blake grated hoarsely. 'How many times have you slept with him? How long have you been lovers?'

'That's none of your business,' Sapphire protested, hot colour flooding her skin. 'I don't ask you about your . . . your love life. . .'

'Love life!' Blake laughed harshly. 'Now there's

an antiquated term if ever there was one. I don't
have a *love life*, my dear wife, I learned the folly of
that years ago, but I do have all the usual sexual
desires. . . Like me to prove it to you?'

'You're disgusting.' Sapphire flung the words at
him as she pulled free of his grip.

'You didn't seem to think so earlier this evening,'
Blake reminded her softly, going back to the
bedroom door where he turned the key in the lock
and then removed it, putting it in his jeans pocket.
'Just in case you have any ideas about going to lover
boy while I'm asleep,' he explained tersely.

What was the matter with Blake? Sapphire
wondered bitterly. He seemed to have a fetish
about her going to Alan. What would he say if he
knew the truth? That Alan wasn't her lover; that
no man ever had been. . . She shuddered; her skin
suddenly too warm, her body weak with the
knowledge that there was only one man she
wanted to make love to her. What would Blake
say if she told him . . . if she asked him. . .

Shocked she pulled her thoughts back from the
precipice on which they teetered. Hadn't she
learned anything at all from the past? Once before
she had begged Blake to love her.

'Don't worry, you're quite safe with me,' Blake
drawled, watching her. 'Unless of course, you
choose not to be.'

'Why on earth should I do that?' Animosity
flared between them; tension tightening Sapphire's
nerve endings.

'Oh any number of reasons,' Blake told her
insultingly. 'You've been up here several days . . .
and it can sometimes be hard denying oneself,
when one's been used to. . .'

'Stop it!' Sapphire demanded, goaded almost beyond endurance, her cheeks scarlet with rage. 'How dare you suggest that. . .'

'That you'd be so hungry for sex that you'd turn to me?' Blake finished coolly for her. 'Why not? After all it wouldn't be the first time, would it?'

He turned his back on her as he spoke, calmly pulling off his sweater and unfastening his shirt, leaving Sapphire seething with temper and pain. How could he throw that in her face? He always had been a cruel bastard, she thought bitterly, but she had never expected anything like this. . .'

'Go on.' His voice was amused rather than contrite. 'Why don't you throw something at me, if that's how you feel.'

'Go to hell,' Sapphire told him thickly. 'God, I hate you, Blake. . .'

'Really?' He paused in the act of unfastening his belt, sitting down on the bed, his eyebrows arching as he studied the warm curves of her body. 'Then perhaps you ought to have a word with your hormones,' he tormented blandly, 'they seem to be getting the wrong message.'

Sapphire had forgotten her nudity, and she froze to the spot, the image of her own body faithfully reflected in the long pier-glass on the other side of the room. Her skin glowed milky pale, her breasts full and softly feminine, crowned with deeply pink nipples that betrayed all too clearly the correctness of Blake's taunt.

'I'm going to have a shower,' Blake told her, standing up and shedding his jeans. Frantically Sapphire dragged her gaze away from the muscled contours of his body, not sure who she hated the most; Blake for tormenting her as he was doing, or herself for being so vulnerable to that torment.

'You can always join me if you want to cool down.' The mocking taunt followed him across the room as he closed the bathroom door behind him. Once he was gone Sapphire struggled into her nightdress. The fine pearl grey silk seemed to emphasise her curves rather than conceal them, the deeply decolleté, lace-trimmed neckline outlining the curves of her breasts in explicit detail. One thing she was sure of. When Blake came back from the bathroom he would find her deeply and safely asleep. As she lay down and pulled the covers over her, keeping as close to the edge of the bed as possible she wondered bitterly if he had come to her room deliberately to torment her, or if he genuinely did believe if he wasn't there to prevent her she might have gone to Alan.

Letting him think that she and Alan were lovers was her only means of protection, she acknowledged, closing her eyes, her body tense. Once Blake found out they weren't, it wouldn't take him long to discover that she still loved him and then she would be completely at his mercy.

Nothing had changed, she thought bitterly, forcing herself to breathe evenly, and then a small inner voice corrected her, one thing had changed apparently. Blake, for some reason, now seemed to find her physically desirable. Or was his desire for her simply a frustrated sexual longing for Miranda who presumably now shared her favours between Blake and her husband? Nausea, deep and wrenching, tore into her as Sapphire pictured them together. No, please God not that, she whispered squeezing her eyes, closed as though she could blot out the pictures. She had been through all this once before and suffered all the torments of the damned picturing Blake with Miranda, imagining their bodies entwined in the act of love; sharing its heated ecstasy and its languorous aftermath—pleasures which had been denied to her, and she wasn't going to endure them again. She *couldn't*.

She heard Blake come back into the room and tensed as he snapped off the lamp, and pulled back the covers. The sarcastic comments she had expected about the way she was huddled on the edge of the bed never came, and to her chagrin within minutes of getting into bed, Blake appeared to be fast asleep!

As she struggled up through dense layers of sleep the first thing Sapphire realised was that at some time during the night she must have turned instinctively towards Blake, because now, instead of lying with her back to him, curled up on the edge of the bed she was actually curved against his body, her head pillowed on his shoulder.

Luckily Blake was still asleep and therefore unable to witness her weakness. As she started to move away from him, the second thing Sapphire realised was that he was sleeping nude. Perhaps she ought to have expected it; but during the brief days of their marriage he had always worn pyjamas, the jackets of which he had invariably tugged off at some time during the night, she remembered. Lost in her thoughts; seduced into inert languor by the warmth of his body, she was reluctant to move, even while acknowledging that she should; surely there could be no real harm in indulging herself in these few brief seconds of pleasure. But her conscience prodded her, and unwillingly she started to move away.

'Going somewhere?' Blake's voice, still husky with sleep, rasped tantalisingly against her sensitive skin, making her shiver with a reaction somewhere between delight and dread.

'It's light,' Sapphire told him unnecessarily, trying to edge away from him without drawing his attention to what she was doing, and failing abysmally as he rolled on to his side, pinning her against him with one arm.

He was so close now that she could feel the intimacy of his body heat; the warm, muskily male scent of his skin clouding her reasoning processes, so that it no longer seemed quite so imperative for her to move. Much more pleasant to give in to the allure of remaining where she was.

'I thought you'd want to be out, checking on the stock.' Conscience made her make the feeble concession to saying what she felt she should, but Blake brushed her protest aside.

'The men will be doing that, because I did the last round last night—we're very democratic up here,' he drawled teasingly. 'I must say it was quite a surprise to wake up and find you in my arms. I seem to remember that last night you couldn't get far enough away from me.'

'I didn't know what I was doing,' Sapphire defended herself, 'I must have turned over in my sleep and when. . .'

'You're used to sharing a bed with someone? Like you do with your lover?' Blake accused harshly, 'Is that what you were going to say?'

'And if it was?' Sapphire flung back at him

recklessly. Anything to keep him from discovering just how much she was affected by his proximity.

'Then there must be other things you're missing, beside a warm body in bed beside you at night,' Blake countered softly. Sapphire couldn't tell if it was challenge or anger that turned his eyes to molten gold, but even as she moved away from him, his fingers clamped into her waist, refusing to let her go. As she struggled to free herself her breasts brushed the taut skin of his chest and even through the fabric of her nightdress she was overwhelmingly conscious of the contact, closing her eyes against a sudden too-painful image of skin against flesh, of Blake stroking and caressing her.

'Open your eyes,' Blake demanded harshly, shattering the erotic bubble of her thoughts. 'You aren't going to pretend it's someone else who's holding you in his arms, Sapphire.'

'Who was it who taught you to be so arousingly responsive?' he muttered, his eyes on the swift rise and fall of her breasts, her nipples pressing urgently against the fine fabric of her nightdress, in wanton supplication of the caresses her mind had envisioned so very recently.

Sapphire felt a wave of shame course through her. How could she be behaving in such an abandoned fashion?

'Who?' Blake pressed. 'Your precious Alan, or another lover?'

'Does it matter?' Hot tears stung her eyes, caused as much by his cruel blindness as her own weakness. He was the only man she had ever met who could touch the deep inner core of her femininity; he was the only man with the ability to unleash her desire.

'Perhaps not.' The heat had gone from his voice to be replaced by a cynical blandness. 'That it has been achieved at all is miracle enough I suppose. When I think of the way you used to shy away from me.'

Shy away? Sapphire stared at him. What about all the times she had willed him to make love to her? What about the times she had lain in this bed praying that he would stretch out and touch her?

'I think it's time we were getting dressed,' she told him hurriedly, trying to dispel her tormenting memories.

'So, you haven't changed completely,' Blake drawled. 'You still run away from situations you find unpalatable. Well, this is one occasion my dear wife, when you can't run. Unless, of course, you want me to pursue you, and carry you back to this bed?'

'Why should you want to do that?' Sapphire tried to sound sophisticated and amused but instead her voice was a breathy, hesitant whisper, Blake's smile telling her that she had not succeeded.

'Do I really have to tell you?' He leaned towards her, the fingers of his free hand curling round the strap of her nightdress and slowly sliding it down her arm. The bedcovers had slipped down to her waist during their earlier struggle, and Sapphire watched like a rabbit transfixed by the hunter as Blake leisurely revealed the creamy slope of her breast.

'You've changed,' he murmured, studying her until the colour ran up under her pale skin. 'You're fuller here,' his thumb skimmed the outline of her breast, resting so briefly against her nipple that she couldn't be sure whether the caress was deliberate or accidental, 'and narrower here.'

His fingers touched her waist, and she shivered convulsively, her throat dry and tight with the aching need she could feel burning up inside her. She wanted to slide her fingers into the crisp darkness of his hair, to hold his head against her breast, and caress the male contours of his body. Shame and fear mingled into a stomach-tensing cramp as she tried to fight against her feelings.

'Do you like this?' Blake slid the nightdress free of her breast cupping it with his palm and stroking his tongue along the valley between it and its twin, his thumb making erotic patterns around its rosy peak.

'No.' Her denial was a choked, strangled lie.

'I think you mean yes.' Blake was so lazily self-assured that Sapphire started to tremble. 'Well, Sapphire,' he pressed, 'did you mean yes?' All the time he spoke to her he was teasing, nibbling little kisses closer and closer to her nipple. Heat coursed through her veins. Part of her wanted to flee; to get as far away from him as she could, and the other part wanted to be so close to him that not even the fragile thinness of her nightdress was between them. She ached for the feel of Blake's mouth against her breast; his hands on her body, but as though to punish her for her fib, his kisses stopped tantalisingly short of their goal, and with memories of past rejections to the forefront of her mind Sapphire could not, would not guide his mouth to the place she most wanted it to be.

'Well, then, perhaps you prefer this?'

She was eased out of her nightdress before she had time to object, the embarrassment of Blake's thorough scrutiny of her nude body outweighing all other considerations as she struggled to tug the bedclothes up over her, and Blake effortlessly restrained her. A mocking smile curved his mouth, but it was the showers of gold lightening glittering in his eyes that made Sapphire tense on a sudden spiral of excitement.

His fingertips stroking her hip and then following the line of her body downwards sparked off a showerburst of heady pleasure that she fought to conceal, swallowing the small gasp of delight that threatened to betray how she felt. She badly wanted to touch Blake as freely as he was touching her, to taste the warm maleness of his skin and feel his body come alive beneath her hands.

'You have the loveliest skin.' Blake was still touching her, drawing spiralling patterns against her thigh which transmitted an intensity of heat totally at odds with the lightness of his touch. His voice had a velvet, mesmeric quality that lulled her tense muscles into languorous relaxation. She wanted to purr almost, like a small satisfied cat, Sapphire realised on a stunned wave of surprise; she wanted to stretch and arch beneath those teasing fingers; to prolong the tormenting love play and instigate some of her own.

'Sapphire?'

The sound of her name made her turn her head to look at Blake, her eyes unknowingly a deep, dense purple blue.

'Open your mouth,' Blake commanded softly, 'I want to kiss you.'

It was heaven and hell, the zenith of pleasure and the nadir of despair. It was life and death; light and dark, and she was no more capable of resisting him than she was of denying that she loved him.

She clung to him, obeying the wordless commands of his mouth, responding with deep, driven intensity of emotion she had not known she could feel, abandoning every last vestige of pride and self-defence as her fingers locked in his hair and she clung with unashamed need to the greater strength of his body.

When at last he released her mouth, he studied its bruised softness for several seconds, his eyes eventually lifting to her bemused eyes, before he kissed her again, this time letting the moist warmth of his lips soothe the sensitive stinging skin of hers.

'You liked that.' It was a statement, not a question, rich with self-satisfaction, the long, lingering look he gave her body that of a man who knows exactly what effect he has had on the woman in his arms. His fingers traced a lazy pattern around and between her breasts, trailing downwards to her waist.

Excitement and urgency arched her body upwards, mutely seeking closer contact with his.

'I think you were right after all. It is time we got dressed.' His words were like snow being trickled down her spine. Sapphire couldn't believe she had heard them. She wanted to protest, to demand to know why he had aroused her so deliberately and turned away from her, but her pride would not allow her to. If Blake could behave as though what had just happened between them meant nothing to him; if he was completely unaffected by the explosion of love and need which had gripped her, then so was she.

# CHAPTER EIGHT

SAPPHIRE deliberately dawdled getting dressed, not
wanting to face Blake. As she had hoped, when
she walked into the kitchen half an hour later
there was no sign of him, but the sight of Alan
sitting morosely at the table, a mug of coffee in
front of him brought her to an abrupt halt.

'So you "hate" him do you?' he sneered bitterly.
'Some way you have of showing it! And to think I
held off taking you to bed because I didn't want to
stampede you! Oh, it's all right, Sapphire,' he
grimaced, the anger deserting him, as he raked
tired fingers through his hair. 'He's told me all
about it; how the two of you decided to give your
marriage another try. I just wish I heard it first
from you that's all.'

'I'm sorry, Alan.' Shakily Sapphire sat down,
knowing that Alan had every right to feel angry
and resentful. 'I didn't tell you over the phone
because . . . because I didn't think it was the right
thing to do. I didn't realise that Blake intended us
to be re-married quite so soon.'

'You're happy with him?' His voice was abrupt,
tight with a pain that made Sapphire's heart ache
in sympathy.

'I do love him,' she told him, avoiding the
question.

'And obviously sexually you're extremely compatible,' Alan shocked her by saying. 'Come on,
Sapphire, I'm not a complete fool,' he told her

134

roughly, 'when a man comes down for breakfast, looking like a well-fed predator, it isn't hard to guess what's put the smile on his face.'

She wanted to protest that he was wrong, but sensibly did not. Perhaps it might make it easier for Alan to accept the situation if he believed that she and Blake were lovers. Sadly she knew that their friendship was now over, and that once she and Blake had parted there could be no going back to Alan. She would miss him as one always missed good friends, but she did not love him, she acknowledged, her feelings from him came nowhere near to those she felt for Blake.

After he had breakfast Alan insisted on leaving. When he had gone Sapphire felt restless. On impulse she decided to go out for a walk, glimpsing Blake working in one of the snow-covered fields—just a small dark figure by a Land Rover, with something familiar in his stance that tugged at her heart.

Shivering in the cold wind she walked back to the house, still too restless to settle. She would go and see her father; she decided visiting him might help to keep her mind off her own problems.

Flaws farmyard was deserted when she drove in. Someone had cleared the worst of the snow away, and although the kitchen was redolent with the yeasty smell of baking there was no sign of Mary.

Terror, sharp and paralysing, gripped her for a second, a dreadful vision of her father, motionless, dying, rising up before her. The vision cleared and she hurried upstairs, her heart thumping; her pulses racing in aching fear as she pushed open the door to her father's room and came to a full stop.

Far from lying close to death's door on his bed

her father was standing by the window, dressed in a pair of disreputable old trousers and a thick woollen jumper. He looked thinner than Sapphire remembered, but otherwise he was still very much the father of her late teens, his weatherbeaten face turned towards the window, his eyes on the distant snow-covered line of hills.

'Back already,' he commented without looking round. 'I'll just have a cup of coffee Mary and then...' He turned and saw Sapphire, shock and something else she couldn't understand leaping to life in his eyes.

'Sapphire!'

The room started to tilt and spin and Sapphire heard a roaring sound in her ears, increasing in volume until it drowned out everything else. Dimly she was aware of her father calling for Mary, of blackness coming down over her, and then a thick, suffocating darkness that seemed to press down all around her.

When she opened her eyes she was sitting in her father's chair, Mary standing anxiously at her side.

'My, you gave us all a shock fainting like that,' she told Sapphire worriedly. 'Are you all right now?'

'Dad ...' Sapphire croaked unevenly, 'when I came in and everywhere was so quiet, I thought...'

Shock, and something else she couldn't name shadowed Mary's eyes. She was about to speak when the door opened and her father walked in. *Walked in*, Sapphire noted dazedly, carrying a mug of tea.

'Come on, drink this,' Mary instructed her. 'It

will help allay the shock.' The 'phone started to ring and as Sapphire took the mug from her father Mary said briskly, 'I'd better go down and answer that.'

When she had gone Sapphire looked at her father. 'Sorry about this,' she apologised huskily, 'but you gave me such a shock. . .'

'Aye, I'm sorry too, lass.' Her father looked sad and disturbed. 'I thought. . .' He shook his head. 'No, we won't talk about it now, Sapphire. You're in no fit state. You stay here and rest for a while and I'll. . .'

He broke off as Mary came in her round face creased into a thoughtful frown.

'That was Blake,' she told them both. 'In a rare old state, wanting to know if we'd seen anything of you.' She looked at Sapphire and smiled. 'That must have been some spat the two of you had to generate so much concern, and the pair of you not a week reconciled yet.'

Knowing that her father was watching her Sapphire summoned a light smile. 'Blake wasn't too pleased when Alan turned up last night,' she told them, hoping she would be forgiven her small fib, but not wanting to let them guess at the real state of affairs between herself and Blake.

'Jealous, was he?' her father laughed. 'Aye well, I suppose it's my fault for sending the laddie over to you, but I thought it best.'

'He's gone now,' Sapphire told them, and explained briefly.

'I'd better get back,' she told her father. She couldn't put off facing Blake for ever. From somewhere she would have to find the determination to remind him that their marriage was a strictly platonic one. Not that he could really want her, she reminded herself bitterly.

'You stay right here,' Mary scolded her. 'You're in no fit state to be driving after that faint. Blake's coming to take you home. He's getting one of the men to drive him over in the Land Rover. He'll be here in ten minutes or so.'

Shakily Sapphire drank her tea. Why had Blake rung Flaws Farm? Had he perhaps gone back to the house this morning and wondered where she was? She frowned, and then tensed as she heard the familiar sound of a Land Rover engine.

'Here he is now,' Mary announced going to look out of the window. 'I'll go down and tell him where we are. No, don't you get up,' she told Sapphire sternly. 'I'm not too happy about that faint of yours. You must try and take things easy for a few days. Put on a few pounds, perhaps. I know it's fashionable to be slim but you seem to have been overdoing things.'

'Now she's back with Blake, she'll soon fatten up a bit,' her father prophesied. 'There's nothing like a happy marriage.'

Sighing Sapphire turned her face away. What would her father say if he knew the truth? But he mustn't know the truth, she thought in panic. She could already see the effect their re-marriage had had on his health; he was marvellously improved. It couldn't last for long of course, but she daren't take the risk of him discovering the truth.

She heard Mary go downstairs and then return several minutes later accompanied by Blake. Where earlier she had been shocked to see how much healthier her father had appeared than she had anticipated, now she was equally startled by the pallor of Blake's skin and the tense, bitter, brooding darkness of his eyes.

'Mary tells me you fainted.' His voice was almost accusatory.

'It was just the shock of finding Dad out of bed,' she told him knowing how feeble her explanation sounded, but not able to tell him in front of her father of her fears when she had entered the strangely silent house.

She started to get out of the chair, but Blake forestalled her, striding over and bending to pick her up, ignoring her protests.

'Let him carry you,' Mary placated. 'I don't want you falling down those steep stairs. No, she's perfectly all right,' she told Blake who had turned to question her, 'she just needs to rest a little and get her strength back.'

When he had installed her in the passenger seat of his car Blake started the engine, his face grim as he drove the car out of the cobbled yard.

'What did you want me for?' Sapphire ventured once they were out on the road. 'You rang Mary to find out if I was there,' she pressed when he turned to frown at her. 'You must have wanted me for something. . .'

'When I went back to the house and found you missing,' Blake told her harshly, 'it struck me that you might have decided to renege on our bargain.'

It took several seconds for the words to sink in. 'You mean you thought I had left with Alan?' Sapphire said incredulously, 'But. . .'

'But he wouldn't take you, believing that you and I are lovers?' There was a cynically bitter twist to Blake's mouth, his eyes as hard and cold as the snow-encrusted stone walls they were driving past.

'No! I. . .' Oh, what was the use trying to get through to him when he was in this sort of mood, Sapphire thought despairingly. Reaction from her faint had started to set in. She felt sick and tense; in no condition to cope with Blake's biting sarcasm. This was the Blake she remembered, she thought miserably; this hard, cynical man who seemed to be driven by demons she could not comprehend; who seemed to take pleasure in humiliating her.

The moment the car stopped outside the backdoor, she reached for her seatbelt, but Blake was too quick for her, moving swiftly round to her door, and lifting her out of her seat, even as she protested that she could manage.

'What made you faint, Sapphire?' he demanded as he carried her upstairs to their room. 'No wonder you put up so little fight when I suggested we re-marry. But you weren't completely truthful with me were you? What happened? Wouldn't he marry you when he knew that you were carrying his child?'

She was too stunned to answer him. He dropped her unceremoniously on the bed, where she simply lay, staring at him.

'Oh, I confess you had me nicely fooled,' Blake said bitterly. 'It never occurred to me that you. . . We can hardly have our marriage annulled now,' he continued sardonically, 'and that being the case. . .'

He walked back to the bedroom door, calmly locking it and pocketing the key while Sapphire watched him in stupid disbelief. Blake couldn't really believe that she was carrying Alan's child, could he? If that had been the case she would

never have consented to this ridiculous re-
marriage. Alan would have married her and
willingly. Anger swept aside pain. How dare he
accuse her of behaving so selfishly? She opened her
mouth to tell him the truth and then closed it, her
eyes rounding in surprise as he stripped off his
sweater and shirt. His hands were on the buckle of
his belt before Sapphire realised what was
happening, her voice croaky and unsteady as she
whispered, 'Blake, just what do you think you're
doing?'

'If you're going to foist the responsibility for
this child off on me, I might as well have some of
the pleasure of fathering it,' he snarled furiously at
her. 'It might not be my child, Sapphire, but you
are my wife, and since it looks like this time I'm
stuck with you, I might as well get whatever I can
get out of it. . .'

'I thought all you wanted was my father's land,'
Sapphire gritted back at him. 'I won't make love
with you, Blake,' she warned him. 'I. . .' Her
breath was trapped in her throat as he stepped out
of his jeans, flinging them on to the floor. Clad
only in dark briefs his body was that of a man
used to an active life. Unwillingly Sapphire felt her
glance slide helplessly over his broad shoulders,
and down across the width of his chest. Dark hair
arrowed downwards across the flat tautness of his
stomach, and a mad desire to reach out and trace
its erotic path rose up inside her. Quelling it, she
tore her gaze away, shaken by the force of her
reaction.

Two strides brought Blake to the edge of the
bed. Leaning down he grasped the lapels of the
cotton blouse she was wearing and Sapphire

tensed, blue eyes meeting gold. Her breath stifled
in her throat as Blake's fingers curled into the
fabric, the glitter in his eyes one of dark menace
as he jerked forcefully at the cotton. Buttons
flew in all directions as the blouse tore, unable
to withstand the violence he was doing it.
Sapphire knew she ought to have felt fear; terror
even, but what she did feel was a wild surging
excitement; a primaeval emotion that seemed to
spring from her innermost being and burst into
life, fuelled by the dark determination she could
read in Blake's eyes.

He found the waistband of her denim skirt,
unsnapping it and sliding down the zip. She tried
to push him away, tensing as she heard the almost
feral snarl of anger he gave as he removed her
clutching fingers, and tossed aside her skirt.

Wearing only her bra and briefs she stared up at
him as he loomed over her, willing her body not to
communicate to his her unwilling arousal. Despite
the rage she could feel emanating from him, she
couldn't forget that this was the man she loved;
and that the mere sight of his body was enough to
bring leaping pulses to life inside her, fuelling a
burning ache that instinct told her only his
possession could assuage. She remembered how he
had deliberately aroused her only that morning
and her eyes darkened unknowingly, her tongue
touching the dry outline of her lips. Above her
Blake growled menacingly, and her eyes met his,
reading the eternal message of rage and desire that
glinted there.

'Thinking about him, were you? Pity you fainted
so unpropitiously this morning,' he taunted,
'otherwise I'd never have suspected you could be

pregnant. Despite it all you still have a look of . . . almost innocence about you.'

His eyes darkened over the last few words, almost as though they caused him pain, and mingled with her own resentment that he could so easily think so little of her Sapphire felt a thread of aching response. She wanted to be in his arms, she acknowledged wistfully; she wanted the warm heat of his body against hers; his hands caressing her, his lips. . . A shudder seemed to tear through her, visible in the brief convulsion of her body, escaping in a faint sigh that was lost as Blake gripped her hair, tangling his fingers in it, forcing her face up so that he could look into her eyes as he muttered thickly, 'Forget him,' and then bent to silence her protest with the fierce possession of his mouth.

This was no tentative, explorative kiss, but an explosion of raw emotions, too strong to be confined in neat pigeonholes labelled 'anger' or 'desire', but instinctively Sapphire recognised and responded to them, unaware that her fingers were digging into the muscled smoothness of his shoulder, until Blake released her abruptly.

'No wonder he wanted you,' he told her hoarsely, his fingers stroking lightly down her shoulder and then erotically over the taut outline of her breast, his warm breath fanning her bruised lips. 'If you always react like that I'm only surprised that he didn't want to keep you—or was it the thought of the child that put him off? Is that why you were so quick to accept my offer, Sapphire? Because you knew he didn't want to marry you?'

Anger flared hotly inside her. 'You already seem

to know all the answers, Blake,' she responded brittly, 'so why ask the questions?'

'Perhaps because I'm hoping I don't.' His thumb was rubbing lightly over the thin silk covering her nipple and Sapphire squirmed slightly beneath the tormenting caress, trying to clamp down on the feelings he was arousing inside her.

'What's the matter? Doesn't my touch appeal to you as much as his? I can make you want me, Sapphire.'

'No!' Her denial was meant as a plea for him not to carry out his threat, but Blake chose to ignore it.

'You think not?' he muttered into her throat, searching for and finding the fast-beating pulse that gave the lie to her denial. She could smell the warm musky scent of his body—inflaming her own with a subtle sexual chemistry that made her languorous and weak. The rough hair on his chest rubbed abrasively against her skin as he moved, biting delicately into her skin, making her shiver almost deliriously with pleasure. The fine silk of her bra and briefs was a barrier between them that tormented her, denying her the intimate contact of skin against skin that she now craved and when Blake's hands slid round her back to remove her bra she expelled her breath in a pent-up sigh of relief he couldn't fail to understand. Soft colour filmed her cheeks as he looked down at her, his smile tormentingly cruel.

'Still expect me to believe you don't want me, Sapphire?'

What could she say? That he had misunderstood her initial remark? She turned her head aside, not wanting him to see the betraying sheen of tears she knew wasn't far away and then gasped out loud as she felt the stinging nip of his teeth against the swollen curve of her breast. Hard on the heels on the initial burst of pain came a pleasure so intense that her eyes widened in acknowledgment of it.

'Don't expect me to believe you haven't been touched like that before,' Blake told her thickly, watching her, 'or like this.'

Ripples of pleasure spread shiveringly through her body as his tongue stroked and teased the aching fullness of her breasts, making her tense and arch in a mindless frenzy of need she hadn't known herself capable of feeling. She dimly heard Blake's suddenly harsh breathing in counterpoint to her own quick shallow breaths, and then his hands slid to her waist, gripping its slenderness until his mouth opened over first one nipple and then the other, tasting, sucking, tugging, while Sapphire felt she would explode with the intensity of pleasure building up inside her.

Unable to stop herself, she moaned Blake's name, reaching up to stroke the hard contours of his back with hands suddenly desperately eager for the feel of his skin against them, scattering wild, impassioned kisses over his shoulder, using her teeth to deliver delicate little nips that drew a hoarse groan of satisfaction from his throat.

All sense of restraint and commonsense abandoned, Sapphire didn't allow herself to think or reason. This was Blake who she still loved as desperately now as she had done when they first married; and if he had accused her so unfairly, well what did it matter now that she was in his arms and he was touching and kissing her with a hunger that her body recognised even if her mind could not. It was a hunger that fed and matched her own, his body whispering to hers that it too had starved and ached for this tumultuous pleasure they were now sharing. Despite the fact that they had never before made love, there was nothing tentative or exploratory in their embraces. Sapphire responded to the intimacy of Blake's touch as intuitively as though they had been lovers for years. Her lips brushed the flat hardness of his nipple and she registered the surprised shock of pleasure jolting through him. His eyes closed, his mouth warm against the indentation of her waist, as she lay half-pinned beneath him, indolently admiring the sculptured perfection of his body.

She ran her fingers lightly down the dark arrowing of hair, stopping when she reached his briefs. He tensed, and then demanded thickly, 'Touch me, Sapphire.'

She let her fingers stray exploratively over the thin cotton of his briefs, her touch slightly hesitant and unsure, her heart thudding violently in response to the small, liquid sound of pleasure emerging from Blake's throat. Heated, muttered words of praise and encouragement overwhelmed all her shyness and reserve. When Blake tugged off his briefs her breath caught in her throat, her eyes unknowingly widening slightly.

'A man could be in danger of forgetting that he's only mortal under a look like that,' Blake told her throatily, sliding his hand round her throat, his thumb under her chin tilting her face up to meet his.

Passion blazed into life as they kissed, her mouth opening willingly to admit the penetration of his tongue, seeking, taking all the warm sweetness she gave up so willingly.

Blake's free hand was resting possessively against her thigh, a heavy warm weight that tantalised and excited her, her own fingers stroking and cajoling the strong muscles of his back, sliding round to investigate the sharp angles of his hips, moving in restless, roving urgency as she responded to the hunger in Blake's kiss.

He released her to tease a chain of moist caresses in a line that investigated the valley between her breast and the slight swell of her stomach.

The restless urgency in the pit of her stomach increased and in obedience to its commands Sapphire brushed her own lips against the firmness of Blake's belly, thrilling to the sudden tension in muscles finely tuned to her light touch. His skin tasted warm and slightly salty, its flavour almost addictive. Lost in the veil of pleasure touching him had revealed to her, she let her lips travel where they wished barely aware of Blake's harsh groan of protest until he snatched her up, rolling her beneath the constraining weight of his body, parting her legs with his thigh, muttering her name like a litany as his fingers touched her intimately, making her yield and ache for his possession.

Far beyond remembering the accusation that had preceded their lovemaking, Sapphire wasn't ready for the unexpected burst of pain. Her muscles tensed immediately, shock mingling with hurt as she fought to understand the too-swift transition from pleasure to pain.

Above her she heard Blake curse, a fiercely bitter sound, his body withdrawing from hers.

Suddenly the pain was gone, and shamelessly she clung to him, refusing to let him go, her eyes pleading mutely with him as her fingers dug into his shoulders, her soft, 'Blake, please ...' dragging an anguished mutter of response from his throat as he tensed and then shuddered and her body melted in welcome to his, her senses singing with pleasure.

Never had pleasure seemed so tangible, her body was awash with it, glowing, so supremely fulfilled that she wanted to tell the whole world. Stretching indolently she turned her head. Blake was lying inches away, his eyes open, his expression sombre. Of course, this wasn't the first time he had experienced such feelings—not by a long way.

'There's never been anyone else, has there?' he asked the question in a flat voice that drained her pleasure as effectively as a tap being turned on. Sapphire shook her head.

'Then for God's sake why didn't you say so?'

No need to ask if he was regretting making love to her. It was there, written all over his face, etching into his scathing voice.

'I didn't think you'd listen.' She turned away from him, not wanting him to see how vulnerable she was. Neither of them had mentioned love ... but silently in her heart she had told him how she felt about him, just as her body told his how much it worshipped and adored him.

'So you decided to let me find out for myself?'

'I didn't think I could have stopped you.'

'Half-a-dozen words or so would have done it— "I'm still a virgin", for instance.'

Sapphire arched her eyebrows, turning back to

face him. 'And you'd have believed me?' She turned away again. 'I'd better get dressed. . .'

'No.' Blake's voice was sharp. He swung himself out of bed. 'No, stay here and rest for a while, I'll go down and make you a drink.'

'I'm not an invalid, Blake,' she protested, flushing as his eyes studied her pale skin and slender body. Still bathed in the warm afterglow of their lovemaking she hadn't bothered to cover herself, but now she felt a need to do so, chilled by the way Blake was studying her. Was he comparing her to Miranda? She felt sick at the thought.

'You're not exactly in the peak of *health* either,' he told her still watching her. There was a dark, brooding quality to his look that saddened her. Was he already regretting what had happened?

She reached out towards him, her eyes unconsciously pleading, 'Blake, I. . .'

'Stay here and rest.' He had his back to her and was already getting dressed. Feeling dejected, Sapphire huddled beneath the bed-clothes. Plainly Blake didn't want to talk to her. She closed her eyes, knowing she should regret what had happened but knowing that she did not. Where was her pride? When Blake left the easy, weak tears of physical release flowed for a few seconds and then stopped. By the time he came back with her tea Sapphire was fast asleep. He stood watching her for several seconds with shuttered eyes, before turning to leave, his face grim.

# CHAPTER NINE

'SAPPHIRE, we have to talk.'

They were sitting in front of the log fire she had lit just before dinner. Blake had suggested they have their coffee there and now she tensed dreading what he might be about to say. She had been awaiting this moment with mingled apprehension and anguish ever since she had woken up this afternoon. Had Blake guessed that she still loved him? Was he going to tell her that what had happened between them had been caused by some mental aberration. That he would never have made love to her had he been in his right senses? Was he going to tell her about Miranda?

She risked a glance at him. He was sitting opposite her on a chair, his upper body leaning forward, elbows braced on his thighs as he dropped his head into his hands and pushed weary fingers through his hair.

A wave of love overwhelmed her. She wanted to reach out and touch him; to wipe away the lines of exhaustion fanning out from his eyes; to touch and caress him, to. . .

'Sapphire!' The tone of his voice warned her that he knew her thoughts were wandering, his fingers steepled together as he watched her over them, the liquid gold of his eyes dulled, their expression almost stark.

'I never intended what happened this afternoon to take place,' he began abruptly, causing a thousand sharp knives to tear jaggedly at Sapphire's aching heart.

'I know that,' she interrupted curtly. 'I do have a memory, Blake, I'm well aware of the fact that you don't find me desirable. When we first married. . .'

'Don't be ridiculous, of course I find you desirable.' Angry fingers raked through his hair again. 'Hell, Sapphire,' he growled impatiently, 'you're not *that* innocent. If I don't desire you what the hell do you think that was all about this afternoon?'

Colour flamed momentarily in her face as she recalled the fierce intensity of their lovemaking; the feeling she had had at the time that both of them were suffering from the same driven compulsion; the same starving hunger. Quickly she reminded herself of the past, of the early days of their marriage. 'You may desire me now, Blake, but when we were first married, you couldn't bear to touch me; you. . .'

'I don't want to talk about the past.' His voice was clipped and brusque, defying her to continue the subject. 'We're living in the present now, Sapphire, and despite everything we said before we re-married, it must be as obvious to you now, as it is to me, that we can't live together platonically.'

Her muscles seemed to be seized in a paralysing grip, her body totally unable to function, and then as the great wave of pain crashed down over her Sapphire knew her immobility was simply a defensive measure; a way of stopping the pain, only it had failed miserably. It seemed to fill every corner of her, drowning out pride and reserve. She wanted to cry out to Blake not to send her away;

she wanted to plead with him to stay with her, but instead she remained unspeaking, dreading opening her mouth in case she voiced her anguished thoughts.

'Well?'

Blake was plainly waiting for a response, and when she didn't make one, said tersely, 'Come on, Sapphire, I know you . . . you were a virgin—and that fact alone merely reinforces what I feel—but you must know that sexually we're extremely compatible, almost explosively so,' he muttered half under his breath.

His words were so totally at variance to what she had expected to hear that Sapphire simply stared at him. 'Come on,' Blake demanded half-aggressively, 'Admit it Sapphire, when I made love to you, you enjoyed it. You. . .'

'Yes.' Her simple admission seemed to rob him of breath. 'I did enjoy it, Blake.'

Colour lay dark red along the ridge of his cheekbones, his eyes the flaming gold she remembered from that afternoon, their gaze trained on her, tracking every betraying expression that crossed her face. He breathed deeply, exhaling slowly, his chest rising and falling with the effort.

'Why were you still a virgin?' He was looking directly at her, and Sapphire knew an insane desire to laugh. Pure nerves she told herself, taking a deep breath of her own to steady her.

'At first when I left here I felt too bruised mentally to even think of loving anyone. Later . . .' she shrugged, 'Well, there just wasn't anyone I wanted, and then I met Alan. . .'

She paused, telling herself that it wasn't really

lying to tell him the truth as she had believed it to be before realising that she still loved him. He didn't want her love, and if he knew how she felt he could easily send her away, when, in reality, all she wanted to do was to stay.

Ignoring the inner warning voices that told her she was courting even greater unhappiness than she had already experienced, she continued softly, '... I wanted to be sure that what we felt for one another was right. Alan felt the same way. Before I came up here we were planning to go away together for a holiday. We were going...'

'To be lovers? In some romantic, idyllic setting?' Blake demanded harshly. 'Mentally you were ready to make love, and because your boyfriend wasn't available you substituted me, is that what you're trying to tell me?' He looked so murderously angry that Sapphire knew a frisson of fear.

'Perhaps, subconsciously,' she lied bravely— anything rather than risk him guessing the truth. 'But no, I didn't consciously substitute you for Alan, Blake.'

'And am I also supposed to believe that we were good together because you thought I was someone else?'

Slowly Sapphire shook her head. She daren't risk trying to pretend that. Blake was angry enough already. Obviously she had touched some nerve of touchy male pride which it would be unwise to press on too hard. 'You're the one with the experience—not me,' she reminded him simply. 'Personally I don't think it would be possible to deceive oneself to that extent, but...'

'It isn't.' Blake's voice was so harsh, his face so shuttered and forbidding that she wondered what personal anguish lay behind the curt words, but could not bring herself to ask.

'So,' he told her, 'given that sexually we both agree that we're extremely compatible, I submit that we change the rules of our partnership.'

'Change the rules?' Sapphire was so surprised that she could only repeat what he had said, staring uncomprehendingly up at him. For an instant there was something in his eyes that warmed the ice-coldness of her heart, but it was gone almost immediately his voice crisp and businesslike as he said firmly. 'Yes. We agreed that our relationship would be a platonic one lasting just as long as. . .'

'My father lives,' Sapphire finished for him, her face white. For a few hours she had forgotten her father's condition. Mentally castigating herself she tried to concentrate on what Blake was saying. 'Now I'm suggesting that we lift that self-imposed ban; that we make our marriage a real one in every sense of the word, to be. . .'

'Set aside when we no longer desire one another?'

'Is that what you want?'

His eyes narrowed as he waited for her response, and Sapphire felt a quiver of apprehension deep down inside her. Had he guessed how she felt? It was pride and pride alone that kept her from crying out that she wanted to be with him for ever; that she wanted to share his life and his bed for just as long as her life lasted. Instead she said lightly, 'Yes, of course.'

A mask seemed to drop down over his features, his eyelids lowering to conceal his thoughts from her. 'Very well then,' he said at last. 'If those are your terms, then for as long as our desire lasts, so does our marriage.' He stood up, stretching lithely, and completely changing the subject said calmly, 'Snow's melting. I'll just go out and check on the foal. Why don't you have an early night? You still look washed out.'

Very flattering, Sapphire thought wrathfully ten minutes later, luxuriating in a deep scented bath of deliciously hot water. She wasn't going to question Blake's abrupt volte-face, nor his suggestion that their marriage continue. Perhaps he was hoping to quench his desire for Miranda with her. Perhaps the fact that Miranda was now married broke Blake's own personal code of behaviour, Sapphire didn't know.

One half of her urged flight and safety, reminding her of all the pain he had already caused her, while the other whispered that life without him had been arid, dead; and that perhaps his desire for her could flower into something stronger and more permanent if it was carefully nurtured and protected.

She lingered so long in the bath, deep in thought, that the water started to cool. A draught from the door as it opened made her shiver and she turned round thinking it must have swung open.

'You've been in here so long I was beginning to wonder if my suggestion was so offensive to you that you'd decided you preferred a watery grave to another night in my arms.'

The sight of Blake standing beside the bath, looking down at her, was so unexpected and startling that she could barely breathe. 'I was thinking,' she told him huskily, shivering again as her skin chilled. 'I'm sorry if you've been waiting for the bathroom.' How formal her voice sounded, her expression hunted as she looked past him to where she had left her towel, trying not to think about the hunger that had started to unfurl inside her at the thought of 'a night in his arms'.

'It's large enough for us to share,' Blake drawled reaching for his electric razor, and wiping some of the steam off the mirror above the basin as he plugged it in and switched it on.

'Blake, it's cold in here. . .' He was halfway through shaving when she finally plucked up the courage to remind him, albeit obliquely, that she wanted to get out of the bath. He finished what he was doing, rubbing his jaw experimentally. 'I thought you always shaved in the morning,' Sapphire muttered crossly. Why couldn't he take the hint and leave her in privacy to get ready for bed?

'So I did,' he agreed blandly, unplugging the razor and turning round to lean indolently against the wall, watching her, 'but married men, my sweet, always shave at night. It saves wear and tear on delicate feminine skin,' he pointed out, grinning openly when she started to blush. The colour seemed to start at her toes and wash up over her body until it reached the swell of her breasts, now barely concealed by the cold bubbles, 'and if you're cold, why don't you get out of the bath?' He saw her tense and instinctively try to submerge more of her body beneath the bubbles and leant towards her. 'Why so shy? You weren't this afternoon.'

How could she explain that that had been different; that then in the heat of passion her own nudity had not disturbed her, but that now in the small confines of the bathroom, with Blake still fully dressed, it did?

All she could manage was a cross, 'You seem to forget that unlike you, I'm not used to . . . to. . .'

'Living with someone? The only person I've ever lived with is you, Sapphire.' As he spoke he was unfastening his shirt buttons. When he had finished he tugged it off, revealing the tautly muscled expanse of his chest. Her breath seemed to lock inside her as Sapphire tried to drag her hungry gaze away from his body.

'Since you won't get out of your own volition, and since I'm too much of a gentleman to let you freeze, I'll just have to help you, won't I?' Blake drawled, and as he leaned towards her, Sapphire realised why he had removed his shirt, and tried automatically to evade him. The small tidal wave her hurried movements caused soaked Blake's jeans, but didn't prevent him from lifting her out of the bath. His chest felt warm and hard against her water-chilled damp flesh, a shivering that had nothing to do with the cold raising goose bumps over her sensitised skin.

'Blake!' Her half-shocked protest was ignored. 'You're soaking wet,' she pointed out breathlessly, trying to clamp down on her rising excitement and totally unable to do so. This close she could see the pores in his skin, the mingled scent of sweat and heat coming off it provocatively arousing.

'We both are,' he agreed, slowly letting her slide to the floor, while reaching for her towel with his free hand, 'but it can soon be remedied.' His eyes never left her face as he enveloped her in the large soft towel and then slowly started to rub her dry.

Within seconds of his touching her Sapphire had forgotten how chilled she had been. Her body seemed to be bathed with heat, consumed by it everywhere he touched her. She had never dreamed that something as mundane as drying her damp skin could be so unbelievably erotic but the gentle friction of the towel against her skin, in Blake's hands became an instrument of exquisite pleasure that delighted and yet intruded unbearably, stopping her from savouring the touch of Blake's hands against her skin—a touch she now burned and hungered for even more than she had this afternoon. He only had to touch her and she went up in flames, she realised shudderingly, almost lightheaded with desire.

'Blake.' His name was a muffled protest and a plea, lost against his chest as she gave in to an overwhelming urge to reach out and touch him, pressing trembling lips to the hard column of his throat, and glorying in his responsive shudder.

'Tell me you want me.' The hoarse command was one she couldn't resist.

'I want you.'

The towel fell away as he picked her up and strode through into the bedroom. Against her body she could feel the fierce thud of Blake's heart, pounding out an unmistakably erotic message, his body, hard and urgent as he deposited her on the bed, tugging off his wet jeans before joining her.

'Show me how much,' he demanded thickly, tracing an erotic pathway downwards along her throat, his fingers burning fiery brands of possession against her skin as he cupped the silky skin of her breast, delicately stroking the hard nub of her nipple. This time Sapphire responded immediately without hesitation, knowing with one corner of her mind that mingled with her desire and love was a tiny thread of desperation urging her to take as much of him as she could while she could—memories to store up to keep her warm on those nights when her bed would be cold and empty without him. As though her yearning hunger reached out and unleashed some deep core of need within him Blake reacted to her passion, touching her, kissing her with a barely restrained ferocity that left her weakly clinging to him like a drowning person to a raft. His touch, his need, the words of passion and hunger he muttered into her ear, took her far beyond the shores of love and out into an ocean so deep she knew that without him she would sink and never ever re-surface.

Fierce tremors of pleasure raced through her body, each lingering caress making her arch and invite with a sensuality that left one corner of her mind half-shocked. Could this really be her, touching Blake with a far greater intimacy than she had ever envisaged; stroking and kissing the taut male body until Blake cried out in a delirium of need, reaching for her, taking the fullness of one breast deeply into his mouth and laving it with the moist heat of his tongue.

Now it was her turn to cry out with pleasure and to experience the fierce shudder of pleasure slamming through Blake's body as he responded to that cry. His fingers stroked circles of fire along the inside of her thigh her body aching with the intensity of her need. He touched her intimately and she melted, twisting and turning, breathing in short, muffled gasps.

'It's no good, I can't wait any longer.' Blake's groaned admission echoed her own thoughts, her body wildly exulting in his swift possession and frenziedly responding to it. The world seemed to explode around them Sapphire crying out with pleasure at each powerful thrust of his body, her nails scoring heatedly along his back as she sought to prolong the contact her body craved even after the climax had been reached and the deep ache inside her soothed.

She felt Blake move away slightly and murmured an incoherent protest. 'Hush...' His mouth covered hers briefly, warm and moist and she was shocked to feel the light spiral of desire twist through her so quickly after she thought it had been sated. She tried to move away when Blake bent his head to suck lightly on her swollen and slightly sore nipples, but the pleasure of his touch seduced her into staying where she was, dreamily contemplating the smooth warmth of his skin, reaching out lazy fingers to stroke idly along the ridge of his shoulder.

When his lips grazed across her stomach she felt too indolent to protest, simply looking down at the thick darkness of his hair and wondering awedly that one person could be so vitally important to her happiness.

Blake's fingers touched her thigh, and she tensed as his tongue touched her so intimately that she almost recoiled from the shock of it, trying to pull away and yet at the same time consumed by the molten heat his intimacy engendered until she was giving herself up to it, abandoning herself completely to the sensual spell he was weaving around her, unaware that she was crying out his name.

This time their coming together was less tumultuous, more leisurely and prolonged; Blake's fierce cry of exultation muffled by her kiss, her arms holding him locked against her body as she savoured the sweet aftermath of their pleasure. She fell asleep still holding him, waking during the night to discover that their positions were reversed and that he was now the one holding her, the heavy weight of one leg thrown across her body, pinning her close against him. Sleepily content she nestled closer to him gloating over the pleasure of being able to do so; of being free to reach out and touch the matted hair on his chest; to place her lips to the pulse thudding slowly in his throat. Maybe he only wanted her, but she loved him and hopefully, God willing, they could yet build a relationship; a marriage that could last.

She fell asleep on that thought waking to find herself alone. Downstairs in the kitchen she found a note propped up against the teapot and a small smile tugged at her lips as she read it.

'Market Day,' Blake had written. 'Don't expect me back until late—suggest you catch up on your sleep!'

She spent the morning in a blissful daze, knowing that she was walking around with a smile on her face like a cat fed on cream, but unable to do a thing about it.

After a light lunch she contemplated going for a walk, and was just about to set out when she heard the sound of a car driving into the yard. From her vantage point in the kitchen she watched Miranda uncurl her slender body from the driver's seat, her face disdainful as she picked her way over the cobbled yard in spike heeled shoes. Her cream

wool suit and expensive shoes were beautiful but
surely completely unsuitable for farm visiting
Sapphire reflected waspishly as Miranda knocked
on the back door.

'If you want Blake, I'm afraid he isn't here,'
she told her curtly, knowing she was being
ungracious but unable to stop herself. It still
hurt bitterly to think of Blake and this woman
being lovers; to know that if Miranda hadn't
married they still would be lovers. It did nothing
to endear Miranda to her to know that at least
some of Blake's desire for her must have been
fuelled by the fact that he was missing *her* and
Sapphire knew some of her feelings must be
reflected in her face.

'It isn't Blake I wanted to see,' Miranda
surprised her by saying smugly, 'Of course I knew
he wouldn't be here. It's market day—we normally
meet for lunch but of course since I got
married. . .' She shrugged dainty shoulders. 'I've
told Blake he can't have his cake and eat it. It's
much pleasanter being a married woman than
being a single one. . .'

'Despite the fact that you had to settle for
second best,' Sapphire threw at her, regretting her
impulsive comment the moment she saw the pale
blue eyes harden.

'Hardly that,' Miranda drawled tautingly. 'As a
lover Blake is first-rate, but as a husband?' Her
eyebrows lifted. 'Hardly. For one thing Jim is an
extremely wealthy man, whereas Blake. . .' She
glanced round the large kitchen disparagingly.
'Being a working farmer's wife is hardly my
metier. . .'

'No, I can see that,' Sapphire agreed drily, 'But

if you haven't come to see Blake why have you come here?'

Settling herself comfortably in a chair Miranda raised calculating blue eyes to Sapphire's darker ones. 'Oh I thought it was time you and I had a little talk—that er, shall we say . . . certain ground rules were laid down. You know of course that Blake and I are lovers?'

'I know you *were*,' Sapphire agreed coolly, hoping that Miranda would never guess how much the admission cost her.

*'Were?'* The thin eyebrows lifted tauntingly, 'Oh dear is that what he told you? And you believed him? Poor Sapphire,' she mocked. 'Blake is far too virile a man to give up what he and I have between us. Oh I grant you, you've grown up from the awkward adolescent he married, but Blake loves me, Sapphire, and all you'll ever be is a pale substitute. Your marriage to him won't last. Blake will tire of you again just like he did before.'

Her taunting words, the look in her eyes, and her own inner insecurities all combined to goad Sapphire into saying with desperate intensity, 'You're wrong; Blake wants our marriage to last.'

'You mean he wants to keep your father sweet to make sure he doesn't lose out on Flaws Farm,' Miranda derided. 'Oh come on Sapphire you know it's true. That's the only reason Blake ever married you, and the reason he wanted you back. Your father threatened to sell his farm elsewhere if he didn't. You'd better pray that he lives a long time if you're counting on seeing more than one wedding anniversary, just as Blake must be hoping that he doesn't.'

The cruelty of her gibe took Sapphire's breath

away for a moment. With tears in her eyes she cried fiercely, 'That's not true, Blake knows that my father only has a matter of months to live . . . I . . .'

'What? What on earth are you talking about?' Miranda snapped obviously disbelieving her. 'Why only last month Jim was telling me how amazed he is by your father's stamina. It must come of coming from sturdy farming stock,' she added, her lip curling fastidiously.

'Oh I know he was seriously ill with pneumonia, but Jim told me he'd never seen anyone recover so quickly from it, never mind a man well into his mid-sixties. If he's told you he's at death's door, he's lying,' she told Sapphire positively. A gleam of suspicion darkened her eyes momentarily, her gaze narrowing as she studied Sapphire with insolent appraisal. 'So that's how he got Blake to take you back,' she breathed triumphantly at last, 'by telling him that he's close to death. Of course! It would work perfectly. Poor Blake, I wonder what he's going to say when he knows he's been deceived. I can't wait to see his face,' she purred viciously. 'I don't think he's going to be too pleased about the way you've trapped him into taking you back. Oh I grant you he's single-minded enough to stay with you until he's got what he wants, but that doesn't mean he'll ever really be yours or that he cares about you.'

She turned and left before Sapphire could retaliate. Not that she had anything left to retaliate with, she thought despairingly, staring helplessly out of the window. Everything fitted together too neatly for Miranda to be wrong. She had thought herself, the last time she saw him, that her father looked better. He had even been out of bed, she remembered. Dear God how could he have done this to her? How could he have put her in this position?

Perhaps Miranda *was* wrong, she thought feverishly ... after all she had only the other woman's word for it that her father had only had pneumonia. Frantically pacing the kitchen Sapphire knew there was only one way to find out. She was already dressed for walking, so pulling on her boots she stepped out into the yard closing the kitchen door behind her.

If Miranda was right Blake would have to be told. She shivered in the cold breeze. What would his reaction be? He had never made any secret of the fact that he wanted Flaws Farm, but there was a big difference in expecting to inherit in say six months' time and waiting perhaps sixteen years? After all her grandfather had lived to his mid-eighties and so had his father before him. Walking quickly to try and blot out her jumbled thoughts, Sapphire headed for Flaws Farm.

# CHAPTER TEN

'YOUR father?' Mary responded in answer to Sapphire's query. 'Yes, he's in his room.'

'How is he today?' Sapphire watched closely as she waited for Mary's response.

'Oh much better,' the older woman beamed. 'In fact he's improving rapidly every day now. As soon as this cold spell breaks he'll probably be able to go outside. He's chaffing at the bit now I'm afraid,' she smiled ruefully, 'not the best of patients, but then that's understandable when one thinks of the active life he's led.'

'But he will be able to get out and about?' Sapphire queried.

'Good heavens yes.' Mary looked surprised that she even needed to ask. 'Pneumonia is serious of course, but these days, with modern drugs, its not dangerous, and of course your father is supremely fit.'

'Pneumonia. . . There weren't any other complications then?' Sapphire asked trying to sound casual while inwardly shaking with dread. So Miranda *had* been right after all.

'Not as far as I know.' Mary looked concerned. 'I know you must be worried about him, but there really is no need you know,' she told her gently. 'For a while he did seem to have reached a plateau stage, but since you came back he's really made progress. I suspect the hope of a grandchild has had some bearing on that. Men hereabouts place a great deal of importance on continuance of the family line. I think when your father was ill he brooded rather a lot on the fact that he was the last male Bell, but he's definitely over that now. Why don't you go up and see him, he'll welcome the interruption. He's working on the farm accounts.' She grinned conspiratorily, 'And you know how he hates that.'

It was amazing what one could see when one knew what to look for Sapphire thought wretchedly, opening the door without knocking and walking into a scene familiar to her from her childhood.

Her father's dog lay curled up at his feet, swear words turning the air mildly blue as he bent his head over his ledgers. Seeing him now with her new knowledge, Sapphire could see that he had been ill and that he was recovering. There was more flesh on his bones for one thing and for another the colour of his skin was better. The door creaked faintly as she let it swing closed and he turned round, his welcoming smile changing to a frown as he saw her pale face.

'Sapphire.' He got up, coming towards her, but she avoided him, sitting down in a spare chair.

'I know exactly what's been going on, Dad,' she said quietly. 'I know you're not . . . not dying. Her control broke as she cried out wretchedly, 'How could you do this to me . . .? How could you trick and deceive . . .?'

'Lass, lass, believe me I thought it best,' he interrupted sadly. 'Your place is here with your husband. I've always thought that.'

'You're free to think what you like, Dad, but to try to force me back with Blake by pretending. . .'

She bit her lip, turning away from the remorse in his face.

'Sapphire, perhaps I shouldn't have meddled, but believe me I thought it was for the best. It was plain to me that you weren't happy in London. You loved Blake when you married him.'

'But he didn't love me, he only married me to get Flaws Farm. That's the only reason he took me back,' she cried wildly. 'Can't you see that? He doesn't really want me, he only wants your land, and the only reason he re-married me was because he thought it wouldn't be long before he inherited it. We made a bargain you see,' she told him wretchedly, 'peace of mind for you, and Flaws Farm for Blake. I agreed I'd sell it to him, once... How do you suppose he'll feel when he discovers how you've tricked him and he *will* discover it...'

'Sapphire, you've got it all wrong,' her father interrupted sternly. 'I've never deceived Blake. He knew exactly what was wrong with me. He wanted you back here as much as I did. Don't you see ... Blake knew the truth ... he knew, Sapphire...'

For a few minutes it was too much for her to take in and then she burst out bitterly, 'I see ... and how were the pair of you planning to resolve this grand charade—a miracle recovery? And to think I fell for it.' Unable to endure any more she wrenched open the door, ignoring her father's anguished cry, half-running through the kitchen and out into the yard. The afternoon was drawing in and the cold blast of air against her heated skin stung, but Sapphire ignored it, head down, hands stuffed into her pockets as she walked doggedly away from the farm, instinctively taking the path that had been her favourite as a child.

It led to a disused quarry, now overgrown and mossy. As a child she had discovered a moss-covered ledge halfway down one of the escarpments, and almost hidden from view by the lip of the quarry.

This had been a favourite refuge of her childhood, and now driven by an intense need to be alone she automatically took the path that led to it.

She could understand what her father had had to gain from deceiving her, but Blake... Had her father perhaps dangled the farm in front of him? Take Sapphire back, give me a grandchild and in return... Her mind shied away from the thought. No, Blake would never allow himself to be manoeuvred like that, he wasn't that type of man, but he was very fond of her father . . . and he did want Flaws' land . . . and he did find her desirable. Given that might he not decide that marriage to her was a reasonable price to pay, especially when he could still be Miranda's lover?

Round and round her thoughts circled, tormenting her with each combination that came to mind. There were so many imponderables for her to consider, so many differing combinations, and only Blake knew the real truth; exactly what had motivated him. But now it would have to end. She couldn't stay with him knowing what she now did. Humiliation seared her soul when she thought about their lovemaking; about the intensity of emotion she had put into it when he had merely been enduring it out of necessity.

On and on she walked, scarcely aware that it

was starting to get dark, setting one foot in front of the other, wrestling with her thoughts.

By the time she reached the quarry it was almost dark, but logic and common sense had long since given way to an instinct for sanctuary which led her to seek out the treacherous path going down to her childhood hiding place.

She found it more by instinct than anything else, stumbling once halfway down and clinging to the quarry face for support as a tiny avalanche of stones crumbled downwards beneath her feet, to eventually splash eerily into the deep pool that had formed at the centre of the quarry crater. This place had been out of bounds to her as a child but it had never stopped her coming here. She shivered suddenly, coming out of the bleak despair that had driven her to seek out this place, swaying lightheadedly. Perhaps she ought to go back; her father would be worrying about her. Remorse overcame her earlier anger. Of course he had been doing what he thought best; to him no doubt she was still the shy seventeen-year-old who had first fallen in love with Blake. And her father *was* old-fashioned. To him marriage vows were sacrosanct and not lightly to be set aside. Sighing faintly Sapphire started to turn round, freezing tensely as she felt the shale beneath her feet shift. The last time she had come down here she had been seventeen—a child bride looking for somewhere to escape the miseries of a marriage that had turned out to be so far removed from her childish imaginings of high romance that now it seemed to be a farce. Even then the path had been dangerous—something she had forgotten when she came down it tonight. She shivered again remembering the remoteness of the quarry and the unlikelihood of anyone guessing that she was up here. If she made it to the ledge she would be stuck there until morning when she might be able to attract the attention of one of the shepherds. If she made it, she thought wretchedly as another part of the path slid away to drop into the pool. The pool. Icy trickles of fear dripped down her spine. The water in that pool was freezing, its sides smooth and worn by time into a glassy slipperyness that made the pool a death trap for anyone foolish enough to swim in it. Closing her eyes and clinging to the wall of the quarry she inched her way carefully down to the ledge, easing her shaking body on to its grassy smoothness.

It seemed smaller than she remembered and as she edged back against the quarry wall, trying to sit down she realised why. Like the path, the ledge had been partially eroded away. Every time she moved she could hear the rattling of shale and small stones. How safe was the ledge? She could die here and no-one would be any the wiser. Would it matter if she did? Was life really worth living without Blake? If one judged life on its quality rather than its quantity then no. Without him her life had no direction; no purpose. Without his love... Wearily her body relaxed into a numbing lethargy that was almost a relief, her mind torturing her with images of Blake and on to the point where death lured her with its promise of oblivion.

Suicide had always been something she had viewed with horror—until she lost Blake, and now with sharp clarity she remembered those first months after she had left him, when she would have given anything not to have had to wake up in the morning. Now she was going to lose him again. The moon slid out from behind a cloud illuminating the still water below. It beckoned to her, casting a spell that seemed to reach out and enfold her until she could almost imagine she was already in its icy embrace. As though obeying the directions of a voice only she could hear Sapphire stood up, drifting like a sleep-walker towards the edge of the ledge where she stood poised, drawn by the inky black depths below, her powers of reasoning clouded by the greater force of her emotions.

'No!'

At first Sapphire thought the taut cry had been torn from her own throat, but when it was followed by her name, called abruptly by a familiar male voice she started back from the edge of the ledge, staring up in disbelief to find Blake looking down at her.

Perhaps it was a trick of the moonlight, but his face seemed oddly white and drawn, his eyes burning as though he had looked into the fires of hell.

'Stand back from the edge Sapphire, and I'll throw you down a rope.'

She was too bemused to question how he had got there, simply obeying the commands he shouted down to her, feeling the coarse fibre of the rope bite into her waist as Blake hauled her back up the quarry face, until she was lying flat on her back, on the ice-cold grass, breathing in great gulps of air, like a landed fish.

Blake's fingers tugged at the knotted rope, unfastening it from around her. His head bent over his self-imposed task, Sapphire resisted the urge to reach out and stroke the thick darkness, but she couldn't restrain the brief quiver tensing her body when she remembered how they had made love.

'Keep still,' Blake's voice was terse, his hands clinically detached as they examined her body. 'Nothing seems to be broken. . . Come on, I'd better get you back and alert the rest of the team.' As she stood up Sapphire saw that his mouth was compressed, his eyes darkly bitter as they studied her.

'The team?' Was that really her own voice, soft and husky almost begging him to reach out and touch her?

'The Rescue Team,' he reminded her in the same clipped voice. 'Your father called them out when you didn't come back. Tom Barnes rang me and asked me to stand in for Geoff Plant—he's away at the moment. I had no idea when I set out that it was you . . .' He broke off and turned away from her, rubbing his forehead with tense fingers. 'I called at Flaws on the way to see if you were there—I thought you might have decided to spend the evening with your father. . .'

'In view of his ailing health I suppose you mean,' Sapphire cut in sarcastically, only to be silenced by Blake's brusque, 'Not now Sapphire. You realise your father's practically frantic with worry, to say nothing of how I felt. . .'

'And how did you feel Blake?' she asked bitterly, suddenly furiously and intensely angry, the adrenalin flowing fiercely along her veins. 'Worried that you might not get Flaws after all? Oh yes, I know all about how the pair of you deceived me. Your very good friend Miranda enlightened me. My father I can forgive because I know he acted in what he believed to be my best interests, but you. . .' Her heated words were silenced by the brief blast Blake gave on the whistle he was holding.

'We can discuss all that later,' he told her curtly. 'Right now, like the rest of the team, all I want to do is get home to bed. You do realise that if I hadn't remembered about this damned quarry, you'd have been there until morning, if not longer, don't you? And just what the hell were you playing at when I arrived, for God's sake?' he shouted at her, fingers clenching into her shoulders as he shook her roughly. Once given life it seemed as though his anger couldn't be quenched, and Sapphire listened in silence as it flowed moltenly over her. Blake was angry. . . It was a phenomenon she had never witnessed before. Before he had always been so cool and in control.

Other members of the team alerted by his whistle were hurrying towards them, and he stopped berating her, turning instead to assure them that she was quite safe.

'She slipped off the path and luckily for her landed on a ledge,' was the explanation he gave his co-rescuers, and after Sapphire had endured some well-deserved chaffing on the subject of her carelessness Blake started to guide her towards where he had left his Land Rover.

'I'll call at Flaws and let Simon have the good news,' one of the men offered. 'It's on my way, and you'll both be wanting to get back home. Hot baths and a good mug of toddy, put the pair of you to rights. . .' He winked over his shoulder at Blake, and Sapphire felt the warmth seep up under her skin as she intercepted the very male look they exchanged. And the worst of it was that deep down inside her she still yearned for Blake to take her into the warmth of his bed and hold her until all the nightmare details of the day faded into oblivion.

Instead she had to sit with him in the Land Rover, the tense quality of the silence stretching between them acting on her nerves with all the torment of a thumbscrew. When the Land Rover eventually came to a halt in the farmyard she was out the moment Blake cut the engine, shocked to discover how weak her legs felt as she clung wretchedly to her open door.

'You should have waited for me.' The terse, unsympathetic words brought tears of weakness and pain to her eyes, but thankfully it was too dark for Blake to see them. She wanted to protest when he walked round to her and hauled her carelessly into his arms, but she knew that she just didn't have the strength to object.

Upstairs she lay on the bed where he had dropped her knowing that she couldn't endure sleeping with him now. Not that he was likely to want to. Her mouth twisted bitterly. Had he, like her father, hoped they might have a child—preferably a son who could inherit the rich Flaws acres he coveted? Was that why. . . Unable to endure the torment of her thoughts she gave a low moan, rolling on to her stomach.

'Can you manage to get undressed or. . .'

Until Blake spoke she had forgotten she was still wearing her outdoor clothes.

'I can manage.' Her voice was colourless and completely dry.

'Sapphire, we have to talk.'

Was that uncertainty and pain she could hear threading through the determined words? Anger hardened her heart. Whatever he might be enduring through guilt and fear of losing Flaws was nothing compared with her own agony. 'Tomorrow,' she told him briefly. 'I don't want to talk tonight Blake . . . I need to think.' It was a lie, but at least it got him out of her room.

When he had gone she struggled exhaustedly to remove her clothes, almost crawling into the bathroom. Her legs were bruised and scraped where they had rubbed against the rough stone of the quarry walls, the abrasions stinging with the hot water. Bathed and dried she went back into the bedroom, tensing as she saw Blake waiting there.

'I already told you, I don't want to talk tonight Blake,' she told him rudely. 'I'm tired, and so if you don't mind. . .' Glad that she had had the forethought to take her nightdress into the bathroom with her, she swept past him with magnificent disdain, hoping that he wouldn't guess how vulnerable and hurt she was really feeling.

'It's a bit late for this isn't it?' Lean fingers reached out and tugged at the fine lawn fabric. 'After last night. . .'

'Last night is something that should never have happened and would never have happened if I'd known. . .' Sapphire gasped out loud as Blake's fingers moved from the frill of her nightdress to the vee of its neckline, stroking softly over the upper swell of her breasts.

'You think not?' Blake's voice was soft, almost detached, but there was nothing detached about the look in his eyes Sapphire realised, her heart starting to thud with powerful, heavy thuds. 'I'm getting tired of playing "let's make believe", Sapphire,' Blake told her thickly. 'Last night you wanted me, and tonight I could make you want me again.'

'No!' The harsh denial was out before she could stop it and the moment it was said Sapphire knew she had made a mistake. It was almost as though something snapped inside Blake, some fine thread whose snapping unleashed a savage tumult of emotions that demanded expression.

Her moaned protest of 'Blake you can't do this', went unheard as he picked her up and carried her over to the bed, stripping off her nightdress with ruthless, hard fingers, his touch a thousand times removed from that of the tender lover of the previous night.

'I know you want me, damn you,' Blake muttered in a tortured whisper against her skin, bruising it faintly with the pressure of lips suddenly savage with pent-up emotions whose origins she could only guess at. His thumb brushed her nipple and Sapphire felt the unmistakable flowering of her body, her cry of despair mingling with Blake's murmured triumph.

As he bent his head to touch her treacherous body first with his tongue and then his lips Sapphire felt the first weak tears of broken pride slide from her eyes. In the darkness Blake lifted his head and stared at her, his thumb touching the dampness of her face.

'You're crying. Why?' If she hadn't known

better Sapphire might have believed that the pain in his voice was real; that the anguish in his eyes was because he couldn't bear to hurt her, but she did know better. She turned her head away from him too weak to stem the tears.

'Don't touch me Blake,' she begged huskily, 'Please    just leave me alone.'

She closed her eyes and felt the bed shift under his weight. When she opened them again he had gone.

Sleep was a long time coming. She could hear Blake moving about in his own room; the noises of the old house as it settled into sleep disturbing tonight instead of vaguely comforting. Tomorrow she would have to tell Blake she was leaving him. No running away this time. She would tell him this time that she was going, and that she was never going to come back. A sob stuck in her throat and suddenly she was crying as she could not remember doing in a long time, tearing, painful sobs that left her chest aching and her eyes sore.

'Sapphire, are you awake?'

Slowly she turned her head. Blake was standing just inside the door, his hair ruffled and on edge, his shirt half-unfastened, a cup of tea in one hand. 'I've brought you a drink,' he told her unnecessarily when she lifted her head from the pillow.

'What time is it?' Sapphire glanced at her watch, dismayed to see that it was midmorning. 'Shouldn't you be out working?'

It was obviously the wrong thing to say. Blake's mouth thinned, anger hardening his eyes. 'It's all right,' she muttered huskily. 'This time I'm not

going to run away. This time when I leave. . .'
She broke off stunned by the sudden blaze of heat
turning his eyes molten gold, which died just as
quickly when she started to finish her sentence.
Surely Blake couldn't want her to stay? Not for
herself, she told herself cynically, but perhaps for
the farm. The thought sickened her as it had done
ever since it had first come into her mind all those
years ago.

'I'd better get up.'

'Sapphire we have to talk.' Blake's voice
sounded thick and hoarse, and now that she
looked at him properly she saw that beneath the
healthy tan of his face he looked drawn and tired.

'We can talk downstairs,' she told him reasonably, feeling very much at a disadvantage in bed
while he stood, virtually fully dressed, in front of
her. She hadn't put another nightdress on after he
had left her and the remnants of the one he had
torn off her body lay on the floor at her side of the
bed.

'No, now. . .' One stride brought him alongside
the bed, the mattress dipping under his weight as
he sat down next to her, one lean arm imprisoning
her against his side should she have any thoughts
of trying to turn away.

'All right . . .' he admitted tiredly when she said
nothing. 'I know I shouldn't have done it . . .
you've every reason to hate me for it, God knows,
I knew when your father suggested it that it was a
crazy idea, but then when a man's as desperate as I
was, any idea, no matter how crazy, has its
appeal.'

'My forebears would be extremely flattered to
know how eager you are to gain possession of

Flaws' land,' Sapphire gritted at him. 'Such a noble sacrifice...' Some demon she had never suspected she possessed drove her on. '... even to the extent of giving up your mistress, but then that wouldn't have lasted would it? How long did you intend to devote your attentions to me? Long enough to get me pregnant—to provide my father with a grandson? And we both know what a sacrifice that would have been, don't we Blake? I should have remembered how much you loathed touching me, instead of deluding myself into...' She broke off as Blake wrenched the bedclothes away, squirming away from him, trying to cover her naked breasts by folding her arms.

'So I loathe touching you do I?' Blake muttered huskily, tugging her arms away from her body and then cupping the rounded warmth of her breasts stroking their pink tips with rough thumb pads. A deep sensual warmth burgeoned somewhere deep within her, increasing in intensity when she felt the fine tremor in Blake's hands. His eyes golden and fiery as the sun seemed to bathe her skin in molten heat, the expression she saw in their glowing depths as he bent his head to touch his lips first to one pink nipple and then the other making her wonder if she had suddenly completely lost her wits. 'Does this feel like I loathe the enticement of your skin beneath my fingers?' Blake demanded rawly releasing her breasts to spread brown hands possessively against her rib cage. 'Or this.' Hot damp kisses filled the valley between her breasts, his lips exploring the tender column of her throat, teasing the line of her jaw, his teeth nipping delicately at the fullness of her bottom lip until her lips parted and the fine tremor of his body became an open spasm of need, his mouth savagely hungry as it possessed hers, his tongue pushing past her teeth to explore its inner sweetness.

Unable to stop herself Sapphire caressed the firm muscles under his skin, stroking his neck and shoulders and feeling the powerful surge of his body's response.

'I love you so much,' Blake whispered as he lifted his mouth from hers, touching its swollen contours with his tongue as though unable to stop himself from doing so, 'that's my only defence. I nearly went crazy when you left me, hoping that you'd come back, telling myself that I'd find a way to get you back, and then when your father told me you were thinking of marrying again. . .' She felt him swallow and saw the unmistakable truth darkening his eyes, shining in the unexpected tears that shimmered in his eyes.

'You love me?' She could hardly trust herself to say the words. How could that be true?

'Always,' he averred.

'But you never made love to me, never. . .'

'Because you were so young,' he told her abruptly. 'Because I knew I'd taken advantage of what was little more than an infatuation, using it to bind you to me when you'd barely had a chance to taste real life.'

'I thought you didn't want me.'

'Not want you.' He closed his eyes, and swallowed hard. 'I wanted you so much I couldn't trust myself within a hundred yards of you, but I wanted you as a man wants the woman he loves Sapphire, not as an adolescent boy wants the first girl he falls in love with. I was terrified. of frightening you away, and yet I knew that once I touched you I wouldn't be able to control myself; that I couldn't play the controlled lover. . .'

'And that was why you went to Miranda?' she asked in a low voice.

'I never "went to her" as you put it. Once, a long time before I fell in love with you she and I were lovers, but never since. . .'

'But the other night. . .'

'I wanted to make you jealous. To make you feel the same agony as I've endured over Alan. I spent the entire evening driving around in my car. After you'd gone out I rang her back cancelling the date.'

'But you wrote her love letters,' Sapphire told him, frowning as she remembered finding that incriminating evidence.

'Love letters?' Blake stared down at her.

'Yes.' Pain ached through her, her eyes clouding. 'When my father told me you married me because you wanted the farm, and after I'd seen what you'd written, I knew I couldn't stay . . . I saw the letter myself Blake, it was so full of . . . of need and love. . .' She couldn't go on, remembering as though it had been yesterday how she had felt.

Suddenly Blake's frown cleared. 'Stay here,' he told her softly. 'Don't move.'

He was gone less than five minutes, during which time she had pulled the bedclothes back up round her body, but the first thing Blake did when he walked back into the room was to pull them down again. 'I love looking at your body,' he told her simply. 'It makes up for all the years when I couldn't. You can't imagine how I felt when I found out you were still a virgin.' His lips caressed one deeply pink peak, bringing it achingly to life, and then as though unable to resist the temptation, transferred to the other, adoration giving way to passionate need as he felt her body's unmistakable response and Sapphire arched achingly, longing to curl her fingers into his hair and hold him against her, but the paper he had dropped on the bed caught her eye and she tensed, causing him to stop and pull her into the warmth of his body so that she was leaning against his thighs her head cushioned against his shoulder.

'Is this what you read?' he asked her gently, offering her the close written sheets. Sapphire only needed to read the first few words to nod an assent.

'And because of this you left me? Oh! Sapphire. . .' His voice broke and she felt the damp warmth of his tears against her skin. 'I wrote them for *you*,' he told her brokenly, 'I wrote what I daren't tell you! What I couldn't in all honour show you. . . You're the only woman I've ever loved and when I saw you standing on that ledge, about to go over into the pool, I didn't know what I wanted to do most—strangle you or strangle Alan for hurting you so much that you felt you needed to end your life because of him.'

'It wasn't him, it was you,' Sapphire told him urgently. Right now it was almost impossible to take in the enormity of what had happened; but that Blake was telling the truth when he said he loved her she didn't for one moment doubt.

'After Miranda told me the truth about my father's illness I knew I couldn't stay with you—not when really you loved her, and yet I didn't know where I was going to find the courage to leave, loving you so much.'

'I've never loved anyone but you,' Blake interrupted fiercely. 'I think you were all of sixteen years' old the first time I realised how I felt about you. Miranda lied to you.'

Because she had been jealous, Sapphire now realised, but she had been clever as well, using her sophistication and experience to drive a wedge between them, no doubt hoping that Blake would turn to her once Sapphire had left him.

'So many wasted years,' she said sadly raising bleak eyes to meet his.

'No ... not wasted. You *were* too young for marriage at seventeen,' Blake told her. 'I would always have felt guilty and uncertain wondering if I had stolen from you the right to make your own choice of husband, but now I know that you love *me*. You do love me, don't you?' he demanded thickly, when Sapphire remained silent.

Part of her longed to tease him just a little, but the rest of her responded eagerly to the plea in his eyes, her body curling into his as she kissed him, lightly at first and then with growing need, breaking away from him only to murmur huskily, 'So much... Blake if you hadn't arrived at the quarry when you did...' A shudder wracked her body and she felt him tense in response. 'Don't,' he commanded her rawly. 'Don't even think about it, just tell me you've forgiven me for lying to you about your father. I hated myself for doing it; for causing you pain—a pain I could see every time you looked at your father, but I was desperate to get you back; willing to do anything to stop you from marrying someone else.'

'And having got me back how did you intend to keep me?' Sapphire teased, forgiveness explicit in the look she gave him as she reached out to push the unruly hair back off his forehead.

'Oh, I'd have thought of something.' The old assurance was creeping back into his voice, but she didn't mind. Now that she had seen his vulnerability she could accept the macho side of his personality more easily. 'Such as?' she whispered, feathering light kisses along his jaw and glorying in his responsive shudder.

'Such as this ... and this...' Blake's voice deepened, raw need underlying the husky words as he caressed her body, kissing her silky skin, words no longer necessary.

Now she really had come home, Sapphire thought contentedly abandoning herself completely into his keeping, revelling in the fierce thrust of pleasure seizing his body as he recognised her surrender, and she was never ever going to leave again. Closing her eyes she murmured the words of love she knew he longed to hear, for the first time saying them in complete trust that she would hear them back in return.

'The stock ...' she reminded Blake weakly long, satisfying minutes later... 'You...'

'To hell with the stock,' Blake responded thickly. 'Right now I've got far more important things on my mind, like making love to my wife, unless of course she has any objections?'

A smile dimpled the corner of Sapphire's mouth. 'Only one,' she told him gravely, 'and that is that you're wasting far too much time in talk instead of action...'

Retaliation was every bit as swift as she had envisaged—and every bit as pleasurable, the words of love she had longed to hear for so long caressing her skin in silken whispers as Blake took her back in his arms.

New York Times bestselling author **Anne Mather** has written since she was seven, but it was only when her first child was born that she fulfilled her dream of becoming a writer. Her first book, CAROLINE, appeared in 1966. It met with immediate success and, since then, Anne has written more than 130 novels, reaching a readership which spans the world.

Born and raised in the north of England, Anne still makes her home there with her husband, two children and, now, grandchildren. Asked if she finds writing a lonely occupation, she replies that her characters always keep her company. In fact, she is so busy sorting out their lives that she often doesn't have time for her own! An avid reader herself, she devours everything from sagas and romances to mainstream fiction and suspense. Anne has also written a number of mainstream novels with DANGEROUS TEMPTATION her most recent title, published by MIRA® Books.

**Look out for THE RODRIGUES PREGNANCY**
**by Anne Mather**
**in Mills & Boon Modern Romance™, March 2001**

# A RELATIVE
# BETRAYAL
## by
## ANNE MATHER

# CHAPTER ONE

'RACHEL'S coming!'

'Is she?' Matthew had had plenty of opportunities during the long nights since Barbara's death to face that possibility—and decide he didn't give a damn.

'Yes.' His mother-in-law pressed the palms of her hands together. 'She'll be staying at the vicarage, of course.'

'Of course.'

Matthew was annoyingly indifferent, and Mrs Barnes shook her head. 'Well, someone had to invite her!' she exclaimed, as if needing to defend her position. 'Barbara was her cousin, after all.'

Matthew abandoned any attempt to answer any one of the dozens of letters that had flooded in since his wife had died, and got up from behind his desk. 'I'm not saying you shouldn't have done it, am I?' he asked wearily, pushing back the unruly weight of hair from his forehead. 'For God's sake, Maggie, you can invite who you like. It's your daughter's funeral, not some bloody garden party!'

'Oh, Matt!'

His harsh words achieved what he had been most hoping to avoid. His mother-in-law dissolved into noisy tears, and Matthew was obliged to take her in his arms and comfort her. But who was going to comfort him? he wondered bitterly, as the garrulous little woman's tears soaked through the grey silk of his shirt. God, he wished this whole charade was over! Perhaps then he'd find some meaning to his life; some peace.

Mrs Barnes at last composed herself sufficiently to draw back from him, patting the patch of wet cloth on his chest with a rueful hand. 'Oh, dear,' she said looking up at him with misty eyes. 'You must forgive me. But I get so upset every time I think about it.'

'I know.' Matthew managed a polite smile, hoping against hope that she would leave now. It was strange, but since Barbara had died the house seemed to have been full of people, and he desperately wanted to be alone, however selfish that might be.

But, of course, his mother-in-law had something more to say. 'I didn't want to ask her, you know,' she confided, and he didn't need to be reminded who she was talking about. 'No. It was Geoffrey—he insisted. But then, she's *his* relation, isn't she? Not mine.'

Matthew heaved a sigh. 'It doesn't matter, Maggie.' He propped his lean hips against his desk and waited. Surely she would go now? He didn't know how much more of this he could take.

'Oh, well.' Mrs Barnes gave him a wistful look. 'So long as you understand I had nothing to do with it.' She paused, and then added anxiously, 'I hope there won't be any trouble. For Barbara's—and for Rosie's—sake.'

'I'm sure there won't be.'

Matthew could hear his voice losing all expression, and he was amazed that his mother-in-law could remain so totally unaware of it. But then, she had never been particularly perceptive, he reflected grimly. Or Barbara would never have succeeded in convincing her that their marriage had ever been anything more than a sham.

'Where is Rosie?' she asked now, and Matthew strove to contain his impatience.

'I don't know,' he replied tautly, glancing towards the long, mullioned windows. 'About the estate somewhere, I suppose. Perhaps she's down at the stables. I really have no idea.'

'You wouldn't like me to find her and take her home to the vicarage, would you?' Mrs Barnes suggested hopefully. 'I mean—I'm sure Agnes does a fine job but she's not like—family. Is she?'

Matthew pushed himself away from the desk. He could imagine his daughter's reaction if he told her she was going home with her grandmother, and it wasn't fit for his mother-in-law's consumption. 'I—think I'd rather she stayed here,' he declared, choosing his words with discretion. 'Agnetha's fairly competent, and Rosie has to get used to—to the situation.'

'I know, but—'

Mrs Barnes looked as if she was about to have a relapse, and, although Matthew despised himself for his lack of sympathy, he had to prevent another display of emotion. 'I think it'll be easier on you this way,' he declared, walking past her to the heavy door and opening it. 'And now I must beg your indulgence and get on. There's such a lot to do; you understand?'

'Of course, of course.' Mrs Barnes dabbed her eyes with the lace handkerchief she had taken from her pocket, and walked reluctantly towards him. 'But you will let me know if you need any help, won't you?' She paused beside him, looking up into his dark face through tear-drenched eyes. 'I know that's probably a silly thing to say. And I'm sure you feel you've all the help you need. But, at times like this, families should stick together.'

Matthew felt as if the smile he offered was merely a stretching of his facial muscles. But it evidently satisfied his mother-in-law, which had been his intention. 'Thanks,' he said, bending to bestow a dutiful kiss on her cheek. 'I'll be in touch.'

'Do.'

She wiped her eyes one more time, raised a hand in farewell and departed. Matthew waited to ensure that Watkins was there to see her out, and then went back into the library and closed the door.

Leaning back against it, he surveyed without emotion the pile of letters and cards awaiting his attention. So many people had written; so many business colleagues, or acquaintances, who had felt it their duty to offer their condolences. They had hardly known Barbara, but that didn't matter. The tragic circun stances of her demise had over-ruled formalities. There was a unifying quality about death that brought people who were virtual strangers together, and it was up to him to respond to their kindness.

But it was difficult, *bloody* difficult, he acknowledged grimly, straightening away from the door and making his way across the room. A tray of drinks resided on a table in the chimney alcove, and it was to this that he headed, pouring himself a stiff Scotch and drinking it straight down. Then, before replacing the stopper in the crystal decanter, he poured another and carried it over to his desk.

'My dear Matt,' he read tersely, 'We were so sorry to read of your tragic bereavement…' The words of the letter on the top of the pile leapt out at him, and he flung himself down on to his chair and closed his eyes. 'So sorry to read of your loss'—'our deepest sympathy in this time of mourning'—'so sorry to hear of Barbara's death'—the trite phrases were endless! He didn't even need to read them to know what each and every one of them would say. They all talked of Barbara's illness, her tragic death at the age of only thirty-two, of his loss. *His loss…*

His nerves tightened. How could you be married to some-one for almost ten years, and yet still feel so little remorse at her passing? He and Barbara had been man and wife; they had produced a daughter, for God's sake! But there had never been any love between them—just a greed for money and possessions on her part, and a desire for revenge on his.

He opened his eyes again and, sitting up in his seat, he swallowed half the whisky in his glass. It was no good, he told himself tautly. He was getting maudlin, and for all the wrong reasons. Barbara was dead. Whatever she had done in life was over. He had to think of the future. Of Rosemary's future, at least. Maggie had been right about one thing. Agnetha was not family—and his daughter took advantage of that.

He groaned suddenly and ran weary fingers through the over-long hair at the nape of his neck. Rachel was coming to the funeral! he thought savagely, acknowledging for the first time the real reason why he had been so impatient with his mother-in-law. It had been all very well telling himself he didn't care what she did when the chances of her taking time off from her job in London and making the long journey to Cumbria had seemed so unlikely. But now, faced with the reality that tomorrow he was going to see her again, his reactions were not half as positive.

A tentative knock at the door put his thoughts to flight and, glad of the interruption, Matthew lay back in his chair. 'Come in,' he called, and Patrick Malloy, his secretary and personal assistant, put his head into the room.

'Sorry to intrude—' he began, and then, realising Matthew was alone, he opened the door a little wider and stepped inside. 'Oh—has Mrs Barnes gone?'

'As you see,' remarked his employer flatly, throwing the remainder of the whisky to the back of his throat. He held his glass out towards the other man. 'Get me another, Pat, will you?'

Patrick closed the door behind him and crossed the floor. 'It's a little early, even for you, isn't it?' he commented, with the familiarity of their long association, but he took the glass and did as he was bidden. 'What happened? Did she tell you she's inaugurating a Barbara Conroy Memorial Fund?'

Matthew's head swung round. 'She's not, is she?' His dismay was evident, and Patrick shook his head.

'Not that I know of,' he reassured him drily, handing over a rather smaller measure of Scotch than Matthew had previously poured for himself. He waited until his employer had taken a generous mouthful. 'You look shattered, do you know that?' He paused. 'So—what did she want?'

Matthew expelled his breath heavily, and then lifted guarded grey eyes to Patrick's face. 'Rachel's coming,' he said simply, and the other man caught his breath.

'I see.'

'Do you?' Matthew got up from his chair again and paced across to the windows. 'Who'd have thought it, hmm? Rachel—coming to Barbara's funeral.' His lips twisted. 'Do you think she's coming to gloat?'

'You know Rachel's not like that,' retorted Patrick at once, but Matthew was unconvinced.

'Do I?' he countered, turning back to face his friend. 'I don't know anything about Rachel any more. It's been over ten years, Pat. Ten years!'

'I know.' Patrick's angular features were troubled. 'So, how do you feel about it?'

Matthew looked grim. 'The truth?'

'Of course.'

'Then—angry. Bloody angry!' said Matthew violently. 'I don't want her here. I wish to God I didn't even have to see her. It's been too long. Too many years. If it weren't for Rosemary, I'd probably never see any of the Barneses again after tomorrow.'

Patrick inclined his head towards Matthew's glass. 'Is that why you're drowning your sorrows in Scotch?' he enquired, not without some irony, and his employer scowled.

'I'm not drowning my sorrows,' he retorted curtly. 'I'm just trying to get through the next couple of days with some dignity.'

'And afterwards?'

Matthew frowned. 'What do you mean—afterwards?'

'I mean after the funeral. Have you thought what you're going to do about Rosemary? Now that—now that Barbara's not here any more, don't you think you ought to consider sending her away to school?'

Matthew sighed. 'Is that what you think?'

Patrick was ambivalent. 'She does need discipline,' he pointed out evenly. 'And unless you're going to spend more time at Rothmere—'

'Take up the life of a gentleman farmer, is that what you mean?' Matthew was sardonic.

'It's what your father would have wanted you to do,' replied Patrick quietly. 'And you know how your mother feels.'

'Yes.' Matthew acknowledged the fact that his mother would prefer him to live at home. But since his marriage to Barbara he had expended more and more energy attending personally to his business interests elsewhere, and spending most of his time away from the estate.

'Anyway,' Patrick could see his employer was becoming broodingly introspective, and quickly changed the subject, 'why don't you take Rosemary over to Helen's this afternoon? It would do you both good to get out of the house, and you know she and Gerald would be pleased to see you.'

Matthew considered the prospect of driving over to his sister's home near Ambleside, and shrugged. The idea of visiting the small hotel they ran overlooking Windermere was appealing, except that people might recognise him, and he wasn't in the mood to be sociable.

'I'll think about it,' he said without enthusiasm, finishing the whisky in a gulp. 'Do you know where Rosemary is, by the way? I haven't seen her since—well, since suppertime last night, actually.'

Patrick gave him a resigned look. 'So what's new?' he remarked, taking Matthew's empty glass from him and replacing it on the tray. 'Do you want me to find her? She'll be around somewhere.'

Matthew hesitated a moment, then he shook his head. 'No,' he said flatly, flexing his shoulders and walking towards the door. 'I'll catch her later.' He paused with his fingers on the handle. 'I'll be in the gym, if you want me. See you at lunch.'

He had skirted the hall and the drawing-room and was passing the morning-room when his mother called his name behind him. 'Matthew! Matthew, wait! Didn't Watkins tell you I was waiting to speak to you? Come into the parlour. I want to talk to you.'

Matthew's sigh was heartfelt, but, short of offending one

of the few people he really cared about, he had little choice but to obey. 'I do have things to do, Mother,' he declared patiently, walking back towards her, and, remembering Watkins' face when he had shown Mrs Barnes out of the library, he guessed the old man had thought better of interrupting him.

'So do I,' responded Lady Olivia Conroy, pausing with her hand on the door, so that Matthew was forced to pass her on his way into the room. 'Ugh—you've been drinking! Matthew, it's barely twelve o'clock!'

'12.02, to be precise,' remarked Matthew evenly, halting in the centre of the softly fading Aubusson carpet. He thrust his hands into the pockets of the worn corded jacket he was wearing and faced her politely. 'What can I do for you?'

'You can stop adopting that supercilious attitude for a start,' said his mother shortly. 'Really, Matthew, I don't know what's the matter with you. I shouldn't have thought Barbara's death would have been such a shock; in the circumstances.'

Matthew regarded her dispassionately. 'What circumstances?'

'Oh, Matthew!' Clearly he was annoying her, but he didn't seem able to help it. 'You know what circumstances. The fact that Barbara had been ill for the better part of a year, and—and…'

'And?' he prompted.

'And you and she hadn't been close for—well, for years!'

Matthew inclined his head. 'I see.'

'What do you see?' Lady Olivia was obviously impatient. 'Matthew, please; I'm your mother. If there's something troubling you, then tell me. Ever since Barbara died I've tried to get close to you, but I can't. You're shutting me out. You're shutting everyone out! Darling, we're your family. Don't you think we deserve some consideration?'

'Oh, God!' Matthew's shoulders sagged. 'I'm not shutting anyone out, Mother. I just need some time alone, that's all.

It's natural enough, isn't it?' He tried to be flippant. 'It's not every day one becomes a widower!'

His mother's expression was eloquent of her feelings. 'I think there's more to it than that,' she declared firmly. 'I'm not a fool, Matt. I know this marriage had its problems.'

'Its problems?' echoed Matthew caustically. 'Oh, yes.'

'So why are you acting as if you're grief-stricken?' countered his mother sharply. 'Helen tells me you haven't been over to see Gerald since you got back. Or the children. You know how Mark and Lucy dote on you. Goodness knows, you've always had more time for Helen's children than you have for your own daughter! What's the matter with you, Matt? Why are you behaving like this?'

Matthew turned away from her pained bewilderment, staring broodingly out of the long windows that overlooked the parterre at the side of the house. At this time of the year the lawns were edged with pansies and dwarf hyacinths, and the deep blue stems of salvias grew among clusters of cream and yellow saxifrage. Beyond the formal gardens, acres of rolling grassland swept away towards Rothmere Fell, and Matthew's eyes were drawn to the purple slopes where only sheep could scratch a living. When he was a boy, he had scrambled up those slopes with Brian Spencer, his father's shepherd, but nowadays he hardly gave them a thought. He left the running of the estate in his agent's hands, and spent his days attending board meetings and business lunches, and fighting a growing propensity for boredom.

'Matthew!'

His mother's voice arrested his wandering thoughts, and he forced himself to turn round again and face her. 'I'm listening.'

'You're not, or I'd have had some answers before now,' replied Lady Olivia tensely. 'What is it? Is it Rosemary? You know, something will have to be done about that child, before it's too late.'

Matthew regarded her frustrated face with some affection for a moment, and then flung himself on to one of the buttoned satin sofas that faced one another across a polished maplewood table. 'Did you know Rachel was coming to the funeral?' he enquired lightly, keeping his tone as casual as possible, and his mother gave a gasp.

'No!'

'Yes.' Matthew considered the toe of the boot he had propped disrespectfully on the corner of the table. 'Mrs Barnes gave me the news this morning. Apparently the Reverend invited her.'

Lady Olivia seemed to require some support herself now, for she sank down on to the sofa opposite her son and gazed at him disbelievingly. 'But why? Didn't he realise it was hardly in the best of taste?'

Matthew shrugged. 'As Maggie said, she is Barbara's cousin.'

'Is she in favour?' His mother was surprised.

'I wouldn't say that.' Matthew grimaced. 'But she's making the best of it. And it's true. Rachel is Barbara's cousin.'

'And your ex-wife!'

'So?'

'Matthew! Surely even you can see the unsuitability of your ex-wife attending your second wife's funeral?'

'Yes.' Matthew's stomach muscles clenched. 'But I can hardly stop her, can I? She is—family.'

'*Family?*' Lady Olivia's echo of the word was scathing. 'I don't know how you can suggest such a thing! I could say she was nothing but trouble from the moment you laid eyes on her. You were engaged to Cecily Bishop, do you remember? That's who you should have married.'

'I know.' Matthew's boot heel ground into the polished wood and his mother winced.

'Matt!'

'All right, all right.' Unable to sit still any longer, Matthew rose to his feet. 'And now, if you'll excuse me—'

'Is this why you've been so—so unapproachable?'

Matthew groaned. 'I haven't been unapproachable, Mother.'

'Yes, you have. You know you have.' Lady Olivia looked up at him despairingly. 'Oh, well—it will all be over to-morrow. Then you can get back to some semblance of normal living. I suggest you tell Mrs Barnes—and her husband—that you'll be incommunicado for a while. You don't want that awful woman coming here, treating this place as she did when Barbara was alive. If you make the position clear to begin with—'

Matthew's oath silenced her. 'Shut up, Mother, will you?' he muttered savagely, and, ignoring her shocked expression, he strode grimly out of the room.

In the gym, he changed into a pair of shorts and a vest, and stretched out on the lifting frame. The sheer physical effort it took to push the weights up the stack gave him some relief from the chaos of his thoughts, and the sweat he worked up helped to compensate for the alcohol he had consumed earlier. Then, when he was feeling pleasantly numb to anything but the physical aches and pains of his own body, he plunged into the jacuzzi and let the hot, pummelling jets revitalise his tortured muscles.

It was then that he admitted that he couldn't entirely dismiss what his mother had said. It was true that since Barbara had died he had felt a certain detachment from the events going on around him. His friends—those who had not been aware of the circumstances of his marriage, his acquaintances—probably thought it was grief; but his sorrow at the way things had turned out was a small thing by comparison. The truth was, Barbara's death had resurrected the past, and it wasn't until Mrs Barnes had told him Rachel was coming that he had realised exactly what he had been thinking.

And he despised himself for it! He couldn't still want her. Not after all this time. Not after all that had gone before. It was as he had told Patrick: he was angry, *bloody* angry, that she should have the nerve to come here.

So what if her uncle had invited her? So what if Geoffrey Barnes had decided the occasion warranted her presence? He was just a Church of England vicar. What did he know?

She should have refused. She should have made some excuse and stayed away, instead of embarrassing all of them by joining in their grief. She wasn't sorry Barbara was dead. What had Barbara been to her? Simply an excuse for severing her marriage, so that she could pursue the career that had always taken precedence in her life.

Matthew was drying himself when Patrick came to tell him that lunch was on the table. 'And Rosemary's disappeared,' he announced, as Matthew stepped into worn jeans and zipped them over his flat stomach. 'Do you want me to go and look for her?'

'I'll do it myself—later,' replied his employer broodingly. 'And I'm not hungry. Make my excuses to my mother, will you? I'll get a sandwich when I feel like it.'

# CHAPTER TWO

THE place hadn't altered much architecturally over the years, Rachel decided. The road, which wound down from the Coniston Pass, still afforded a magnificent view of the valley, with Rothmere itself lying still and silent at its foot. From the pass, it was possible to see the roofs and chimneys of the house that stood at the end of the lake. Lower down, sturdy pines and spruce trees provided a protective screen from inquisitive eyes, except from the lake itself, where it was possible to catch a glimpse of the lawns and terrace at the front of the house. But, from the pass, Rachel looked down on the house that had once been her home, and knew a fleeting sense of nostalgia.

However, it didn't last. She had no wish to resurrect the past. She wouldn't be here at all were it not for Uncle Geoff, and she had no illusions that her aunt had endorsed the invitation. But Barbara had been her cousin, her uncle's only daughter, and if he wanted her here she owed him that, at least.

The village of Rothside, which was her destination, lay approximately halfway along the lake shore, with the waters of Rothdale Beck tumbling down from the fell and splitting the main street into two halves. Although there had been few structural changes, Rachel noticed how many of the cottages were now advertising accommodation available, and the old water-mill had been transformed into a café and gift shop. Evidently tourism had reached Rothside at last, and Rachel recognised her own profession's responsibility for that. It was due in part to the very successful job the media had done in promoting the Lake District that so many people now flocked to this most beautiful area of northern

England. And, while she regretted some of the changes that
had been made, the jobs the tourist industry had brought
had to have been welcome.

St Mary's church, and the vicarage that stood close by,
were situated on the outskirts of the village. But Rachel was
in no hurry to reach her destination. Instead, she parked her
car outside the general stores—which she noticed had been
converted into a mini-market—and went inside.

She hadn't expected to see anyone who knew her, but the
elderly woman in charge of the till was familiar. Mrs Reed
must have lived in Rothside for the past sixty years at least,
and she had always been regarded as a busybody. However,
not surprisingly after so long, she didn't immediately recognise Rachel in the slim, elegantly attired young woman
who stood just inside the door, and as Rachel's clothes were
evidently expensive she gazed at her inquisitively.

'Can I help you?'

Rachel hid a smile and shook her head. 'I can manage,
thank you,' she said, picking up one of the wire baskets and
glancing along the shelves. It all looked very neat and ef-
ficient, but she missed the familiar counter with its tempting
display of sweets and chocolate. Still, the familiar things
were there, if you looked for them: locally produced honey,
and Kendal mint cake. It was only the way of exhibiting
them that had changed. Much like herself, she reflected cynically.

She carried her basket back to the check-out, and set it
on the low counter so that Mrs Reed could ring in on the
till the cost of the two items she had bought. Then, as she
retrieved her purse from her handbag, Mrs Reed remarked,
'I don't suppose you got that tan in England?'

'No.' Rachel responded tolerantly. 'Um—the South of
France, actually,' she added, picking up her purchases.
'Thank you.'

But Mrs Reed was not about to let her go so easily. Trade
was obviously slack at this hour of a Monday afternoon,
and, leaving her seat, she accompanied Rachel to the door.

'I thought so,' she said. 'It's too early in the season for you to have caught any sun in this part of the country. You're not from around here, are you, dear?' Two beady brown eyes scanned Rachel's cool features. 'Yet, there's something about your face...'

Not wanting to have to identify herself now, Rachel reached for the handle of the door and pulled it open, just as it was propelled inwards from the other side. A girl of perhaps nine or ten years of age practically tumbled into the shop, regaining her balance with evident difficulty, and directing a hostile gaze at Rachel, as if she were totally to blame for what had happened.

'Oh—Rosemary!' exclaimed Mrs Reed, her expression registering a surprising amount of sympathy for the child. 'You haven't hurt yourself, have you, dear? You just opened the door at the wrong moment.'

'It was her fault!' retorted Rosemary, tossing back a single braid of night-dark hair, and fixing Rachel with an accusatory stare. 'Why don't you watch what you're doing? I could have broken my leg!'

Rachel caught her breath. 'Your neck would have been more appropriate,' she essayed smoothly, keeping her temper with an effort. 'Do you always stick it out so far?'

'Oh—there, don't take any notice of Rosemary's sulks!' exclaimed Mrs Reed quickly, evidently torn between the thought of losing an old customer and offending a new one. 'Rosemary's one of my best customers, aren't you, dear? Are you all right? No bones broken?'

But Rosemary was evidently not prepared to let anyone else speak for her. 'I should watch what I was saying, if I were you,' she informed Rachel, splaying her feet and placing balled fists on her jean-clad hips. 'My father's an important man in Rothside. One word from me, and you could find yourself in a load of trouble!'

Rachel gulped, strung between laughter and outrage. 'Are you threatening me?' she enquired, realising she was playing into the girl's hands by even taking her seriously, but unable to resist.

'Rosemary's not threatening anyone,' put in Mrs Reed, trying to make light of it. 'Are you, dear? And how is your dear daddy? You will tell him I was asking after him, won't you? We're all thinking about him, you know.'

Rosemary made no response to this, her small jaw jutting a little more aggressively as she met Rachel's amused gaze. Obviously, she was trying to think of something even more outrageous with which to shock her listeners, but the elderly shopkeeper forestalled her by asking what she wanted.

'Some sweeties?' Mrs Reed suggested, adopting a hopeful tone. 'Or how about a nice cold can of Coca Cola? I can get you one out of the fridge—'

'Just twenty kingsize, that's all,' the child interrupted her, pointing to the brand of cigarettes she wanted. 'Put them on Daddy's account. He'll settle with you later.'

'Now, Rosemary, you know I'm not supposed to sell cigarettes to a little girl of your age,' began Mrs Reed unhappily, and Rachel, seeing a chance to get away, decided to make good her escape. After the events of the last few minutes she had even less desire for Mrs Reed to recognise her, and she stepped outside, quelling the urge to retaliate.

But she hadn't even unlocked her car before the girl emerged from the store, opening the pack of cigarettes Mrs Reed had evidently not withheld, and putting one between her lips. If it was an act of defiance, it was one she had attempted many times before, thought Rachel irritably, trying to concentrate on juggling her purchases and her handbag, and getting the key in the lock. The way Rosemary extracted a book of matches from her pocket and applied a light to the cigarette proved it, and Rachel tried to tell herself it was nothing to do with her if the child's father sanctioned the offence.

'I hope you drive better than you walk!' Rosemary commented now, puffing on the cigarette, and, although she had at last got the car door open and was about to step inside, something inside Rachel snapped at the deliberate provocation.

Swinging round, she snatched the cigarette from the child's lips and the pack of cigarettes from her hand. Then, dropping them both on to the pavement, she ground her heel into them, watching Rosemary's face with an almost childlike sense of triumph as the pale, sallow features erupted into fury.

'How—how dare you?' she screamed, launching herself at Rachel with flailing arms and legs that somehow connected despite her diminutive size. 'You wait until I tell my father about you! You'll wish you'd never been born!'

'Let's both tell him, shall we?' taunted Rachel, losing all sense of reason with the situation. Twisting the child's hands behind her back, she turned her round so that Rosemary was unable to go on kicking her, adding, 'Where do you live? You might as well tell me. I'd like to meet this father of yours. I'd like to tell him what a disgusting little brat he's got for a daughter!'

'Let go of me!'

Rosemary continued to struggle, but it was obvious she was losing the battle, and there was a suspicious break in her voice that hinted of emotions hitherto not in evidence.

'Tell me where you live,' Rachel insisted, not making the mistake of losing her grip, and then sighed with some frustration when Mrs Reed came charging out of the shop.

'For heaven's sake!' she exclaimed, taking in the scene with horrified eyes. 'What is going on here? Rosemary, my dear! Is this lady bothering you?'

'You have to be joking!'

With a word that was not at all ladylike, and which Mrs Reed evidently recognised, judging from her expression, Rachel let the girl go and turned to the other woman. And Rosemary, who had evidently just been waiting for such an opportunity, took immediate advantage of the situation. While Rachel was forced to make some explanation of her actions, Rosemary aimed a booted foot at the wing of

Rachel's car before scooting off across the footbridge over the stream.

Rachel was almost speechless. 'That—that child,' she choked, struggling to control her voice, 'that child is totally undisciplined!' She bent to examine a ladder in her dark tights and the purpling bruise below it. 'For heaven's sake, why did you serve her? I assume you knew the cigarettes were for her.'

'Of course I didn't.' Mrs Reed was not prepared to admit to that. 'Do you think I want to lose my licence? No—I thought they were for her father. And now, if you'll excuse me, I have work to attend to.'

'But who is she?' demanded Rachel testily, only to find she was talking to herself. Mrs Reed had apparently decided she had said too much already, and, with a feeling of frustration, Rachel flung open the door of the car.

It was then that she saw the dent in the panelling. Until that moment, Rosemary's fit of retaliation for the destruction of her cigarettes had scarcely registered. But now she saw what the child had done, and an anger she had scarcely known she possessed gripped her. The selfish little brat! she thought infuriatedly. If she could get her hands on her...

Coming to an impulsive decision, she closed and locked the car door again, and, grimacing at the heels of her hand-made Italian shoes, she started off across the footbridge. She knew the village like the back of her hand, and unless Rosemary had disappeared into one of the cottages facing the beck she might just have a chance of catching her. The girl would not expect her to follow her, and might be dawdling. Rachel could only hope that luck was on her side now.

She attracted the attention of several pairs of eyes as she crossed the road at the other side of the stream and started up the steep lane that led away from the beck. Tourists in this area invariably wore comfortable walking shoes or boots, and dressed for the most part in hiking clothes and wind-cheaters. Rachel's long-jacketed suit of navy and white houndstooth and the fine white muslin blouse she wore beneath it were definitely not casual, and her air of purposeful assurance drew a curious speculation.

She wondered if anyone had recognised her yet, or whether her new hairstyle and town clothes were blinding people to her identity. Surely she hadn't changed that much? And with the funeral tomorrow they ought to make the association.

She abruptly abandoned these thoughts at the sight of a child loitering ahead of her. Although she was some distance away, the dark plait of hair was unmistakable. It was Rosemary; it had to be. And, as Rachel had supposed, she was totally unaware that she might have been followed.

Rachel took a deep breath and quickened her pace. There was no place to hide, and if Rosemary should happen to glance back and see her her chance might well be lost. And now that she was almost within reach of her goal she was curiously loath to prolong the agony. There was something unwillingly vulnerable about the girl's bent head and drooping shoulders. Without the memory of that scene outside the village stores, Rachel might almost have felt sorry for her. Who was she? Where was she going? And, more expediently, where did she live?

The lane, which was backed by the walled gardens of cottages that faced the fell, gave on to open countryside just a few yards further on. It was a narrow winding track that climbed between dry stone walls and rocky crags to the summit of Rothdale Pike. It was mostly used by sheep, or less adventurous climbers who wanted to reach the peak by a less arduous method than striking up the rock-face. Whatever, it was not really the kind of route for a girl of Rosemary's age to go wandering up alone, and Rachel searched her mind, trying to remember if there were any farms within walking distance.

And then Rosemary glanced back and saw her.

Rachel didn't know what had drawn the child's attention. Maybe her heels had clattered on one of the loose stones that covered the track. Although it had been resurfaced at some time, snow and frost had left deep delves in the paving, and there were plenty of pebbles lying about. In any event, the girl had now recognised her and, although her expression revealed her indignation, she was evidently not prepared to stay and fight another losing battle.

Scrambling over the crumbling wall beside her, the child struck off across the sloping hillside, her rubber-soled shoes moving swiftly over the uneven surface. Although Rosemary's legs were shorter than her pursuer's, Rachel guessed she hadn't a snowball in hell's chance of catching her in her high heels, and she clenched her fists frustratedly when the child turned and raised her fingers in an insolent salute.

But even as Rachel stood, impotent beside the dry stone barrier, a movement beyond Rosemary's taunting figure drew her attention. A rider had appeared from the trees that marked the lower slopes and was coming swiftly towards them. The man—for she could see that the rider was too big to be a woman—was mounted on a great black horse, and even from this distance it was possible to observe his expert horsemanship. It was years since Rachel had been on a horse, and even then she had never achieved the skill and sense of balance she was presently admiring. The man and his mount moved as a single entity, and Rachel's appreciation was such that she briefly forgot her objective.

Rosemary, however, seemed unaware of anyone but her pursuer, and it was only when the horseman seemed in danger of riding the child down that Rachel realised her vulnerability. Objectionable she might be, but Rachel had no desire to see her get hurt, and, resting her hands on the wall, she yelled, 'Look out, behind you!'

Rosemary's expression turned from scorn to disbelief to shocked awareness, all in swift succession, but before she could move or get out of the way the rider was upon her. He didn't ride her down though. On the contrary, with a skilled shortening of the reins he brought the powerful animal to a halt beside her, and as Rachel watched, open-mouthed, he swung the child up in front of him.

For a moment, Rachel was too shocked to do anything. She wasn't even sure what she was witnessing, or indeed if the scene that was being enacted before her eyes was really happening. It was a bright day, and concentrating on Rosemary's diminutive form in the face of a lowering sun had caused spots to dance before her eyes.

She blinked several times, and as she did so the horseman swung his mount around to head back the way he had come. There had been no cry of protest from the girl, and Rachel could only assume that she knew her rescuer. But that didn't absolve her of the damage she had done to Rachel's car, and, cursing her narrow skirt, Rachel clambered over the wall.

'Wait!'

Her cry hardly carried across the open moorland, competing as it did with thrushes and curlews, and the distinctive call of a blackbird. But her actions must have caught the man's attention, for he turned his head to look at her and she saw his face for the first time.

Dear God, it was *Matt*! she realised disbelievingly, the knowledge hitting her with a force she had never expected. For a moment it was as if the last ten years had rolled away, and her heart was pounding as it used to do every time she saw him. Nothing in her experience had prepared her for the shock of seeing him again, and although she fought to hold on to her composure she was suddenly trembling with the violence of her emotions.

But with this awareness came another shattering conclusion. The child—Rosemary—must be *his* daughter. Her stomach clenched and her mouth dried. His daughter! The daughter he and Barbara had had soon after his divorce from Rachel herself.

But it was sobering, too, and as the proud stallion and his equally proud riders picked their way towards her she managed to salvage a little dignity. But never in her wildest dreams had she expected to meet Matt in circumstances like these, and she prayed she had the strength to hide how shaken it had left her.

She had no idea when Matthew had realised who she was. But as the enormous horse came nearer his guarded expression revealed that he had definitely identified her now. Not that that was any consolation. It was perfectly obvious that he was not pleased at meeting her like this. The grey eyes that she remembered so well were glacially distant, and the hands wrapped around the reins were taut within his wrist-length leather gloves.

Rosemary, meanwhile, was looking as if she was torn between the urge to confess her side of the story before Rachel had a chance to speak, and the equally strong suspicion that by saying nothing she could deny everything. You could almost see her weighing the pros and cons of confession, Rachel thought bitterly. No wonder Mrs Reed had refrained from making any derogatory remarks about the girl. The Conroys owned the vast proportion of the land hereabouts, and, like many of the cottages in Rothside, the lease on the store was owned by them.

The horse and his riders had reached her now, and Rachel thought how typical it was that she should be put at such a disadvantage. Her height had never put her on eye-level terms with Matthew, but on foot she had never had to look up at him this way. As it was, the ignominy of her position was not lost on his daughter, and Rosemary's lips curled maliciously as her trailing shoe drew temptingly close to Rachel's chin.

Deciding the best method of defending her position was by ignoring it, Rachel looked up at him with what she hoped was a cool, unflustered gaze. 'Hello, Matt,' she said evenly, briefly enjoying Rosemary's startled deflation. Evidently it had never occurred to her that Rachel might know her father.

She was not a pretty child, thought Rachel dispassionately, fleetingly aware of the similarities between her and her father. They were both dark, of course—dark-haired, and dark-skinned—but whereas Matthew's features were strong, and still disturbingly attractive, Rosemary's face was thin and decidedly sulky.

All the same, it was difficult to make any real assessment of the child with Matthew looking down at her. A different Matthew, yet still so familiar, despite the flecks of grey in his hair and the broader contours of his body. The Matthew she remembered had looked approachable, good-natured—not remote and brooding like this man. The Matthew she had fallen in love with would never have regarded her with quite that look of detachment, through eyes that, even narrowed, conveyed his raw dislike.

But Rosemary could not see her father's withdrawn expression, and his polite, 'Rachel,' in answer to her greeting was a cause for consternation.

'Daddy, I didn't do it!' she exclaimed, without waiting any longer for Rachel to incriminate her. 'It wasn't me! It was someone else! Oh, tell her I couldn't do a thing like that—'

Matthew drew his gaze from Rachel's face to look down at his daughter. 'What?' he demanded blankly. 'What are you talking about?' His eyes shifted unwillingly back to the young woman beside him. 'Do you know something about this?'

Rachel took a deep breath. 'Yes,' she admitted, half unwillingly now, and with a grim exclamation Matthew swung himself down from the saddle.

The horse shifted uncertainly at the sudden shift of weight from his back, but Matthew's hand on his muzzle swiftly reassured him. 'Rosemary?' he said, with an unmistakable inflection in his voice. 'Perhaps you'd explain. I'm waiting to hear what this is all about.'

Rachel expelled her breath warily. The annoyance of Rosemary's attack on her car was fast losing significance. Indeed, the more she thought about it, the more ridiculous it seemed for her to have come charging after the girl, when she was so unsuitably attired for such an expedition. As it was, her heels were scuffed, her tights were laddered, and whatever conviction she had started out with was rapidly diminishing.

'It wasn't my fault—' began Rosemary again, defensively, and, realising this was getting more complicated by the minute, Rachel intervened.

'We had—a—a misunderstanding,' she said, meeting the girl's sullen stare with determined coolness. Then, sensing that Matthew was looking at her again, she transferred her gaze to the open neck of his dark blue sweatshirt. 'It was something and nothing.' She shrugged. 'I didn't know who she was.'

'Would that have made a difference?'

His voice was clipped and without expression, and Rachel knew a rekindling sense of resentment. They were both the same, she thought. Father and daughter alike. They were both treating her with the kind of arrogant contempt more suitably reserved for an inferior, and, although moderation warred with defiance, she refused to let either of them walk all over her.

'No,' she replied now, turning to make her rocky retreat over the pile of stones. She refused to stand there and argue with him like some recalcitrant minion. She would pay for the repairs to her car, and to hell with him. She had no intention of begging compensation from the Conroys.

But, as she struggled to climb back into the lane, and her feet slid ignominiously over the rocks, Rosemary giggled. It was a boastful little sound that jarred Rachel's senses, and she was unbearably tempted to turn back and take up the attack. Her fingers itched to wipe the triumphant smile from the girl's face, but she resisted the impulse. Discretion is the better part of valour, she repeated to herself, like a mantra, and concentrated on getting over the wall and safely on to solid ground.

'Rachel!'

Matthew's harsh use of her name was briefly compelling,

scraping over her nerves like a rough hand on soft skin. How many times had she heard him use that word in just that way when he had been making love to her? she wondered unwillingly. How many times had he been compelled to abandon whatever plans he had to haul her back into his arms and lose himself in her willing body? Her hands clenched. Just as he had lost himself in Barbara's body, she appended bitterly. She mustn't forget that.

By the time she had slithered down into the ditch at the other side of the wall, Matthew was waiting for her. His booted feet had made short shrift of the crumbling rocks, and he offered her his hand to breach the gap between the ditch and the road. Pretending she hadn't seen it, Rachel made her own progress up on to the road, and then stopped to make another examination of her appearance. Damn! she swore. There were at least half a dozen runs in her stockings now, and her hands were scraped and sore. So much for revenge, she thought frustratedly. All she had succeeded in doing was making a complete fool of herself.

'Rachel!'

Matthew's hand on her arm would have swung her round to face him, but she shrugged it off and started back down the lane. To hell with the Conroys—all the Conroys, she thought childishly. She should never have agreed to come here. It had definitely been a mistake.

'Rachel, for heaven's sake!' Matthew's tone was distinctly angry now and, after ordering Rosemary to get down from the horse, he came striding after her. 'You might as well tell me. You didn't come after her just for the fun of it.'

Rachel halted reluctantly. 'It's not important,' she declared coldly, angry herself that her quickening breath wasn't just a result of her exertions. 'I've got to go. Uncle Geoff will be wondering where I am.'

'To hell with Uncle Geoff!' retorted Matthew unfeelingly, glancing back over his shoulder to assure himself that

Rosemary had indeed done as he had said. Then, transferring his gaze back to Rachel, he arched dark brows. 'Well?'

'I'm not a child, Matt.' Rachel resented his high-handed demand that he should be put in the picture. 'As I said, it's not important. Now—if you'll excuse me—'

'Rachel!'

Instinctively he reached out and grasped her wrist, his action born of his frustration, but Rachel was furious. Lifting her eyes to his, she forced herself to stare him down and, after a pregnant moment, he released her.

'Goodbye, Matt,' she said distantly, and, refusing to prolong a situation that she was no longer certain she could control, she stalked stiffly away.

# CHAPTER THREE

'I'LL see you back at the vicarage.'

Rachel stood beside the long black saloon that was waiting to take her aunt and uncle back to Rothmere House, cool and remote in her black suede skirt and matching jacket. The sombre colour of her outfit drew attention to the silvery lightness of her hair, and, although she kept it shorter these days, and swept back behind her ears, its paleness accentuated the unnatural pallor of her cheeks.

She knew she looked pale. She could feel it. The service in the village church had been more of a strain than she could have realised, and the awareness of Matthew and his mother in the pew in front of her had added to her discomfort. What had he been thinking? she wondered. What feelings of grief and remorse had filled his thoughts to the exclusion of all else? Sadness, of course, and pity; but was he as heartbroken as Aunt Maggie had maintained? Somehow she doubted it. The man she had met out on the fells had not looked heartbroken. Bitter, perhaps, and angry. But not torn by any overwhelming pangs of emotional anguish. And why should *she* expect anything else, after what he had done to her?

The Bishop of Norbury had conducted the service, leaving Uncle Geoff to mourn the loss of his daughter in private. And afterwards Barbara's remains had been buried in the family plot in the adjoining graveyard. The bishop himself had read the eulogy, before the heavy, iron-bound casket had been lowered into the ground, and the sound of Aunt Maggie's weeping had echoed off the surrounding headstones.

But now the ceremony was over, and a long stream of

limousines was already transporting family and friends back to the house, where a cold buffet was waiting. Personal respects would be endorsed, sympathy would be offered, and then everyone would depart about their own business, guiltily relieved that their responsibility was over.

'What do you mean?' Rachel's aunt demanded now, putting aside her grief to lean out of the car window and gaze up at her niece with an aggravated impatience. 'You'll see us back at the vicarage? What is that supposed to mean?'

'Please, Maggie!' Geoffrey Barnes put a detaining hand on his wife's arm, but she shook him off.

'Stop it, Geoff!' she exclaimed irritably. 'Well, Rachel? I'm waiting for an answer.'

Rachel glanced about her; unwillingly aware that their exchange was attracting curious eyes. Not least because their car was holding up at least half a dozen other limousines.

'I think it would be better if I went straight back to the vicarage, Aunt Maggie,' she responded quickly. 'I—well, it's not as if I'd be a welcome visitor at the house, and I'm sure I'd save us all a deal of embarrassment if I left you and Uncle Geoff to accept everyone's condolences alone.'

Her aunt's face suffused with colour. 'You should have thought of that before you came here,' she hissed angrily, her grief apparently taking second place to her indignation. 'But you had to come, didn't you? You had to have your— your pound of flesh!'

'Aunt Maggie!'

Rachel was horrified that her aunt should believe she had come here with some perverted desire to bear witness to her cousin's demise. Whatever Barbara had done, she had not deserved to die, and Rachel felt only pity now for the woman who had destroyed her marriage.

'Maggie, for goodness' sake!'

Geoffrey Barnes's face mirrored his distaste at this unpleasant scene, and Rachel felt the unaccustomed sting of tears behind her eyes. Dear God, and she had felt obliged to come here because she had thought—foolishly, she now realised—that they needed her.

'I don't care.' Her aunt was unrepentant. 'She's here now, and I will not have people saying that she wasn't invited to the house. How do you think that would look? People talk, Geoffrey. Before you know it, they'd be saying that Matt didn't invite her because he's afraid to see her—'

'Oh, Aunt Maggie!' Rachel was almost speechless with emotion. 'That—that is absolutely—ridiculous!'

'I know it and you know it, but *they* don't,' retorted her aunt grimly. 'Now, will you get in the car and stop behaving as if your presence at Rothmere had any importance—any importance at all?'

Rachel hesitated, but to argue any further would only aggravate an already embarrassing situation, and when her aunt thrust open the door she unwillingly stepped inside. But, once installed on one of the folding seats facing her aunt and uncle on the leather banquette opposite, she spoke to her uncle.

'What do you think, Uncle Geoff?' she asked him tensely. 'Don't you feel it would be better if I didn't accompany you?'

'Geoff—' began her aunt warningly, but for once Geoffrey Barnes didn't need his wife's admonishments.

'I suspect Maggie may be right,' he ventured, to Rachel's dismay, running a nervous finger around the inside of his clerical collar. 'Rothside isn't like London, Rachel. And people do gossip, I regret to say. Your coming here is bound to have caused conjecture, and avoiding speaking to Matthew will only fuel the fires of speculation.'

Rachel caught her breath. 'Then why did you invite me?'

'You might well ask,' declared her aunt darkly, dabbing at her eyes with a lace handkerchief.

'I invited you because Barbara is—was—your cousin, and I saw this as a way to resolve our differences,' declared Geoffrey Barnes firmly. 'Rachel, when your father thrust the responsibility of your upbringing upon us all those years ago, I did not see it only as a physical duty. You are our niece, whatever else. Can't we forgive the past?'

Rachel moistened her lips and looked out of the window of the car. Forgive the past? she echoed silently. How was that possible? Obviously Aunt Maggie forgave nothing, and, for herself, she wanted no part of any attempt at reconciliation with the Conroys.

'You do see how it would look, don't you, Rachel?' her uncle persisted now, and Rachel managed a slight inclination of her head in his direction. But inside she was a churning mass of nervous tension that not even her media training could totally control.

The procession of cars was sweeping through the stone gates that marked the southern boundary of Rothmere House now, and Rachel's fingers clenched around her handbag as the remembered lawns and paddocks opened out beside her. Rothside had been recognisable to her, but the grounds of Rothmere were unbearably familiar. Yet, if it hadn't changed in over two hundred years, why should she have expected it to change in only ten? Didn't it only go to prove that no one was indispensable? The passing of Rachel Barnes Conroy hadn't even ruffled the surface of the lake that lapped the pebbled shore below the house.

The house itself was solidly built of lakeland stone, with long mullioned windows glinting in the late afternoon sunlight. It was built on three floors, with many turrets and chimneys, and Rachel had always thought it had many of the characteristics of one of the fortified manor houses of earlier times, but Matthew had declared it was because it had been added to so many times that it had lost its own identification. But, in spite of everything, Rachel had loved the house, and seeing it again now was a particularly painful experience.

Watkins was waiting on the gravelled forecourt, to open car doors and welcome his employer's guests to Rothmere, and his old eyes widened in some amazement when Rachel stepped first from the limousine.

'Why—it's Miss Rachel!' he exclaimed. And then, recollecting the circumstances, his lined features sobered. 'Um—good afternoon, Mrs—*Miss* Barnes.'

'Rachel will do,' she responded gently, acknowledging his look of gratitude as she turned away to draw a deep breath. Well, here she was, she thought tensely. Let battle commence!

Her aunt and uncle were climbing out of the limousine now, and, meeting Aunt Maggie's accusing gaze, Rachel guessed she had witnessed the exchange between herself and Watkins. But what of it? she asked herself defensively. She had always had a soft spot for the elderly butler, and of all the servants at Rothmere he had been the first to accept her as Matthew's wife. If only Watkins were the only one to meet.

In the event, she was able to join the subdued group of people thronging the hall of Rothmere House without incident. Remaining behind her aunt and uncle, she attracted little immediate attention, and only when they made their way across the room to speak to Matthew and his mother did she feel the urge to hang back. But Aunt Maggie was having none of that, and, grasping her by the arm, she forced her to accompany them.

'You must remember the good times, Matt,' someone was saying as they approached, and with a pang Rachel wondered how popular Barbara had been.

'Matt, we're here,' Maggie was saying now, interrupting the speaker to tug arrogantly at Matthew's arm, and Rachel wished the floor would open up and swallow her. She didn't want to be here. She didn't want to be a part of this very personal occasion. And, most of all, she didn't want to speak to the man who had once been the whole core of her existence.

He was looking exceptionally composed for a bereaved man, she thought bitterly. Tall, and dark, and attractive, his sombre attire only adding to his air of controlled sophistication. He didn't look like a man who had just lost his much-loved wife, but then Matt had always had the uncanny ability to hide his feelings, she remembered.

'Maggie, Geoff,' he responded now, allowing his mother-in-law to bestow a fervent kiss on his cheek before his eyes moved beyond her to the young woman who hung back from their intimate circle. 'Rachel,' he added stiffly, and she had, perforce, to step forward and offer her own condolences.

'I'm sorry,' she said, aware that his use of her name had attracted more than one pair of eyes. 'Please—believe me.'

'Oh, I do.'

But Matthew's eyes were cold, his expression as hard and unforgiving as that of the slim, elderly woman standing at his side. Lady Olivia had reacted violently to his use of Rachel's name, but like her son she would not make a scene in public.

'Rachel,' she echoed, but her lips were thin and forbidding. It was obvious how she felt, and Rachel shivered in spite of the press of bodies around her.

'Lady Olivia,' she responded, steeling herself against the almost uncontrollable urge to escape. 'This is a very sad occasion.'

Matthew's mother's lips twisted. 'Yes,' she said. 'It is.' But the meaning behind her words was obscure, and Rachel was glad when someone else came to claim Lady Olivia's attention.

Several white-coated attendants, hired for the occasion, were making their way among the guests with trays of glasses containing sherry or whisky, and the huge doors to the dining-room had been opened up to display the sumptuous cold buffet laid out on damask-covered tables. As people relaxed, and cigars were lit, a haze of tobacco smoke rose above the gathering, and the level of sound gradually rose in volume.

Rachel, compelled to accept at least one drink before making her escape, allowed herself to be engulfed in the mêlée. Her aunt and uncle were paying little attention to her now, her aunt, at least, enjoying the dubious notoriety of being the mother of the deceased. Her uncle seemed less aware of his surroundings, and she guessed that for him this was something of an ordeal. But at least he had his faith to sustain him, she thought ruefully. For herself, she had no such panacea.

It was time to leave, she decided grimly. She had done what Aunt Maggie had demanded she do and paid her respects, but now it was time for her to go. Perhaps, in spite of Uncle Geoff's invitation, she should have stayed away. It was obvious that Matthew's mother thought so. And Matt, too, although he was probably enjoying her discomfort. Whatever, she couldn't wait to put as many miles as possible between herself and this painful exhumation of the past.

Putting down her glass, she began to thread her way back across the hall. Occasionally someone recognised her, and rather stilted greetings were exchanged, but on the whole she avoided any further embarrassment. Happily, they were all too busy helping themselves to the mouth-watering canapés that were presently being circulated, and swallowing more of Matt's extremely good Scotch. It had turned into just another cocktail party, thought Rachel, somewhat cynically, depression settling like a heavy weight upon her shoulders.

She was within a few yards of the door when the accident happened. Someone stepped back heavily on to her toe, and she had to choke back the automatic protest that sprang to her lips. But even as she struggled to restrain her indignation the perpetrator of her injury pushed rudely past her, and she realised belatedly exactly who it was.

'Wait a minute!' she exclaimed, forgetting for a moment where she was as she lunged forward awkwardly and grasped the child's arm. Balancing on her uninjured foot, she swung the girl round to face her, only to wish she hadn't when she saw Rosemary's tear-stained face.

'What do you want?' the little girl asked defensively, ev-

idently recognising her, and Rachel wondered what particular malevolent god had chosen that she should make one
abysmal mistake after another.

'Um—nothing,' she said abruptly, releasing her and lifting the offended foot from her shoe to rub it tenderly against
the calf of her other leg. 'Forget it.'

Rosemary hesitated. 'I suppose you're expecting me to
thank you for not telling my father what happened yesterday,' she declared suddenly, and Rachel looked up from
examining the purpling bruise on her instep to find the child
still confronting her.

'I beg your pardon?'

'Is that why you're here?' Rosemary demanded suspiciously. 'I heard Grandma tell Daddy that you wouldn't dare
to come here to the house, but you're here now, so is that
why?'

Rachel slid her foot back into her shoe and expelled a
careful breath. 'Your—your mother was my cousin,' she
said, after an awkward moment. 'That's why I'm here.
Not—not for any other reason.'

Rosemary frowned. 'Then why haven't I seen you before?
If you're really Mummy's cousin, why haven't you come
to visit?'

Rachel hesitated now. 'It's a long story—'

'And not one for your ears, rabbit,' remarked a cool, crisp
voice behind them. 'What's going on here? Aren't you supposed to be helping Mrs Moffat in the kitchen?'

Rachel stiffened. The dark, velvety tones of her ex-
husband's voice were unmistakable, and she didn't need to
see Rosemary's instinctive reaction to his words to know
who had joined them.

'I don't want to help Mrs Moffat,' Rosemary mumbled
now, casting an appealing look in her father's direction.
'You only want me to stay out of the way. You don't really
care what I want to do!'

Matthew moved into Rachel's line of vision, and,
although she was loath to study his dark features, his daugh-

ter's words were so startling that she felt compelled to observe his expression.

'I think you've done quite enough, Rosemary,' he declared, his tone still even, but icily remote. 'And as you prefer to be defiant rather than enjoy yourself in the kitchen, I suggest you find Agnetha and have her put you to bed. You'll really be out of the way then, won't you?'

'No!'

Rosemary's cry was anguished, a mixture of indignation and desperation, a frantic appeal to his finer feelings, but Matthew was not to be persuaded.

'Bed, Rosemary,' he said implacably, gesturing towards the inner hallway and the staircase which, Rachel knew from experience, curved elegantly around its panelled walls.

Rachel wanted to protest. She found herself wanting to say that perhaps Matthew's judgement had been a little harsh, and that Rosemary's remarks might have a grain of truth in them. But she didn't. She didn't know enough about the situation to warrant making some unguarded comment, and besides, her own experiences with Rosemary were hardly grounds for encouragement. It was nothing to do with her, she told herself firmly. Just because, for a moment there, she had felt a reluctant pang of sympathy for the child, there was no reason to get involved in what was possibly a long-running battle between them.

There was a pause then, when Rachel half expected the girl to exhibit some further show of defiance, but it passed. With artificially bright eyes and only the faintest reddening of her nose to betray her emotions, Rosemary marched away towards the stairs, and Rachel was left to confront the child's father with her defensive shell not quite intact.

Around them, the silence which had descended when Rosemary had challenged her father was quickly replaced. Although Rachel was sure that Matthew's other guests would all have liked to go on listening to their exchange, politeness, and embarrassment that they might be observed, forced them to contrive an air of normality.

'Matt,' she murmured stiffly now, using his name as both an acknowledgement and a farewell, then, walking rather gingerly on her still-painful instep, she started again towards the door.

'Rachel!'

Matthew's impatient summons was all too familiar, but she pretended not to hear. If she could just make it out on to the forecourt, she was sure she could persuade one of the liveried chauffeurs from the funeral directors to take her back to the vicarage, and once there she intended to pack and leave before her aunt and uncle noticed she was missing. Cowardly perhaps, but justifiable under the circumstances.

'Rachel!'

This time, Matthew's hand gripping the yielding flesh of her upper arm was determined. It was not like that other occasion, when there had been only the sheep and the birds that inhabited Rothdale Pike to observe them. Here, not only were they the cynosure of those eyes near enough to see what was happening, but their words could be overheard by as many people as cared to listen.

Clenching her teeth, she looked up at him, willing him as she had done before to let her go, but this time he chose not to obey her silent command. 'I think we should talk, Rachel,' he said, his voice just as cool and deadly as it had been when he'd spoken to his daughter. 'Now—or later. It's all the same to me.'

Rachel took a steadying breath. 'Why?' she countered tensely, refusing to let him intimidate her, and his eyes narrowed.

'Why do you think?' he retorted. 'I want you to tell me why you followed Rosemary from the village yesterday. You were following her, weren't you? In spite of what she says.'

'What does she say?' asked Rachel unwillingly, curious to know how the child had defended herself, but Matthew was having none of that.

'I want to hear your story,' he told her, without releasing her arm, and Rachel's face flamed. He was treating her like a child, too, she thought indignantly. And embarrassing her as well, today of all days.

'I should have thought you had more important things to think about,' she countered hotly, keeping her voice low with an effort. 'Matt, please—are you trying to humiliate me? Wasn't what happened ten years ago enough for you?'

Matthew's grey eyes narrowed. 'Humiliating *you*?' he echoed, barely audibly, and this time she had no fear that anyone else could overhear his harsh denial. 'Humiliating you? Oh, Rachel, you don't know the meaning of the word!'

'Matt! Matt, I've been looking everywhere for you!' As Matthew's hand fell away from Rachel's arm, Lady Olivia insinuated herself between them, her eyes, so like her son's, assessing in an instant the potential danger in the situation. Lady Olivia hadn't been looking for Matt, decided Rachel bitterly—although her interruption had probably not come a moment too soon. She had known exactly where he was all the time, and she had undoubtedly made a beeline for them. 'There are people waiting to speak to you,' she added, sliding her arm through his and circumventing any further exchange between the protagonists. 'Rachel,' she murmured, in much the same way as Rachel had used Matthew's name earlier, and, refusing to be diverted, she drew her son away.

With no further obstacle to her departure now, Rachel felt suddenly loath to go. Even though she was aware that the little scene that had just concluded had not totally removed the covert glances being cast in her direction, she no longer felt the need to escape. The worst had happened. Matt had revealed his hatred for her, and embarrassed her in front of his friends. What more could he do to her?

# CHAPTER FOUR

IN THE event, Rachel had to send for a taxi to take her back to the vicarage. And, in consequence, she was still gathering her things together when she heard the crunching sound of a limousine's wheels on the gravel of the drive.

Her room, the room she had occupied when she had lived at the vicarage, was a small room at the front of the house, and so she could look down at the long black car without impediment. For a heart-stopping moment she wondered if it was Matt, come to continue his denunciation, but it wasn't. Her aunt and uncle were climbing out of the limousine, and her heart sank abruptly at this obvious obstruction to her plans.

Leaving her case still open on the narrow bed, she hesitated only a moment before going downstairs. Favouring her left foot, she trod the creaking treads of the stairs with some misgivings. But the vicarage was old, and there was no way she could avoid the bald announcement of her presence.

Her aunt and uncle were in the drawing-room, and as Rachel pushed open the door she could hear her aunt's stifled sobs. In spite of everything, she felt incredibly sorry for her. Her aunt was going to miss Barbara a lot, not least because she had always contrived to give her daughter the best, and Barbara's eventual marriage to Matthew Conroy had been the ultimate triumph. Without any other children to compensate them, her aunt and uncle had no one else— which was one of the reasons why Rachel had allowed herself to be persuaded to come here. But she knew now that it had been a mistake, and the malevolent face her aunt turned in her direction only emphasised the fact.

'Er…' Rachel looked towards her uncle, who had risen

to his feet at her entrance, and sought for words. 'I—er—I thought I'd be going—'

'Going?' echoed her uncle blankly.

'Going where?' demanded her aunt, with sudden animation.

Rachel moistened her dry lips. 'Um—back to London,' she managed, after a moment. 'Home,' she added, for good measure. 'If I leave now, I should—'

'But this is your home, Rachel.' Her uncle was gazing at her with anxious eyes. 'My dear, have you forgotten already what we were saying as we drove to Rothmere? Don't you see? This is our chance, our opportunity to be reconciled.'

Rachel didn't know what to say. It was certainly not what she had expected, and, looking at her aunt, she still couldn't believe she had any part of this plea for reconciliation.

'Uncle Geoff,' she began awkwardly, 'I do appreciate what you say, but—well, I can't stay here. My work—my friends—are in London—'

'He's not asking you to live here,' broke in her aunt abruptly. Drying her eyes with impatient fingers, she, too, got to her feet. 'But you can't leave—not yet; not tonight. It wouldn't be right. What would people say?'

Rachel was getting a little bit sick of worrying about what other people might say, or think. It was ten years since she had left the area. Ten years since she had had to care what anyone might say or think about her actions. That was one advantage of living in London. She could come and go as she pleased, with no one to feel answerable to. She had got used to being free, uncommitted, and if sometimes she found her life a little empty, it was the price she paid to guard her independence.

'I don't see how my staying on here for another night will silence any speculation,' she said at last, looking at her uncle rather than Aunt Maggie. 'And, as I say, I do have a job—'

'Another night?' exclaimed her aunt, with irritation, and

Geoffrey Barnes rubbed his hands together nervously as he was left to explain their wishes.

'We thought—well, that you might stay on over the weekend,' he ventured, giving Rachel a hopeful look, and she sighed.

'But it's only Tuesday, Uncle Geoff. That's *five* more days!'

'Little enough, I should have thought, after what we've done for you,' retorted her aunt bitterly. 'What would you have done all those years ago if we hadn't taken you in, that's what I'd like to know? All those years we gave you a home, and now you can't spare five days to give your uncle and me a little support when we need it.'

'Oh, Aunt Maggie—'

'Maggie, my dear, we don't want Rachel to stay because she feels she owes us something—'

Rachel and her uncle spoke together, but Maggie Barnes was unrepentant. 'Why not?' she demanded, responding to her husband's reproachful words. 'She does owe us something, and if this job of hers was important enough to break up her marriage for, then surely she can take a couple of days off when she feels like it without its causing the whole television station to close down!'

Rachel bent her head. They all knew that the idea that she and Matt had separated because she had been offered a better job in London was just a myth, but this was hardly the time to resurrect those old grievances. And her aunt knew it. That was why she was using it now. Because she knew Rachel wouldn't—*couldn't*—contradict her. Not with Barbara's body lying scarcely cold in its grave.

'We would be grateful if you could stay, of course,' her uncle murmured now, evidently torn between his desire to please his wife and his Christian duty to be fair. 'But only if you feel you can,' he added awkwardly. 'I mean, we'll understand if you have to get back to London.'

Would they? Rachel wondered. She doubted that her aunt would forgive her if she chose the latter course, and, while she might tell herself that subsequent events had destroyed the normal family ties there should have been between them, nothing could alter the fact that they had given her a home when her father had died.

'All right,' she said at last, feeling an undeniable sense of entrapment. 'I'll stay until Sunday. But I'll have to ring Justin Harcourt. He's expecting me back in the office to-morrow morning.'

'Justin Harcourt?' muttered Aunt Maggie scornfully, gathering her bag and gloves together and making for the door. 'What kind of a name is that for a man? *Justin!* I suppose he's one of those left-wing intellectuals, with long hair and Jesus sandals!'

'Nevertheless, he is my boss, and I have to call him,' replied Rachel, biting back the urge to defend Justin to them. The brilliant, bulky editor of *Network Southeast* didn't need any defending, and she was not about to play into Aunt Maggie's hands by extolling the awards he had won for television journalism, or announcing that the programme they both worked on was presently the number one current affairs programme in the UK.

'You can use the telephone in my study,' said her uncle helpfully, more than relieved at her capitulation, and Rachel forced a smile.

'Thanks,' she said, as her aunt made a sound of impatience before disappearing upstairs. 'I'll make the call now.' Then, aware of the clammy after-effects of her exchange with Matt, she added, 'And then I'll take a bath, if you don't mind. I'd like to freshen up.'

Justin was predictably peevish when she told him she wouldn't be back at work until Monday. 'You said two days, Rachel,' he reminded her irritably, and she could hear his pencil beating a tattoo on his desk—a sure sign of his uncertain temper.

'I know I did,' she conceded ruefully, perched on the edge of Uncle Geoff's worn leather armchair. 'But—well,

Barbara was my cousin, and—and I can't just walk out on them.'

'Your aunt and uncle?'

'Yes.'

'The aunt and uncle who've made no attempt to see you in ten years?'

Rachel sighed. 'Yes.'

'Oh, Rachel!'

'Well…' She was defensive now. 'Look, circumstances alter cases. You know that. And—and it's different now, now Barbara's—Barbara's—'

'Dead?'

'Not here,' amended Rachel uncomfortably. 'Justin, she was their only child. It's only natural that they should feel bereft.'

Justin was silent for a moment. Then he said harshly, 'And are you planning on taking your cousin's place? Now that Barbara's dead, do you feel differently about what happened between her and your ex-husband? Have you seen him, by the way? You must have, I suppose. Is he part of this sudden desire to assuage your aunt and uncle's grief? Perhaps you're hoping you can assuage his grief, too?'

*'No!'* Rachel was incensed at his words. 'That's not true. None of it. To start with, Aunt Maggie would be the last person to want me here, and as for taking Barbara's place— well, I couldn't. I wouldn't want to. My home's in London now. I'm happy there. The last thing I need is for you to start putting ideas like that into Dan's head. Five days more and I'll be back. And that's a promise.'

'I'm sure our inestimable producer will be glad to hear it,' remarked Justin drily. 'But you still haven't mentioned Conroy. How's he taking it? Or would you rather not say?'

'You are a bastard, Justin.' Rachel's fingers clenched around the receiver. 'Matt—Matt's upset, of course.' Or was he? She had seen no evident signs of it. 'And naturally I've see him, and—and spoken to him. It was no big deal. We are civilised human beings. Or, at least, some of us are.'

'All right, all right.' To her relief, Justin appeared to accept her protestations at face value, and Rachel breathed a little more easily. 'OK. So we can expect you back in the office on Monday morning, right? Bright and early, hmm? Just in case we're swamped with mail.'

'Right.'

Rachel made her farewells and replaced the receiver, not realising until after the phone had been put down that she was trembling. It was ridiculous, she thought impatiently. It wasn't as if Justin had been particularly objectionable. On the contrary, if anything, he had been fairly easy on her, and she knew he would intercede with Dan Stern on her behalf. No, her call to Justin was not to blame for her present state of upheaval. She had been on edge ever since yesterday, when she had had that run-in with Matthew and his daughter. And his attitude towards her today in no way reassured her that the past was literally dead and gone.

Sitting comfortably in the bath some fifteen minutes later, however, she was more inclined to dismiss her earlier apprehensions. Lying back in the water, made soft by a little of Aunt Maggie's bath salts, she endeavoured to relax. What were five more days, after all? she asked herself logically. At home, in London, five days could pass incredibly quickly, particularly if she was obliged to work on Saturday mornings too. And spending a few days in such spectacular surroundings ought to be an advantage. She had always loved the scenery of the Lake District, and she could surely put up with her aunt's ill-humour if it meant so much that she should stay.

And, however much she tried to avoid the fact, she did owe her aunt and uncle quite a lot. She had often wondered what might have happened to her if her father's brother and his wife had not taken her in. Twenty years ago, the alternatives of either a foster home or an orphanage had not sounded at all inviting, and she had been unutterably relieved when Mr Jennings, her father's solicitor and the executor of his will, had informed her she was to live with her relations.

All the same, it had been a daunting experience, travelling north to Cumbria to live with an aunt and uncle she had never even met. Her father had been totally unlike his brother, so Mr Jennings had told her. Her uncle had been quite content to enter the Church and live a quiet existence, whereas her father had chosen to help his fellow man in a totally different way. After qualifying for the medical profession, he had taken himself off to Africa, where he had considered his talents could be put to best use. He had married her mother, a nurse he had met working in Nigeria, and for the first five years of Rachel's life Lagos had been her home. Then, tragically, her mother had died in one of the seasonal outbreaks of some intestinal disease that was prevalent in the area, and her father, grief-stricken by his loss, had packed up himself and his small daughter and moved back to England.

But from then on, until his death some six years later, they had never settled in one place for longer than a few months. Her father, once a caring, conscientious physician, had started drinking, and although Rachel was too young to understand all that was happening she soon realised that their nomadic existence and her father's growing dependence on the bottle were linked.

Nevertheless, when he died she was devastated. He was all she had had, and she had loved him very much. She was frightened, too, by the knowledge that, although she was almost twelve years old, and had been taking care of the various apartments and rented houses she and her father had lived in for the past six years, the authorities were not going to allow her to live alone and look after herself.

That was when Percy Jennings, her father's solicitor, had come to her rescue. It was he who located her father's brother and informed him of Philip Barnes's death. Until that time there had been no communication between the brothers—not since before Rachel was born, anyway—and when she was told that he had offered her a home she had known an overwhelming sense of relief. In spite of her father's addiction, her experiences of family life had all been good, and although she had been a little apprehensive on that journey north she had never doubted that she would be made welcome.

Consequently, it had been quite a surprise to encounter hostility in her new home, almost from the first day. It soon became apparent that Geoffrey Barnes's sense of responsibility for his orphaned niece was not shared by his wife and daughter. Aunt Maggie had taken an immediate dislike to her, and Barbara had resented her. From the tentatively happy anticipation of making a new life with her new family, Rachel had sunk into a chasm of despair, and the first few months she had spent at St Mary's vicarage had been the most miserable time of her life.

Of course, she had rallied. She was not her father's daughter for nothing, and she made friends of her own who compensated for her cousin's spitefulness. And Uncle Geoff had always treated her with affection, she acknowledged honestly. The trouble was, he had always seen the best in people, particularly in his own family, and in consequence he'd never known the many minor injustices Rachel was made to suffer.

The water was getting cold now, and, wrapping the rather rough towel which Aunt Maggie had provided around her, Rachel stepped out of the bath. It had all happened a long time ago, she told herself firmly, determining not to brood about the past. Just because she was here, in Rothside, in the vicarage where it had all started, there was no reason to start remembering events that no longer had any bearing on her life.

After ensuring that the landing was deserted, Rachel scuttled back to her room, shivering in spite of the evidence that the central heating had been set in motion. The ancient pipes and radiators were clunking their way into action, filling the old building with odd bangs and clangings. That was a sound Rachel remembered well from winter mornings, but, aware of the dangers of remembering, she resolutely dismissed the thought.

Matthew stalked down to the stables in a foul mood. The morning had begun badly, and it showed no signs of improving. The conversation he had had with his mother at breakfast had been partly to blame. She was concerned about Rosemary. She was upset about the way he had boorishly banished her to bed the previous afternoon. But she could have no idea of the anguish he had felt when he had found his daughter talking to Rachel. He had wanted to punish them both. But, of course, he couldn't do that. So, instead, he had used Rosemary as a convenient scapegoat and taken his anger out on the child yet again. He wasn't proud of what he had done. He had felt bloody awful about it for the rest of the day, as a matter of fact. Thank God for the anaesthetic effects of alcohol, he thought broodingly. At least, he had been able to induce a blessed state of unconsciousness for a while.

But seeing Rachel again had hit him harder than he could have anticipated. He found that wounds he had thought healed and, if not forgotten, at least invisible, were dangerously vulnerable. She had hurt him—hurt him badly—and scars like that just didn't fade away.

Of course, his mother suspected what was wrong. That was why she had intervened. And although, at the time, he had been furiously angry at her interference, later on he had acknowledged that it was probably the safest thing.

Nonetheless, their conversation this morning had been just as acrimonious. Just because Rachel's name had not been mentioned, it did not mean it was not uppermost in both their minds. And then, to cap it all, when his conscience drove him to find Rosemary and make amends by taking her over to Ambleside for the day, once again she was nowhere to be found.

Agnetha had not improved matters, by reporting that she

had found both cigarettes and matches in Rosemary's bedroom that morning. 'She is very naughty girl, *ja*,' she declared, giving Matthew a winning smile that completely contradicted her words. She fluttered long, feathery eyelashes at him. 'You vish I should help you find her, Mr Conroy? I come with you, *ja*?' Her gaze lingered on his well-formed mouth. 'Ve help each other, no?'

'No.'

Matthew had been curt and abrupt, but he had no time now for Agnetha's flattery. He wasn't a conceited man, but he had been aware for the past six months that the Swedish girl was hoping he might be attracted to her. And the way she was looking at him at this moment convinced him that sooner or later she would have to go. He had put up with it while Barbara was alive. To have given the girl notice would have aroused too many awkward questions, and Barbara had been hysterical enough as it was. But now Barbara was gone. He had no further reason to procrastinate. And it was only his impatience to find his daughter that prevented him from telling her there and then.

The lake lay beneath a mantle of grey vapour, and, in spite of his knit shirt and hacking jacket, Matthew shivered. Yet it was the time of year that he liked best, when the high peaks still carried a cap of snow, but down in the valley bluebells made a carpet beneath his feet.

There was so much colour, he reflected, reluctantly diverted by his awareness of nature. Daffodils and tulips still grew beneath the copse of silver birch and cypress trees that screened the stable block from the house, and almond and cherry blossom sprinkled the paths that led into the cobbled yard. And a dusky pink clematis would soon be growing over the wall of the stables, its delicate flowers sheltered from the winds that blew from the west.

Jim Ryan, his head groom, was just emerging from a barn as his employer strode into the yard. The diminutive Irishman had worked for Matthew, and his father before him, for almost forty years, and although he was in his late fifties now he was still as spritely as ever.

'Morning, Mr Matt,' he saluted the younger man cheerfully, in much the same way he used to address Matt's father when he was alive. 'It's a dull day. Are you thinking that it's likely to get out?'

'Let's hope so.' Matthew's response was crisp, his eyes intent as he glanced round the yard. He acknowledged the shouted greeting of a boy curry-combing a bay mare in the middle of the yard, and thrust his hands into his pockets as he surveyed the surrounding stalls.

'Would you be wanting Saracen saddled?' enquired Ryan tentatively, sensing his employer's mood and not wishing to draw attention to it. 'Sure, and he'd be glad of the exercise, wouldn't you know?'

Matthew expelled his breath slowly. 'Is Rosemary here?' he asked after a moment. 'I thought she might be.'

'The little one?' The Irishman frowned and shook his head. 'No, sir. I haven't seen the young lady this morning, I'm afraid. You'll be looking for her, then?'

'As you say.' Matthew took another breath, trying to control his irritation. Where the hell was she? She ought to know better than to go wandering off. And if she wasn't riding her pony, had she cut across the fells to Rothside yet again?

'Would you have me send young Peter over there to help you?' Ryan was asking now, but Matthew shook his head.

'No,' he said shortly. And then, realising he was being boorish, he softened his words with a slight smile. 'No, I'll find her. Thanks for your help, Jim. I'll let you know if there's anything you can do.'

Striding back towards the house, Matthew remembered he hadn't asked Jim Ryan about the cigarettes, but he decided that could wait. Besides, it was hardly likely that one of his stable-boys would have given them to her. He thought they had more sense, particularly as they knew they were not indispensable, and it would hardly be worth risking dismissal for such a ridiculous offence. No, Rosemary had to be getting them from somewhere else. But where? Agnetha didn't smoke, so he couldn't blame her.

Fifteen minutes later he was behind the wheel of the Range Rover, on his way to the village. None of his staff knew where Rosemary was, and he was rapidly losing patience with the whole affair. All the same, he couldn't help remembering his daughter's face when he had bawled her out the previous day. He hoped to God she hadn't done anything really rash, like thumbing a lift into Penrith or Carlisle. She was reckless enough to do it, and his anger was tempered now with an unwilling sense of anxiety.

He was halfway along the lake shore when he saw them. A mile beyond the gates of the estate the road dipped down towards the lake, and in summer tourists parked above a shingly stretch of beach, and launched windsurfers and dinghies into the shallow water. Presently, however, it was too early for holiday-makers, during the week at least, and the woman and child who were exploring the rocky inlet were completely unaware of anyone's observation.

For a moment, Matthew was almost blinded by the anger he felt at seeing them together yet again. Then, without even thinking what he was doing, he stepped on his brakes, bringing the Range Rover to a screeching halt in the middle of the road, only realising his mistake when a van behind set up a noisy protest.

*'Blast!'*

Raising a hand to placate the driver behind, Matthew thrust the vehicle violently back into gear and drove it on to the parking space above the beach. Instead of being able to come upon his daughter and her companion unawares, the noisy horn-blowing had drawn their attention to his ignominious arrival, and when he climbed from behind the wheel Rosemary already looked as if she was on the point of taking off.

But it was the woman who took the initiative. As if assessing Rosemary's feelings, she took the little girl by the hand and faced him with cool condemnation, her green eyes meeting his without any trace of intimidation.

'Were you trying to frighten us?' Rachel enquired coldly, as Matthew strove to regain his composure. 'Was it absolutely necessary to make such a noise? We're not blind. We would have seen you, sooner or later.'

Matthew's jaw clamped. 'It wasn't my fault,' he declared, between his teeth. 'What do you take me for? Some kind of moron? I stalled the car, that's all. Someone else blew their horn.'

Rachel regarded him doubtfully. 'Then who was it?'

'The idiot behind,' retorted Matthew, not altogether charitably. It had been his fault, after all. He took a steadying breath. 'Might I ask what's going on?'

'Rachel's been showing me how to play ducks and drakes,' put in his daughter quickly, evidently feeling confident enough to loosen her hand from Rachel's. 'Look!' She bent and picked up a flat pebble, and made an amateurish attempt to send it skimming across the water. 'Rachel says you used to be good at it. Were you, Daddy? Were you? Will you show me?'

The child's prattle had given Matthew time to gather his thoughts, however, and his initial anger at finding his daughter with the woman he had believed would be safely back in London hardened.

'Never mind about that, how dare you leave the estate again without my permission?' he demanded fiercely, catching the child's arm in a purposeful grasp and jerking her swiftly towards him. 'Do you realise I've spent the past hour looking for you?'

'Daddy!'

Rosemary's cry was painful, but Matthew was in no state to care if he was hurting her. His own feelings were too raw and chaotic to pay much attention to his daughter's.

'For goodness' sake—'

Rachel was evidently shocked by his behaviour, but

Matthew hardly cared what her reaction might be. 'It didn't occur to you that people might be worried about her, did it?' he snarled. 'After all the publicity there's been about children wandering off on their own, and being picked up by some pervert, you happily let her stay with you, indifferent to any upheaval it might be causing.'

Rachel stiffened now. 'You can hardly pretend that it's the first time,' she stated, aware of Rosemary's anxious eyes upon her, and Matthew scowled.

'Whether it is or not is no concern of yours,' he retorted. 'The fact remains, you didn't give a—' He broke off at this point and rephrased his statement. 'You didn't *care* that her absence might create a panic. It's bad enough that you should be the one to find her, without—'

'I didn't know that you were looking for her!' Rachel interrupted him abruptly. 'And it's not been my impression that you particularly care where she is, in any case.'

Matthew's free hand balled into a fist. 'And what would you know about it?' he demanded, as Rosemary started to squirm about in an effort to free herself. 'As far as I know, you've only met my daughter on one other occasion—'

'Two other occasions,' Rachel corrected him swiftly. 'We spoke together yesterday, remember? Before you ordered her off to bed!'

Matthew was incensed. How dared this woman stand there and accuse him of ignoring his daughter's needs, when she had never had a child of her own and obviously knew nothing about children. She hadn't even *wanted* a child, he remembered, with bitter loathing. All those months, when he had hoped she might get pregnant and she had been using a contraceptive. The memory was painful; it exposed an unprotected nerve.

He stepped towards her then, infuriated enough in that instant to do her some physical injury, and, sensing her father's distraction, Rosemary chose that moment to break free. With a rueful grimace in Rachel's direction, she darted off along the beach, ignoring Matthew's angry summons to,

'Come back here, at once!' and plunging between the trees that edged the lake shore at that point.

There was a moment's shocked silence, while both of them turned to watch Rosemary's departure, but when Matthew would have started after her Rachel stepped into his path.

It was a brave thing to do, even Matthew had to give her that, but he was in no mood to respond to courageous gestures. Rosemary was disobeying him, and at this point it was the final ignominy.

'Get out of my way!' he exclaimed, pushing Rachel aside without compunction, but she was lighter than he had imagined. Instead of making her step back, his hasty propulsion sent her sprawling on to the sand, and there was an ominous thud as her head struck a rock.

'Oh, *hell*!'

His pursuit of Rosemary forgotten, Matthew dropped down on to one knee beside Rachel's now still form and, laying his hand against her neck, he felt the fluttering pulse. Dear God, she was unconscious, he realised sickly. She must have hit her head harder than even he had imagined, and the realisation that he might have caused her some irreparable damage caused his heart to accelerate in horror.

He was hardly aware of Rosemary's return until she, too, dropped to her knees beside Rachel. 'She—she's not dead, is she, Daddy?' she exclaimed, her pale face even whiter than usual as she lifted her head to look at him, and he found himself giving her an impulsive hug of both relief and reassurance.

'No, she's not dead,' he declared, although his mouth was dry as he said the words. 'She's just—lost consciousness, that's all. I think she hit her head when she fell. She'll come round in a minute.'

'How did she fall, Daddy?' the little girl asked, evidently emboldened by his unaccustomed display of affection, and Matthew sighed.

'She just—fell, that's all,' he said, not altogether truthfully. He took off his jacket, and laid it over Rachel's unconscious form. 'God, I wish she'd open her eyes!'

'I think she's bleeding!' Rosemary burst out suddenly. She pointed to the trickle of blood that was darkening the rocks near Rachel's head. 'Oh, Daddy, she is going to be all right, isn't she? She's not going to die like—like Mummy?'

'I hope not,' muttered Matthew absently, hardly aware of what he was saying as he rolled Rachel's head to one side to expose a small but deep cut at the base of her scalp. Then, realising what he had said, he reached out and squeezed the child's hand. 'No. No, of course she's not going to die,' he repeated, with more vehemence than conviction. 'But we're going to have to get her to a doctor. And quick.'

A tear trickled from the corner of Rosemary's eye. 'You won't let her die, will you, Daddy?' she persisted. 'I liked her. I really liked her. And—and I think she liked me.'

'Don't say *liked*!' For a moment, Matthew's composure slipped. Putting one hand beneath Rachel's neck, and the other behind her knees, he lifted her into his arms. 'You *like* her,' he amended, getting somewhat unsteadily to his feet. 'Present tense. Not past.'

It was doubtful that Rosemary understood what he was saying, but she seemed sufficiently reassured to hurry ahead of him to open the door of the Range Rover.

'In the back, Rosemary,' her father directed, and the little girl swung the rear door open. 'Now, you get in the other side and try and keep her head still. It's going to be a bumpy ride.'

Moving her had caused the wound on Rachel's head to bleed more freely, and the darkening stain on the velour upholstery spread with frightening speed. Giving her one last look, Matthew was forced to get into the driver's seat and take control, but it was difficult to concentrate on what he was doing when his thoughts were all with the woman lying so motionlessly on the back seat.

Dear God, he prayed silently, let her be all right. You know I never intended this to happen.

He drove straight to Rothmere. The house was nearer, and he knew it would be easier for the doctor to come to them than the other way about. Even so, his arrival at the house caused no small upheaval, and the situation wasn't improved when Lady Olivia appeared just as he was carrying Rachel upstairs.

'Matthew!' she exclaimed, gazing up at him from the bottom of the stairs, her eyes wide with accusation. 'In God's name, what is going on?'

'Watkins will tell you,' replied Matthew, not pausing in his ascent. 'Oh, and will you ask Agnetha if she has a night-gown Rachel can borrow? Her sweater and jacket will have to come off.'

'But what has happened?' demanded his mother fiercely, but her son had gone. Matthew, with Rosemary skipping anxiously at his heels, had disappeared along the corridor that led to the west wing.

# CHAPTER FIVE

HER head hurt. That was Rachel's first thought. As she stirred on the pillow she felt the restrictive pressure of something that was bound about her head, and when she lifted a curiously weak hand to explore the reasons her fingers encountered the unmistakable fabric of a bandage.

A *bandage*! She blinked, and found that hurt, too. In fact, her whole head ached; so much so that she didn't even have the strength to lift it off the pillow. But what was she doing lying in bed, in the middle of the day, wearing a bandage? It didn't make sense. She hadn't put the bandage on her head, so what was it doing there? Of course, her head did feel as if it was definitely not misplaced, but how had it happened?

And then she remembered. Or at least, she thought she did. She had been down at the lake, playing ducks and drakes with Rosemary; and Matthew had found them...

A sense of dizziness swept over her at this thought, and she gripped the quilt that was covering her with suddenly sweating fingers. But even the quilt was unfamiliar, and when she cautiously opened her eyes again she realised she was lying in a totally unfamiliar bed.

For a moment the room swam before her dazed eyes, but then, unbelievably, she realised where she was. Oh, the room had changed, of course. When she had used it, it had been decorated in shades of cream and lilac, and the floor-covering had been a dusky Aubusson that she had chosen herself. Now the walls were covered with peach silk, and the rug had been replaced with a white pile carpet, but no one could alter the size and dimensions of the room Rachel had occupied when she was eighteen years of age. She was at Rothmere, she acknowledged disbelievingly. But why?

She frowned, trying hard to think, but her brain felt like a sponge. All she was certain of was that it had had something to do with Matthew—and Rosemary. She tried to shake her head and winced. Surely he hadn't attacked her for playing with his daughter?

Her efforts to bring some coherence to her thoughts were arrested when the door of the bedroom opened. She heard the sound, even if she couldn't turn her head to see who had entered. For a moment she was tempted to close her eyes again and pretend to be asleep. There was always the possibility that it might be her ex-husband, come to see how she was, and she didn't think she had the strength to face him right now. But the figure that swam into her vision was not tall enough to be Matthew, and her eyes widened to encompass the uniformed figure of a nurse.

'Ah, you're awake!' she exclaimed, with evident relief. She came towards the bed. 'How are you feeling?'

Rachel moistened her dry lips. 'Thirsty,' she admitted. 'What am I doing here?'

'First things first,' said the nurse, who was younger than Rachel, and very attractive. She slipped a hand beneath Rachel's shoulders, and helped her to take a sip of water from the glass she held in her other hand. 'There. Is that better? I must say, you do have a little more colour.'

Rachel tried to be patient. 'But why am I here?' she protested. 'What happened? What time is it?' Now that she noticed it, the pale sunlight filtering through the half-drawn curtains did seem awfully low. 'My uncle—he'll be wondering where I am.' She shifted agitatedly beneath the nurse's soothing hands. 'Has anyone thought to tell my aunt and uncle where I am?'

'Of course, of course.' The nurse was coolly unperturbed. 'Naturally, your family have been told where you are. Mr Conroy saw to that himself. And I expect they can come and see you later, after Dr Newman has examined you again.'

'*Again?*' Rachel's head was throbbing, but she had to know what was going on. 'What do you mean? Has he examined me already?'

'Has he examined you already?' The young nurse chuckled at her words. 'Don't you remember?'

Rachel swallowed. 'Obviously not.' She tried not to panic at the thought. 'When—when did Dr Newman examine me?'

'At the hospital,' said the nurse firmly. 'In Penrith. You don't remember going to the hospital?'

Rachel made a negative gesture.

'Oh, well—' the girl was unbearably casual about it all '—not to worry. You will. It often happens like that.'

Rachel's hands clenched. 'What often happens?' she demanded unsteadily. 'What happened to me? Please—you've got to tell me!'

'Now, now, don't go getting upset.' At last, the nurse seemed to realise that Rachel was getting really scared. 'You fell. Do you remember that? By the lake?' she prompted. 'You hit your head.'

'By the lake?' Rachel massaged her temple with a shaky hand.

And then it all came back to her. There had been an argument, she remembered that. Or was *argument* too mild a description of the heated exchange she had had with Matthew? In any event, he had been furious, partly because he hadn't known where Rosemary was, and partly because when he'd found her she had been with Rachel. And she hadn't helped matters by goading him into—into what? Surely he hadn't hit her, had he? She thought there had been a moment when she had half expected he might, but then— then something had happened... Yes, that was it. Rosemary had run away, and when she had tried to stop him from going after her, he had pushed her out of the way—

'You do remember, don't you?' The nurse's anxious voice broke into her thoughts and, wincing, Rachel nodded.

'Most of it,' she agreed. 'But I don't remember anything about a hospital. Did—did Matt take me there?'

'Actually, no—' began the girl, and then broke off abruptly as the door opened again, this time to admit a slim, dapper man, with a thin moustache and sideburns.

Dr Newman? wondered Rachel doubtfully, and then felt a sudden return of panic when her ex-husband followed the other man into the room.

'The patient's awake, Doctor.' Unknowingly answering Rachel's unspoken question, the nurse moved back from the bed. 'She remembers what happened—or most of it, anyway. And she's had a drink of water.'

'Good. Good.' The doctor took the nurse's place at Rachel's bedside, and took her limp wrist between his fingers and thumb. He smiled at her as he took her pulse, and then replaced her arm on the quilt and folded his hands together. 'So—Miss—Mrs Conroy, how does your head feel?'

Conscious of Matthew standing behind the doctor, listening intently to everything that was going on, Rachel found it difficult to speak audibly. 'Um—sore,' she managed, after a moment. And then, clearing her throat, she added, 'When can I go home?'

'Well, not yet,' declared Dr Newman frankly, casting a swift glance over his shoulder at Matthew. 'You've had a mild concussion, Mrs Conroy. I recommend that you stay where you are for at least the next twenty-four hours. Then we'll see.'

'Twenty-four hours?' Rachel was horrified. 'But—I can't.'

'Why can't you?'

Matthew spoke for the first time, coming round the doctor to look down at her with a dark, enigmatic gaze, and Rachel licked her lips. 'Because I can't!' she exclaimed, looking at the doctor and not her ex-husband. 'Dr—Newman, is it?'

And at his nod, 'I don't know what you've been told, Doctor, but I have to get back to London on Sunday.'

'In three days' time?' Dr Newman shook his head. 'I don't think so, Mrs Conroy.'

'Three days' time?' Rachel was confused. 'No, not in three days' time. Today's Wednesday—'

'I'm afraid it's Thursday, Mrs Conroy,' the doctor corrected her gently. 'You were unconscious for over twelve hours.'

'Tw—twelve hours!' Rachel's head was pounding now. 'No. No, I can't have been—'

'You were,' said Matthew, with rather less vehemence. 'Believe it.'

Rachel could feel the hot prick of tears behind her lids now. This couldn't be happening, she thought wildly. She couldn't have lost a whole day! It wasn't possible.

'Besides which, you lost a great deal of blood, Mrs Conroy,' Dr Newman was continuing steadily. 'You cut your head, you see. If Mr Conroy hadn't had the foresight to bring you straight to Rothmere, it might have been a great deal more serious.'

'No—'

'I'm afraid it's yes,' declared the doctor firmly. 'Your local doctor was able to stanch the bleeding until an ambulance could be sent out from the Infirmary, and you were in a stable condition by the time you reached the hospital.'

Rachel could hardly take it in. 'I don't remember,' she murmured blankly. 'I don't remember anything after—after—'

'After I knocked you down,' Matthew finished for her tersely. 'Don't worry. I've told the doctor what happened. It was all my fault.'

Rachel steeled herself to look up at him then. 'I fell,' she said distinctly. 'You didn't knock me down. I stumbled, that's all. I—someone stood on my foot yesterday—I mean, on Wednesday—and it must have buckled when I put my weight on it.'

Matthew's mouth tightened. 'If you say so,' he essayed stiffly. 'In any event, you're staying here until you're fully recovered.'

Rachel wanted to protest. She wanted to say that Rothmere was the very last place she wanted to be, and that no one, least of all his mother, would welcome her being here. Aunt Maggie, for one, would be furious. She'd see it as a deliberate attempt to insinuate herself into Matthew's life again.

'I think Mr Conroy is right, you know,' said Dr Newman now. 'Wounds to the head should never be taken lightly, and, no matter how important it is for you to get back to London, you would be extremely foolish to risk your health in that way. My opinion is that you should spend at least one more day in bed, and even then you'll find that getting up is not as easy an option as you seem to think.'

Rachel caught her lower lip between her teeth. 'But— couldn't I go back to the vicarage?' she ventured, but even before Matthew voiced his objections she had realised how impractical that would be. Aunt Maggie might not like her staying at Rothmere, but she certainly wouldn't welcome taking the responsibility upon herself.

'There simply aren't the facilities at the vicarage that there are here,' Matthew informed the doctor impatiently. 'And Rachel knows it. She—well—I imagine she feels it's hardly suitable that she should be staying here, in the circumstances, but—'

'You mean because your wife has just died?' suggested Dr Newman thoughtfully, and Matthew nodded.

'That, of course, but also because of our past—relationship.'

'I see.' The doctor nodded now. 'Well, I'm sure that, the present circumstances being what they are, no one could doubt the veracity of Mrs Conroy's presence.'

'No.' Matthew inclined his head in assent. 'Do you agree, Rachel?'

Her lower lip trembled, and she bit on it hard to disguise

the obvious weakness. 'Do—do I have a choice?' she responded tautly. She determinedly looked at the doctor. 'And—how long do you expect me to be—inactive?'

'Mmm...' He frowned. 'Well, shall we say—two weeks?'

'*Two weeks?*'

Rachel fairly squeaked the words, and he gave her a rueful smile. 'At the very least, I would say,' he declared firmly. 'I'm sorry, Mrs Conroy, but I really don't see you withstanding any mental strain for some time.'

By the next morning Rachel had learned enough about her condition to realise that Dr Newman's prognosis had not been as exaggerated as she had thought. Her strength, which she had thought was lying dormant while she was in bed, had simply deserted her, and it was frustrating to find that she really was as helpless as a baby. Even sitting up to swallow some of the chicken broth that Mrs Moffat had prepared for her left her feeling weak and shaky, and she didn't argue when the nurse, whose name she had learned was Linda Douglas, insisted Rachel didn't attempt to get out of bed when she wasn't there.

'Don't worry,' she said, when Rachel expressed anxiety at her own helplessness. 'You'll be surprised how much better you'll feel in a few days. What really upsets your system is the shock. Once you've had time to get over that, you'll find your strength will return fairly rapidly.'

'I hope so.' Rachel spoke with urgency. 'As soon as I can, I'd like to return to the vicarage.' She caught her lower lip between her teeth. She could just imagine what a juicy item of scandal this was providing for the gossiping tongues of Rothside.

The nurse made no comment as to when she might be able to leave Rothmere, but Rachel was determined to make it sooner, rather than later. In all honesty, she planned to return to London as quickly as possible, convinced that any recuperation that was needed could be accomplished equally as well in her own home.

But she would have to speak to Justin again before Monday. She frowned. What day was it? Thursday? No, Friday. Her calendar was twenty-four hours out of date. Which meant she must speak to Justin the day after tomorrow. She sighed. She dreaded telling him she wouldn't be returning as she'd promised. Like her Aunt Maggie, he would probably think she had engineered the whole thing.

She should never have told him about her relationship with Matthew, she reflected ruefully. In his opinion, Matthew was a selfish bastard who deserved everything that was coming to him, and Rachel had done the only thing possible in getting a divorce.

Of course, when she had related the whole story to him it had been over a drink at the end of a particularly long and arduous day, and she had held nothing back. It had been soon after she'd moved to London, while she was still feeling raw and betrayed, and she had cried very easily in those days. But he had been so sympathetic, and she had badly needed a shoulder to cry on.

Naturally, she had got over it—eventually. But the trouble was, Justin still remembered how distressed she had been then. And when she had asked him for time off to attend Barbara's funeral, he had initially refused permission. Only her avowed intention of going anyway had swayed his judgement, but subsequent events would only reinforce his original impression.

Dr Newman arrived to examine his patient just as Nurse Douglas was helping Rachel back from the bathroom. Dressed in only the flimsy polyester nightdress Matthew's au pair had lent her, Rachel couldn't help feeling rather exposed, and this sensation was made all the more embarrassing when Matthew again followed the doctor into the room.

With scarlet cheeks, Rachel stumbled hastily into the bed, dragging the covers over her trembling form. Who the hell did Matthew think he was, walking into her room unannounced? she thought indignantly. It wasn't as if he had any right to be here. He wasn't a doctor, and he wasn't a friend. He was simply a man she had once been foolish enough to marry, and it had to be said—if it weren't for him, she might not now be in this ignominious position.

'Well,' said Dr Newman, after the nurse had hastily straightened the covers Rachel had so untidily hauled over herself. 'And how are you feeling this morning?'

Rachel wished she could say she felt much better. She wished she was able to announce she was well enough to get up out of the bed, and leave Rothmere before anything more disastrous happened. But she couldn't.

'Tired,' she admitted instead, avoiding Matthew's careful appraisal. 'I don't think I slept awfully well last night.'

'No.' Dr Newman did not sound too surprised. 'Well, I think we should have a look at your head, don't you? Perhaps I can do something to make you feel a little easier.'

Rachel nodded. 'All right.'

But her eyes moved to Matthew, and, as if sensing her reaction to the other man's presence, Dr Newman turned his head. 'I think it might be as well if you left us, Mr Conroy,' he declared smoothly. 'You can come back when we've finished. I think Mrs Conroy would prefer it.'

There was a pause when Rachel half thought Matthew was going to protest, but then, with a brief nod of his head, he departed. But not before Rachel had noticed how Nurse Douglas's eyes followed him from the room.

Removing the dressing from her scalp was painful, and, lying with her face buried in the pillow, Rachel was hardly conscious of the muffled exchange going on between the nurse and the doctor. She didn't know how big the cut was, but it felt enormous, and she wondered if they had shaved her head around the injury. She wanted to groan. Things just seemed to get worse and worse. How would she look with a bald patch behind her ear? she fretted. If only she hadn't gone for a walk on Wednesday morning. If she'd not had that argument with Aunt Maggie over borrowing her rubber boots and walked out of the house, none of this would have happened. She should have stuck to her guns and gone back to London on Tuesday night, as she had intended. She could bet Aunt Maggie was wishing she had, too.

'There we are.' While she had been thinking of other things, the dressing on her head had been renewed, and Dr Newman assisted her back on to her pillows with gentle hands. 'Does that feel easier? You must tell me if it doesn't.'

Rachel winced as her movements caused her head to throb, but it did feel less rigid. 'Yes,' she murmured. 'Yes, it does feel a bit better.' She frowned. 'There's no problem, is there?'

'Not really.' Dr Newman smiled, but Rachel didn't like the qualification.

'Not really?' she echoed. 'Does that mean there is? I'd really rather know, Doctor. Please don't keep me in suspense.'

Dr Newman sighed. 'I'm not. Believe me. It's just that— well, with wounds of this kind there can be complications.'

'What kind of complications?'

Rachel was anxious, and, shaking his head, the doctor seated himself on the side of her bed. 'It's nothing serious,' he assured her. 'Just a little swelling around the wound, that's all. I'm sure that by tomorrow it will have disappeared. But for the moment I'm going to ask Nurse Douglas to give you an antibiotic, just to be absolutely sure. All right?'

Rachel bit her lip. 'If you say so.'

'I do.' He smiled again, and rose to his feet. 'And now I think you should rest. I'll tell Mr Conroy that I don't think you should have any visitors just now.'

Rachel was grateful for his understanding, and she was glad to close her eyes for a little while. But when she opened them later and discovered it was already late afternoon, she felt a helpless sense of panic. It was frightening to realise how little control she had over herself at the moment.

She looked about her, and found she could do so without

encountering the throbbing pain that had previously accompanied any movement of her head. She could even lever herself up on to her pillows without any attack of dizziness, and although the effort tired her it was definitely an improvement.

She wished Nurse Douglas had been there to see it, but the young nurse was not in the room. Perhaps she was downstairs talking to Matthew, thought Rachel cynically, recalling the revealing look the girl had cast in his direction. Matthew had always had that effect on women, she remembered, unwillingly aware that the knowledge still had the power to scrape a nerve.

She sighed frustratedly, not really wanting to entertain thoughts of that kind. It shouldn't matter to her what Matthew did, or with whom. He wasn't her concern any longer. If he found Nurse Douglas attractive—so what? All she wanted to do was go to the bathroom. That was more important to her than speculating about Matthew's present sexual activities.

Remembering the nurse's admonition that she shouldn't attempt to get out of bed without assistance, she lay for a few more minutes, waiting for Nurse Douglas to return; but she didn't. And the situation was getting quite desperate. Short of hammering on the floor, there was no way she could attract attention, and as she knew this suite of rooms was in the west wing, and remote from the more regularly used rooms on the ground floor, that means of attracting notice was not very practical.

Deciding she would have to disobey instructions, after all, she weakly pushed back the covers and slid her legs over the side of the bed. Her head swam a little as she pulled herself upright, but she was relieved to find she felt a little stronger than she had done earlier in the day.

Gaining a little confidence, she tested her weight before getting to her feet, and then looked across the room at the bathroom door, in much the same way as a marathon walker might view the winning post. It was only a few yards, she told herself firmly. And it wasn't as if she was an invalid. All she had done was cut her head, for goodness' sake!

The filmy nightgown billowed about her as she painstakingly made her way across the floor. Just a few more steps, she breathed encouragingly, letting go of the rail of the bed to totter the few steps to the bathroom door. With her hand clasping the handle, like a lifeline, she looked back towards the bed with a feeling of disbelief. Had she really come so far? she thought, aware of the film of sweat that had broken out all over her body. Dear God, she hoped Nurse Douglas would come to help her back to bed. She really didn't think she could make it on her own.

All the same, it was a great relief to gain her objective, and afterwards she leant over the basin, dousing her hot face with cool water. She felt hot and shivery all at the same time, and her legs were like jelly as she straightened up and reached for the towel.

The sound of the bedroom door being opened reached her as she was folding the towel back on to its rail. The relief she felt was tremendous, and, supporting herself with the door-frame, she moved to show herself. 'I'm here,' she was saying wearily, quite prepared for Nurse Douglas to be angry with her, but it wasn't Nurse Douglas who had come into the bedroom; it was Matthew.

The sight of his tall figure, dark and disturbing in black jeans and a matching black silk shirt, was like a body blow. He was the last person she had expected—or wanted—to see in her present condition, and she swayed against the woodwork, wondering how she was going to make it to the bed now. Why couldn't it have been Nurse Douglas? she fretted. All she really wanted was to crawl back between the sheets.

'You ought not to be out of bed,' said Matthew abruptly, dropping whatever it was he had been carrying and starting across the room towards her. 'Where's Nurse Douglas? Does she know what you're doing?'

'Don't—don't come any nearer!' exclaimed Rachel

weakly, lifting one trembling hand and holding it out in front of her. She had just remembered the scarcity of what she was wearing, and, while modesty was of little importance in her present situation, she still had some pride left.

But Matthew ignored her. Brushing her protest aside, he swept her up into his arms and carried her back to the bed. Then, after settling her against her pillows, he drew the soft quilt about her.

It was a relief, she had to admit it, but that didn't prevent an automatic sense of outrage. This ought not to be happening, she thought, staring up at him frustratedly. They were divorced, for God's sake! His second wife had just died! And yet she could still feel the strength of his arms about her, and the heated warmth of his body had been unbearably familiar.

'Are you all right now?' he enquired, as she fumbled for a tissue to blow her nose, and Rachel nodded cautiously.

'I'd have managed,' she muttered, avoiding his eyes, and concentrating instead on the creamy wisp of paper he had rescued for her from its box. 'What are you doing in here anyway? I didn't realise my being an invalid in your house gave you the right to walk into my bedroom unannounced!'

'You should be glad I did,' said Matthew shortly, folding his arms across his chest as if to control some latent desire he had to retaliate in kind. 'What were you doing exactly? You've got water all down the front of your nightdress.'

Rachel felt her cheeks reddening, and was furious. For heaven's sake, she was far too old to start blushing again. But a covert examination of her nightgown proved that he was not lying and, to add to her embarrassment, in places the damp material was clinging to her breasts.

Drawing the quilt even higher, she said tersely, 'I was washing my face and hands. I didn't realise I'd splashed myself. Thank you for drawing my attention to it.'

'Don't be ridiculous!' Matthew's mouth compressed. 'I just can't imagine why you couldn't have waited until Nurse

Douglas came back. You looked to be on the point of collapse when I came in.'

'Well, I wasn't.' Rachel knew she was being ungrateful, but she couldn't cope with Matthew right now.

'If you say so.' His features hardened. 'But for goodness' sake stop behaving as if I'd never seen you in the nude before—'

'I'm not in the nude!'

'No.' But his expression said as good as. 'Even so, I have been married for a great number of years. The female form is no great novelty, believe me!'

Rachel gave him a bitter look. 'Oh, I do,' she countered tautly. 'So—do you mind telling me what you're doing in my room?'

Matthew sighed, and turned to pick up the object he had dropped when he had charged across the room earlier. 'I collected your things,' he declared, setting the small suitcase on the padded ottoman at the foot of the bed. 'I thought you might prefer to wear your own nightdress.' He paused, and then added grimly, 'Your attitude makes me wish I'd never bothered.'

'Oh.' Rachel didn't know what to say. Contrition warred with self-justification, but the former won. 'I'm sorry.'

'So you should be!' Matthew spoke vehemently at first, but then, as if prepared to give her the benefit of the doubt, he shook his head. 'It wasn't easy, you know,' he went on. 'Your aunt wasn't exactly pleased to see me. Not when I told her why I was there. I think she's wishing you had decided to go straight back to London. Your being here— well, you can guess how she feels.'

'And she's right,' murmured Rachel ruefully, shredding the tissue between her fingers. 'I shouldn't be here—'

'You didn't have a lot of choice,' retorted Matthew drily. 'And it was my fault, after all. Besides, surely we can deal with this like civilised adults? It's not as if your being here can hurt Barbara now.'

'No.' But his reference to Barbara was unsettling, just the

same. How had he really felt about her cousin? she wondered. And why had she started asking herself that question, when the answer could be of no interest to her?

'So,' he said, after a moment, 'how are you feeling? Um—Maggie and Geoff are coming to see you tomorrow. Your—er—your uncle sent his best wishes.'

'Thank you.' Rachel caught her lower lip between her teeth. She was not looking forward to seeing either her aunt or her uncle, but she could hardly tell him that. Indeed, she found it incredibly difficult to say anything to him in her present position, and, remembering how she had stood up to him by the lake, she marvelled at her own audacity.

'You scared me half to death, you know,' he added suddenly, his hands falling to his sides, and her pulses quickened at the violence in his voice. Until that moment his attitude had not led her to believe that what had happened had affected him very deeply, but suddenly there was an element of raw emotion in the room. 'I thought I'd killed you,' he continued, pushing his hands into the back pockets of his jeans. 'You'd be amazed how that focuses the mind!'

Rachel could not let him go on. She didn't want to know what it had focused his mind on, and, striving for something to say, she thought of his daughter. 'Did—did you find Rosemary?' she asked, rather inanely, as he was unlikely to be standing here talking to her if the child was still missing, and, although he frowned at the obvious *non sequitur*, he eventually nodded.

'She came back,' he said briefly, lifting his shoulders, and then letting them fall as he breathed out again. 'Believe it or not, she was worried about you.'

'Was she?' Rachel's lips lifted. 'I'd never have believed it.'

'No.' Matthew's eyes were disturbingly intent. 'Are you going to tell me why?'

'No.' Rachel sighed. 'I don't think so. Not right now, anyway.'

Matthew tilted his head. 'That presupposes that we'll be

talking to one another again,' he pointed out evenly, and she forced herself to look up at him.

'And won't we?' she challenged, meeting his eyes for the first time, and he actually smiled.

'Maybe,' he agreed. 'If that's what you want.'

'I'm in your house, Matt,' she told him tersely, not quite having got the answer she had expected. 'What I want doesn't come into it.'

Matthew's smile disappeared. 'You don't have to adopt that attitude, Rachel. I thought we were beginning to communicate at last.'

'Communicate?' Rachel almost choked on the word. 'Yesterday—no, two days ago—you were practically foaming at the mouth because I was playing with your daughter.'

'That's an exaggeration!'

'Is it?' Rachel's nails dug into her palms. 'I thought that was how I came to be here.'

Matthew scowled. 'That was below the belt!'

'Yes. Yes, it was.' Rachel shifted a little desperately against the pillows. If he didn't go soon, she was going to humiliate herself completely by bursting into tears. But she didn't want Matt to be kind and considerate. She didn't want him to offer her sympathy and conciliation. She felt much safer when he was looking at her as he was now.

'So—do I take it you don't want to see me again?' he enquired harshly, taking his hands out of his pockets and balling them at his sides, and she closed her eyes against the treacherous desire she had to reach out and touch him.

'I—just think I'm rather—tired,' she got out unsteadily. 'Thank—thank you for getting my things. I do appreciate it.'

'No problem,' he responded, the clipped detachment in his voice eloquent of his feelings. 'I'll tell Nurse Douglas you want to rest, shall I?'

'If—if you would.'

Rachel opened her eyes again, and for a heart-stopping moment she caught his brooding gaze. And it was electric.

The look that passed between them owed nothing to the conversation they had just had. Indeed, it might never have been. There was such a searing intimacy in that exchange that, in spite of the fact that she was lying down, her lower limbs went weak.

And then it was gone, as quickly as it had appeared. Like a fire that was suddenly extinguished, his lids descended, and she was left with the uncanny suspicion that she had imagined the whole thing.

*Wishful thinking,* she thought bitterly, as the door closed behind him. But why? *Why?* Why, after all these years, was she even considering that she might have made a mistake by walking out on him...?

# CHAPTER SIX

RACHEL was seventeen when she first met Matthew Conroy.

Although she would have liked to have stayed on at school and taken her A level examinations, her cousin Barbara, who was nine months her senior, had left school at sixteen, and naturally it was expected that Rachel should do the same. After all, she had no money of her own to support her, and it wasn't fair that her aunt and uncle should bear the burden of her education for a further two years.

So, instead of staying on at the comprehensive school, she got herself a job in Penrith, and enrolled at night-school. Of course, it wasn't always easy getting home from Penrith after the classes, particularly during the winter months, when the roads around Rothside became icy or snow-bound. But she was determined to finish the course, and the encouragement of her tutors more than made up for any disparagement she received at home.

Barbara hadn't yet got a job, considering the kind of employment Rachel had settled for to be beneath her. Manning the check-out at a supermarket was not something she would even consider, and ultimately her parents were prevailed upon to send her to a private secretarial college.

Meanwhile, Rachel was working hard to pass her examinations. But it wasn't always easy, when the supermarket didn't close until eight o'clock in the evening, and she had then to go home and tackle an analysis of one of Arthur Miller's plays. On the evenings when she had a class, and finished early at the supermarket, she didn't go home at all between leaving work at five-thirty and attending night-school at seven. In consequence, during those winter months, she was chilled to the bone by the time she got to the night-school, her fingers so cold they could hardly hold a pen.

Oh, she went into a cafeteria for part of the time, but there was a limit to the length of time one could make a burger and a mug of coffee last, and the proprietor of the café grew to regard her continued presence with a jaundiced eye.

Then, one evening, she missed the last bus home. It wasn't her fault. Immersed in a discussion of the war poets, she hadn't noticed the build-up of snow against the windows of the college, and it wasn't until she emerged and found it lying several inches deep that she discovered what had happened. Because of the conditions, the bus service had had to be suspended, and Rachel was left with the unhappy realisation that she was stranded.

What was worse, all her friends from the college had dispersed by the time she came hurrying back from the bus station. They were used to her dashing away as soon as classes were over, and no one wanted to hang about on a night like this.

Endeavouring to suppress the sense of panic that gripped her as she contemplated the seriousness of her situation, Rachel tried to think positively. There were always taxis, of course, she acknowledged steadily, if she had had the money to pay for one, which she didn't. Or she could walk the seven and a half miles to Rothside. But, given the conditions and the fact that it was dark, that was hardly a credible alternative. And yet what else could she do?

She thought, at first, that the man emerging from the college buildings at that moment was her English tutor. In the faint light filtering from the few windows that were still illuminated, and with snow driving into her face, it was a reasonable error. But as soon as she hurried across the car park she realised her mistake. Mr Evans was not as tall as the man presently turning up his collar against the cold, and when her quickened breathing caused him to turn his head and look at her she saw that he was much younger than the English professor. Besides which, she recognised him!

Until that evening, her knowledge of the Conroys had been limited to the glimpses she had had of them about the village. Although her uncle had sometimes visited the house, on one charitable pretext or another, those were not really social occasions. Aunt Maggie had never gone with him, and her aunt's only invitations to Rothmere had been to organise the annual church fête, which was traditionally held in the grounds of the house. In consequence, all Rachel knew about them was what she had heard, and read in the local newspaper, and Aunt Maggie's gossip, which was not always reliable.

Nevertheless, she recognised Matthew Conroy instantly. Only months before she had been among the crowd of sight-seers standing outside the village church when his sister had married Gerald Sinclair, and as Matthew had been one of the groomsmen he had been much in evidence. Indeed, his presence had been the cause of much excited speculation from Barbara and her friends, who all regarded him as the local heart-throb.

And he was good to look at, Rachel had to concede, although at this particular minute his appearance was the least of her concerns. The disappointment at discovering he was not Mr Evans, and therefore not someone she could ask to lend her the taxi fare home, was of greater importance, and her face fell when he arched dark brows in her direction.

'I'm—I'm sorry,' she stammered awkwardly, backing away from him. 'I—er—I thought you were someone else.'

'That's a shame!'

Matthew's mouth lifted in a rueful grimace, but Rachel was in no mood to respond to his lazy teasing. She was wondering if there was anyone left in the building whom she could ask to help her, and she didn't even take the time to wonder why he might have been visiting the college.

'I know you, don't I?'

His next words took her completely by surprise, and,

dragging her eyes from the lighted windows, she gave him a wry, disbelieving, look. 'Do you?'

She didn't believe him, of course. She was used to boys making passes at her, and, although she didn't consider herself a beauty, she knew green eyes and blonde hair could disguise a multitude of failings. But Matthew Conroy wasn't a boy, he was a man—and definitely a complication she couldn't afford.

'Yes,' he said now, startling her into an involuntary protest. 'You're from the vicarage,' he added, taking the steps to close the gap between them. 'But you're not the daughter, are you?' He frowned. 'You're the niece.'

Rachel caught her breath. 'How do you know that?'

Matthew's lips curved. 'I've got eyes. I've seen you around the village. And you know who I am, too, don't you? Don't pretend. I can see you do.'

'Oh, can you?' Rachel lifted a woolly gloved hand to wipe flakes of snow from her lashes, thinking how ridiculous it was that they should be standing, having this conversation, in a snowstorm.

'Mmm.' Matthew cast a look around the car park. 'Are you waiting for somebody?'

'Um—no.' Rachel took a deep breath.

'So what are you doing hanging about here?' he prompted drily. 'It's late. Oughtn't you to be at home?'

Rachel hesitated. And then, taking the most momentous decision of her young life, she said recklessly, 'I've missed the last bus home. At least, I haven't missed it, exactly— it's been suspended. Because of the weather. I was hoping to find someone to lend me the fare for a taxi. That's why I'm here. I—I don't suppose you would—?'

'Are you serious?' Matthew's lean, dark face mirrored his sudden change of mood, and Rachel swallowed hard.

'Yes—'

'You must be crazy!' He glared down at her with eyes that glittered, even in the gloom. 'You were going to ask a complete stranger for a taxi fare?'

Rachel stiffened. 'I wasn't going to ask a complete stranger!' she retorted. 'If you hadn't—hadn't been here, I had intended to ask my English tutor. That's who I thought you were. But don't worry. I'm sure there's someone else—'

'Wait!' As she would have stalked away, he caught the strap of her haversack and swung her round to face him. 'You mean—you're a member of this faculty?'

Her cheeks flamed. 'If you mean do I take classes here, then yes,' she told him indignantly. 'What did you think? That I was trying to pick you up?'

Matthew heaved a sigh, but he didn't let her go. 'Forget it,' he said abruptly. 'I'll take you home.'

'You won't.' Rachel was too incensed to think sensibly. 'I don't need your assistance, Mr Conroy. Now—if you'll excuse me,' she added, with heavy sarcasm.

'Don't be stupid!' Matthew wound the strap of the bag more securely round his hand. Then, casting a brief glance up at the thickening snow, he went on, 'What makes you think a taxi-driver will risk the journey to Rothside tonight? Remember, he'd have to make the return trip.'

Rachel pressed her lips together, trying not to show how worried she really was. But he had a point. What if no one was prepared to drive her home?

'Why should you be willing to take me home?' she asked at last, and, sensing her acquiescence, Matthew unwound his hand from the plaited denim.

'Why not?' he countered flatly. 'Call it my good deed for the day. Come on. My car's over here.'

She trudged after him to his car, her booted feet moving with some reluctance, in spite of her tacit acceptance of his offer. After all, for all her knowledge of his identity, he was as much a stranger to her as any taxi-driver would have been. And at least with a taxi-driver she would have felt she was paying for his services. What kind of payment might Matthew Conroy exact?

The car, a huge, light-coloured Mercedes, was parked on

the college car park, and for the first time Rachel wondered why that should be so. Unless he was taking classes too, she reflected. But that didn't seem likely, bearing in mind that he was reputed to have a university degree from Oxford, or somewhere like that.

'Get in.'

While she had been worrying over his motives, Matthew had unlocked the car and got inside. And now he was thrusting open the door beside her, urging her to join him. The comparative warmth from inside the car swept out to envelop her in its enticing folds, and she swayed a little unsteadily as the snow spun in a spiral about her. But, although she still had reservations, necessity overcame discretion and, taking a determined breath, she stepped into the car.

She tried to slam the door behind her, but it didn't catch properly, and Matthew leant across her to deal with it himself. For a moment, the hard muscle of his shoulder was pressed against her chest, and she was disturbed by the strength of feeling it aroused. None of the youths she had danced with at church socials, or allowed to kiss her in the vicarage porch afterwards, had ever stirred her emotions in quite that way, and her breasts were tingling quite alarmingly when he withdrew his arm.

'Can you fasten the seat-belt?' he enquired, securing his own in place, and Rachel felt the colour invade her cheeks once again.

'I have ridden in a car before,' she retorted, more sharply than was warranted, but she was troubled by her reaction to him and the words were out before she could prevent them.

'OK.' Matthew's response was mild by comparison, and he started the car as she was fumbling for the anchor point. 'I should have known better than to ask. You don't like accepting my help, do you?'

Rachel thrust the clasp home at last, and sank back against the velour upholstery. Then, turning her head sideways, she murmured helplessly, 'I'm sorry.'

'Hmm.' Matthew had reversed out of the parking bay, and was now driving fairly slowly across the car park. The roads would be easier, with the constant movement of traffic to keep them clear, but the college car park was never full in the evenings, and the snow had been allowed to drift. 'You don't have to worry, you know. I almost never get involved with older women!'

For a moment, Rachel didn't understand him, but then, realising he was trying to put her at her ease, she allowed a soft laugh to escape her. 'Nor I with younger men,' she countered, beginning to relax at last. She paused a moment, and then added, 'I do appreciate this, you know, even if it hasn't sounded that way up until now. I could have phoned the vicarage, of course, but—well, I don't think Uncle Geoff would have welcomed turning out on a night like this. And—and who was to know the buses would stop running? You never know, it might not be snowing in Rothside.'

There was a long silence after this statement, and she wondered, somewhat anxiously, what he was thinking. The last thing she wanted to do was imply that her uncle and aunt wouldn't care how—or even if—she got home. It might be true—in Aunt Maggie's case, anyway—but she would never say so. Some things were too personal to share with anyone else.

She turned her head and looked through the window at the driving snow. The car was a cocoon of warmth in a cold white world, and she shifted a little uneasily against the cushioned back of her seat. She wondered what it must be like to take a car like this for granted, and decided that in her world people would always be more important than possessions.

There was some traffic about in Penrith, but by the time they had negotiated its one-way system of streets and emerged on to the dual carriageway that led to the motorway the cars they passed were few and far between. The road to Rothside crossed the M6 just west of Penrith, and then left the A66 a few yards further on to follow the route to Rothmere.

'It's a filthy night,' remarked Matthew at last, as Rachel was racking her brains, trying to think of something to say, and she nodded in relief.

'You—you might have been right about the taxi,' she murmured, settling the haversack more comfortably beside her feet. 'I don't know what I'd have done if I hadn't met you. Do you think they might have allowed me to sleep in the bus station? After all, it wasn't my fault that the service was closed down.'

Matthew glanced her way, and the false illumination from outside the car mirrored his thoughtful expression. He really was a very attractive man, she thought unwillingly, her eyes drawn to his lean, narrow-boned features. Individually, heavy-lidded eyes above a prominent nose and a thin-lipped mouth would not have struck her as sexy, but he was. His skin was dark, as she knew, and although she guessed he would have shaved before leaving home that evening there was already a darkening shadow around his jawline. And his hair, damp now, and sparkling here and there with melting drops of snow, should have looked a mess because it was too long. But it didn't. It brushed his collar at the back, and fell over his forehead in untidy strands—and she had the most ridiculous urge to run her fingers through it and brush it back against his scalp—

'I don't think bus companies work that way,' he was saying now, and it took her a minute to comprehend what he was talking about. A wave of heat swept over her body at the realisation of what she *had* been thinking, and she struggled to find an answer before he noticed something was wrong.

'Um—oh, well, I'd have had to find a hotel room, then, wouldn't I?' she muttered hurriedly, smoothing her damp palms over her knees. 'I'm glad I didn't have to do that.'

'Particularly with no money,' observed Matthew drily, and she pretended to be absorbed in adjusting her seat-belt.

'So—what course are you taking at college? And couldn't you have missed it for one evening?' He shook his head. 'If I were your uncle, I don't think I would have let you go into town tonight.'

'He didn't. That is,' Rachel licked her dry lips, 'I didn't come into town this evening. I—I work in Penrith I went straight from work to night-school. I'm studying English to A level.'

Matthew's dark brows descended. 'I see.' He hesitated. 'And do your employers pay your expenses?'

'Heavens, no.' Rachel almost laughed now. 'I don't think they'd consider it important to understand Shakespeare, or even twentieth-century literature, if it comes to that.'

'Why? What do you do?'

Rachel sighed. 'I work in a supermarket. At least, until I pass my exams, anyway.'

Matthew was silent for a few minutes, considering her words, and she wondered what he was thinking. Probably that she was very different from the young women he usually associated with, she decided. Particularly Cecily Bishop, whom her aunt said he was going to marry.

'And what do you want to do?' he said eventually, and it took Rachel a minute to realise he was talking about her career.

'Oh—well, I'd like to work in journalism eventually, but the chances of doing that aren't very good around here. There aren't many local papers, you see, and there are dozens of people with the same ambitions as me. In my class alone there are at least four others who'd like to work on a newspaper, and when you consider that newspapers are closing down all the time…'

She was talking too much, and she knew it, but she couldn't help it. It was important that he shouldn't become conscious of her awareness of him, and at least when she was talking she was not staring at his hands on the wheel.

'Journalism,' he echoed thoughtfully now, and she nodded.

'That's right.' She took a breath. 'I like writing, you see. It's the only thing I'm any good at.' She grimaced. 'But I'll probably have to move to London or somewhere like that to find a job.'

'Will you?'

The snow was driving more thickly now, and Matthew set the wipers on a faster speed to keep the windscreen clear. For a while, it took all his concentration to distinguish the outline of the road ahead, the hedges, which were so pretty in summertime, spilling their frozen burden as the car went by.

As they neared the lake, however, it got a little easier. Nearer the water the snow was not lying so thickly, and the dark shadow of the lake was a familiar guide-mark in a totally white landscape. Even Rachel thought she could have found her way along the lake road, and Matthew, who had been born at Rothmere, knew it even better.

'Almost there,' he murmured, as they passed the private drive that led to the Rothmere estate. 'Your aunt and uncle must be worried about you. You don't suppose your uncle might have set out to look for you, do you?'

Rachel shook her head. 'I don't think so,' she replied, knowing that however concerned Uncle Geoff might be, her aunt would not countenance him turning out on a night like this. Besides, she argued reasonably, what was the point of her uncle risking getting stranded in a snow-drift?

'No?'

Matthew was looking at her now, and she was glad he couldn't see the wave of colour that swept up her cheeks at his words.

'I don't think so,' she repeated, avoiding his gaze. 'Oh, look! There's the church. Doesn't it look pretty?'

'Mmm.' Matthew gave the church only a cursory look before bringing the Mercedes to a halt at the gates to the vicarage. But, as Rachel released her seat-belt and bent to pick up her haversack as a preliminary to getting out of the car, he said quietly, 'You didn't tell me your name.'

'What?' She sat back in her seat and looked at him blankly. 'Um—oh, it's Rachel. Rachel Barnes. My father was Uncle Geoff's brother.'

'Yes. I know the relationship,' declared Matthew surprisingly. 'Your father was a doctor, wasn't he? You had no inclination to follow in his footsteps?'

'No.' Rachel shook her head, forbearing to mention that even if she had—which she didn't, luckily—there was no way she could have afforded the years of training needed for such a profession.

A brief spillage of light across the snow-packed drive revealed that someone had peered through the vicarage's sitting-room curtains, and Rachel guessed that her aunt had heard the car. Of course, she wouldn't know what it was doing at the gate, but when her niece appeared it wouldn't take her long to put two and two together. Rachel had been hoping to pretend she had caught the bus, as usual. She was loath to discuss Matthew's kindness with her family. Knowing how her aunt and Barbara could reduce the most innocent of acts to something dirty, she had hoped to keep this experience to herself.

But now, realising that the longer she stayed in the car, the more suspicious her aunt would become, she reached for the handle of the door.

'I—thanks for bringing me home,' she murmured ruefully, guessing he had seen the revealing twitch of the curtains, too. 'You probably saved my life.'

'But not your reputation, hmm?' he remarked lazily, and now she was sure he had seen the betraying glimmer of light.

'Oh—' Rachel lifted her shoulders in what she hoped was a dismissing gesture. 'I—I'm sure my aunt and uncle will be very grateful to you.'

'Are you?' Matthew did not sound convinced, but although sitting here, talking to him, was both pleasurable and exciting, Rachel had the sense to realise it was dangerous, too. He was far too easy to talk to, and, while this

might just be an amusing diversion for him, she sensed it
could mean more than that to her. And that was just plain
stupid!

'I must go,' she said, gathering the haversack to her chest,
as if by creating a physical barrier between them she could
protect her innocence. Because she *was* innocent compared
to him, and she had no intention of making a fool of herself.

'OK.'

He made no demur when she pulled the handle and
opened the door, and the still-falling snow made any prolonged farewells impractical. Instead, he just leaned across
the passenger seat and said, 'Good luck!' before slamming
the door again and driving away.

# CHAPTER SEVEN

RACHEL had assumed that that would be the one and only occasion she would get to speak to Matthew Conroy. In the normal course of events their paths simply didn't cross, and even when she'd discovered that his reasons for being at the college that night had been to deliver a guest lecture on computer technology she had had more sense than to imagine it might be repeated. And even if it were, the chances of her running into him again were a million to one.

No, she was quite prepared to accept her aunt's opinion that she had virtually forced him to offer her a lift home, and that she had probably caused her uncle a great deal of embarrassment. In Aunt Maggie's opinion, she should never have gone to the evening class in the first place; as soon as she'd realised the weather was worsening, she should have come straight home. And she was probably right, Rachel decided in the days that followed. But then, Aunt Maggie hadn't wanted her to attend night-school from the very beginning.

And that was that—until the letter arrived.

The plain white oblong envelope was waiting for Rachel when she got home from work a week later. It was obvious that both her aunt and her cousin were curious about the letter, but, assuming that it was something to do with the course she was taking, they allowed her to open it in private. And Rachel was glad that they had when she read what was inside. It was an invitation to attend an interview at the Penrith studios of Kirkstone Television. If the interview was successful, she would be offered the chance to train as a receptionist, with the opportunities of advancement if and when she acquired the necessary qualifications.

With trembling fingers, she turned to the end of the letter, convinced that Matthew Conroy must have had some hand in this, but the signature was disappointingly unfamiliar. Even so, he had to have had something to do with it, she was sure, and her heart palpitated rapidly at the realisation that he hadn't forgotten her.

Her aunt and cousin were predictably pessimistic. Unaware of Rachel's suspicions that Matthew Conroy must be responsible for the invitation, they assumed that the tutor at the college had arranged the whole thing.

'He obviously has no idea how difficult it is to get a job—any job—in television,' remarked Barbara, tossing the letter on to the sofa. 'He probably knows someone who's arranged for you to have an interview, but that's all. It's getting the job that's the hard part. Not being invited to an interview.'

Rachel knew she was right—about the interview, at least. But that didn't stop her spirits from rising. The idea of working in television, in however small a way, was exciting, and her dreams of becoming a journalist could be realised, if she was ever successful enough to join the station news team.

It was six weeks before she saw Matthew Conroy again, and by then she was a trainee telephonist, working behind the desk at Kirkstone Television. Her interview had been successful, and for the past three weeks she had been learning a variety of skills necessary to the job. She hadn't found it hard. Talking to people had never been a problem. And by the time Matthew appeared she had gained more confidence, due in no small part to the clothes allowance which was part of her salary.

Even so, when Matthew walked into the reception area her excitement at seeing him again almost left her speechless. And when later in the day he invited her to have coffee with him, she could hardly get up from her chair and follow him into the boardroom.

Of course, it had been crazy getting involved with him, she acknowledged now, but at the time she had been blind to the possible consequences of her folly. Where Matthew was concerned, her common sense had seemed to desert her, and although she had known he was engaged to someone else she had convinced herself there was no harm in being friendly. After all, he had been instrumental in getting her this job, she consoled herself, having learned in her first few days at the television station that he was an active member of the governing board.

But in the weeks that followed it had soon become apparent that Matthew's interest in her went beyond the bounds of a casual relationship. It had become obvious when he invited her to go sailing, and, instead of taking her to some public marina, he brought her to Rothmere. She hadn't needed his mother's steely-eyed air of disapproval to know that what he was doing was both foolish and reckless, and that, although there might only be a few years between them in age, there was a world of difference in background.

But it was while they were out on the boat that Rachel had begun to realise just what she was taking on. Matthew might have been only eight years older than her seventeen, but he was inconceivably older in experience. And when, inexperienced as she was, she had stumbled and fallen into the bottom of the yacht, there had been nothing remotely immature about the way he picked her up.

One minute, she was lying in the bottom of the boat, stunned by the sudden transference from perching on the gunwale to being flat on her back, and the next, Matthew had lifted her up into his arms, holding her between his knees as he perched on the cabin roof, his long, hard fingers digging into her bare midriff.

Somehow, she never quite knew how, the cotton shirt she was wearing under her life jacket had separated from the waistband of her jeans, and Matthew's probing fingers took full advantage of the fact.

'Are you all right?' he demanded huskily, his breath warm against her throat, and she could only nod vigorously. 'I'd never forgive myself if I hurt you,' he added, gripping her waist with strangely possessive hands. 'I think I should examine you, just to make sure there are no bones broken.'

'Oh—no. That's not necessary!' She almost choked on the words, but when she met his gaze she discovered he was grinning.

'We're a little old to play doctors and nurses,' he commented wryly, though he still made no attempt to let her go. 'But if you're game, I have no objections. Who's going to be the patient first?'

Rachel didn't know how to respond to him, and, as if sensing her bewilderment, his hands slid from her waist, along her bare arms to her wrists. Then, bringing each of her hands to his lips in turn, he kissed each individual finger, stroking the sensitive pads with his tongue and turning her bones to water.

He let her go then, as if realising he had gone too far, but it was already too late. It was impossible to hide her feelings for him after that, and, although she sensed that Matthew was not so deeply involved, it was obvious he was attracted to her.

Of course, Rachel tried to be sensible. She even asked him about his fiancée who, Barbara had spitefully told her, had been away with her parents for the past three months. But Matthew always changed the subject when she mentioned Cecily. And, although she knew deep down inside her that she was a fool for letting him get away with it, the temptation to ignore the truth was easier by far.

Cecily had come back from Australia at the beginning of June, just as Rachel's aunt and uncle and Barbara were going on holiday. They had always taken a cottage on Exmoor for a couple of weeks every year, and, although Rachel had usually gone with them, this year she wasn't able to. Apart from the fact that it would have been difficult to get time off, when she had only been working at the television station for a few months, her first-year exams at college were looming, and, although Uncle Geoff had been loath to leave her, his wife and daughter had no such reservations.

Barbara made her feelings clear the night before she went away, however. 'Now we'll see how long your job at Kirkstone lasts,' she taunted, coming into Rachel's room as the other girl was getting ready to go to bed. 'Did I tell you Colonel Bishop is a member of the board, too? You can imagine what will happen when he discovers Matthew Conroy has installed his latest girlfriend in reception.'

Rachel made no comment, although the news that Cecily's father was involved with Kirkstone Television wasn't welcome. Nevertheless, since Barbara and her mother had realised that Matthew had had a hand in offering her the interview at the station she had had to suffer many such accusations, and arguing didn't make things easier, it just prolonged the agony.

Still, the news did persuade her that perhaps she was being a fool in allowing her association with Matthew to continue. As Barbara had cruelly informed her, now that Cecily was home again he wouldn't need her any more, and, no matter how painful the truth might be, she had been only a substitute.

So, for the first week her family was away, she avoided seeing him, not answering the phone when she suspected it might be him, and getting the other receptionists to make excuses for her absence if she glimpsed his now familiar car driving into the car park at the station. Her friends were sympathetic. She was a likeable girl, and most of her contemporaries, who had envied her the attention Matthew Conroy had shown towards her, were willing to help. Of course, there were exceptions. Girls like Barbara, who had been jealous of her success all along. But she could stand their sniggering; it wasn't likely to last long.

In the event, it proved easier to avoid him at work than she had thought. Lynn Turner, who worked for Simon Motley, one of the associate producers of the local features programme *Newsreel*, was pregnant, and as she was having a particularly difficult time with morning sickness a temporary stand-in was needed. All the girls who manned the reception desk were offered the chance to try for the job, but as it entailed working longer hours, with no obvious advantages, Rachel was the only one to volunteer. And she got it. In consequence, the next day she moved on to the floor above, sharing an office with Simon and his secretary. And the excitement of being part of actual programme production at last helped in a small way to assuage the loss of Matthew.

It seemed her affair—if such a word could be used to describe her relationship with Matthew—was over, and the long summer days stretched ahead of her, bleak and lonely. She had had no idea she would miss him so much, and she was glad her aunt and uncle, and Barbara, were away as she struggled to contain her grief—it would have been so humiliating if they had known she cried herself to sleep at nights. In the morning she could disguise her puffy eyes with make-up before anyone at the television station saw her.

The weekend was the worst. There was no *Newsreel* on Saturday and Sunday evenings, and, although work did go on on the programme during the weekend, she was not involved.

Consequently, her spirits were at their lowest ebb on Saturday evening when Matthew came to the door. Rachel had been in the kitchen, preparing herself cheese on toast in lieu of supper, and she hadn't heard the car. Afterwards, she supposed she should have checked who her visitor was before so precipitately opening the door, but she wasn't thinking clearly, and the practicalities of the situation didn't occur to her.

Therefore it was something of a shock to discover the man who was causing such an upheaval in her life standing with his shoulder propped against the framework of the porch. And she didn't even have the time to regret the unflattering aspects of her appearance before he had straightened and stepped inside, closing the door behind him and forcing her back along the hall.

She thought at first that he was angry, but anger didn't begin to describe Matthew's feelings at that moment. He was simply furious, and as she backed away along the hall she knew a moment's panic.

'What the hell do you think you're playing at?' he demanded, cornering her in the kitchen, where the cheese on her toast was beginning to burn, and she thought uneasily how attractive he was, even when he was angry. It was a warm evening, and he wasn't wearing a jacket, and his dark blue shirt was open at the neck. He wasn't an especially hairy man, but there were hairs at the base of his throat, curling over the opened shirt and glistening with the heat.

'I don't know what you mean,' she answered him now, stretching out a hand to rescue the toast, but he thrust her arm aside. Instead, he turned off the grill, allowing the smoke of the burning cheese to billow into the kitchen, and, grasping her by the wrist, he pulled her after him out of the room.

By a process of opening one door after the other he eventually found the sitting-room, and, dragging her inside, he practically threw her down on to the couch. 'Now,' he said, standing over her, the taut muscles of his thighs barely inches from her knees as she sat there, 'are you going to tell me why you've been avoiding me? And don't pretend you haven't. I'm not a complete fool.'

'Nor am I,' retorted Rachel tremulously, chancing a brief glance up at him, then wishing she hadn't when she met his cold, hard gaze.

'Am I supposed to understand something from that remark?' he countered dangerously. 'Rachel, I'm warning you, my patience is running thin. Either you tell me what this is about, or—or—'

'Or what?' she muttered, hunching her elbows on her knees and cupping her hot face between her palms. 'What can you do to me that you've not already done?'

'You're not serious?' His response was as much bemused

now as violent. 'For heaven's sake! What have I done to you, Rachel? I thought we were—*friends*!'

'For how long?' she exclaimed, scuffing at the carpet with her bare toes. 'You know very well that now—now that Cecily's back, you don't need me any more.'

Matthew swore. 'Who told you that?'

'I didn't need to be told.' Rachel wouldn't look at him. 'You know it's the truth, so why don't you admit it?'

'It's not the truth.' With a muffled oath, Matthew came down on the couch beside her, the depression of his weight causing her to tip automatically towards him. But when he would have put his arm about her shoulders she stiffened and pulled away from him.

'You're crazy,' he said frustratedly, and when she would have turned away he put out his hand and grasped her chin, tilting her face towards him. 'Crazy,' he repeated harshly, rubbing his thumb across the vulnerable curve of her mouth. 'I'm not interested in Cecily. I've told you that before.'

'But you're going to marry her anyway.'

'No, I'm not. Why don't you believe me?' He sighed. 'Have I ever lied to you?'

Rachel quivered. 'I don't know, do I?'

'Yes, you do.' Aware that she was weakening, albeit against her will, his hand slid under her chin to cup the gentle hollow of her throat. 'Just because I haven't slept with you yet, it doesn't mean I haven't wanted to.'

Rachel caught her breath. 'I—I wouldn't let you anyway.'

'Wouldn't you?' His eyes dropped sensuously to her lips, and the quickened rise and fall of her small breasts. 'My darling, if that was all I had wanted you wouldn't have been able to stop me.'

'Because you're so irresistible? Is that it?' she retorted, trembling uncontrollably, and he shook his head.

'Just sure of you,' he amended huskily, and, as if unable to control himself, he leant forward and touched her startled lips with his tongue. 'Stop trying to create a situation of contention when there is none,' he whispered, his breath

moistening the hollows of her ear. 'And don't pretend you
don't want to see me again, or I might not be responsible
for my actions.'

Rachel jerked back. 'But what about Cecily?' she persisted, getting abruptly to her feet. 'You won't ever talk
about her. Whenever I mention her name, you change the
subject.'

Matthew groaned. 'You don't listen, do you?' he declared, and when she turned her back on him he got to his
feet, too, and came to stand right behind her. 'What do you
want me to say?' he demanded, in a low voice, and she
lifted her shoulders as if to ward off an attack. 'For heaven's
sake, Rachel, don't make this any harder than it already is!
Why can't we just go on as before? What has happened to
make you change your mind?'

'Cecily's come back, hasn't she?' she mumbled, her bent
head exposing the vulnerable curve of her nape. 'Everyone
knows. It's common knowledge in the village. They're all
saying you'll be getting married now, and speculating when
it's going to be.'

'Oh, *God*!' His plea was heartfelt, and she flinched when
his hands descended on her shoulders. 'Cecily's been back
in England since the beginning of May. Just because she's
not been here, in Rothside, it doesn't mean I haven't been
in touch with her.'

Rachel's spine became rigid at his words, but when she
would have pulled away he wouldn't let her. Instead, his
fingers probed the fine bones that the thinness of her cotton
T-shirt could not disguise, kneading and massaging the
bunched muscles that her tenseness refused to relax. 'Stop
fighting me,' he said, bending his head to brush his lips
against the side of her neck. 'Ask me what I was in touch
with her about, if you must. It wasn't to arrange a wedding.
Quite the reverse, actually.'

Rachel took an unsteady breath. 'Then why has she come
back?' she exclaimed.

'This is her home,' replied Matthew evenly. 'Where else

would she go? You're not the only one with pride, you know.' He paused. 'And perhaps she's hoping that I'll change my mind.'

Rachel made a disbelieving sound, moving her head jerkily from side to side. 'Why—why should I believe you?'

'Why should you not?' he countered harshly, his hands sliding sensuously down her arms to her elbows. His thumbs brushed the sides of her breasts, and she heard his sudden intake of breath. 'In any case, we shouldn't be having this conversation. Not yet, at any rate. You've still got another year before you finish school.'

Rachel quivered. 'What has that got to do with anything?' she protested, hardly daring to believe what she was hearing, and he expelled a weary breath.

'You *know*,' he muttered unevenly, and then, as if losing all control of the situation, he hauled her back against him. 'I'm trying to be reasonable,' he breathed, against the silky weight of her hair. 'How I've stopped myself from touching you these past few months is beyond me!' His hands slid round her midriff, and rubbed back and forth against the undersides of her breasts. 'I don't want you to feel I'm trying to rush you. I just want us to go on as we were before— before you ruined this otherwise perfectly good week of my life.'

Rachel swallowed. 'And—and what if I don't want to go on as—as before?' she whispered convulsively. 'Wh—what then?'

Matthew dragged her closer, his arms enfolding her against his taut body, and for the first time in her life she felt the unmistakable thrust of a man's arousal. His hardness swelled against her bottom, its heat barely confined by the tightness of his cotton jeans, and a rippling sense of excitement filled her at the realisation that she could do that to him.

'Don't—don't play games with me, Rachel,' he said, and for the first time she heard the harsh edge of emotion in his voice. 'Making me prove that you want me just as much as

I want you isn't very sensible. So, if you want to get out of here with your virtue intact, you'd better take that back right now.'

He meant it! *He really meant it!* Rachel's pulses were racing wildly now, and acting purely on instinct, she flexed her shoulders against his chest. The buttons of his shirt felt unbearably sharp against her sensitised flesh, and taking the initiative now, she ran her hands down the seams of his jeans.

'Perhaps you didn't—understand me,' she murmured, and he sucked in some air. 'When I said I didn't want to go on as before, I didn't mean we shouldn't see one another. As you said before—quite the contrary.'

Matthew shuddered then, and for a moment he pressed even closer. But, as if common sense and his own innate sense of decency grimly prevailed, he steeled his aroused body and dragged himself away from her. But not far. With hands that were not quite steady, he turned her to face him, though he carefully kept a foot of space between them.

'You don't understand—' he began thickly, but she interrupted him.

'No. *You* don't understand,' she retorted, her emotive gaze sweeping over his dark, frustrated face, and down over the muscled planes of his body. Her eyes lingered longest at the revealing junction of his thighs, before returning to confront his narrow-eyed stare. 'What makes you think I need to finish school before knowing what I want? I'm not a child, Matt. I'm not.'

'Even if you sometimes act like one?' he countered, trying to make light of the situation, but she wouldn't let him.

'Do you think I'm a child?' she persisted, arching brows that were several shades darker than her hair, and he bent his head to avoid her knowing gaze.

'No,' he agreed huskily. 'No, I don't see you as a child. But that doesn't mean anything. I see what I want to see, I guess, like everyone else.'

'And—and what do you see?' she prompted, leaning towards him so that only the strength of his fingers gripping her upper arms prevented her from touching him.

Matthew lifted his head, his features taut with the control he was putting on himself. 'I see—temptation,' he muttered, expelling his breath on a heavy sigh. 'Rachel, let's go out somewhere and discuss this. I'll take you for a drive, if you like. We could even go over to Windermere and have dinner. You won't be wanting burnt toast—'

'Why can't we stay here?'

Rachel's softly spoken words stopped him dead for a moment, but then, as if tormented beyond measure by her irresponsibility, he let her go and turned abruptly away. 'You know why,' he grated, striding angrily towards the door. 'I'll call you tomorrow. Perhaps then we can have a serious conversation.'

'Oh—wait!' Impulsively, Rachel went after him, catching him before he had a chance to open the door and sliding her arms around his waist from behind. 'Matt! *Darling!*' she breathed, against the warm hollow of his spine. Her breath moistened the fine material of his shirt, and the scent of his skin was intoxicating. 'Don't go. *Please*, don't go. I'm sorry if I've made you angry, but you don't know how you make me feel.'

'Don't I?' Matthew stood stiffly within her embrace. 'I shouldn't bank on that, if I were you.'

'What do you mean?' Rachel's hands curled over the buckle of his belt, and she felt the shudder that swept through his body.

'I mean—oh, God help me!' He twisted round to face her, and jerked her roughly into his arms. 'I mean, I've been trying to fight what *you* make *me* feel!' he groaned harshly. 'But a man can only stand so much, and you are driving me *insane!*'

'Matt—' she began unsteadily, shivering at the sexual urgency of his words, but he didn't let her go. His hand at her nape tipped her face up to his, and his mouth came down on hers with a driving urgency.

Rachel's senses swam at the first touch of his lips on hers. The undisguised hunger of his caress sent the blood rushing thickly through her veins, and no experience she had had thus far had prepared her for the eager response of her own body. Until that moment she had been unaware of the possibility of losing her head, but as Matthew's hands slid down her back, moulding her yielding softness to his hard, muscled frame, she was completely incapable of offering any resistance.

Not that she really wanted to. Any latent sense of restraint was totally eclipsed by the unfamiliar needs raging inside her. The weeks of being with Matthew, of being tantalised by his dark good looks and lazy charm, had stirred her senses, and the accumulation of their mutual desires was now blazing out of control.

'Oh, Matt...' she breathed, when he released her mouth to seek the palpitating pulse below her jawline, and he made a strangled sound of protest.

'Don't—don't ask me to stop,' he told her unevenly, and she made a little negative movement of her head.

'I—I wasn't going to,' she whispered against his neck, and with a shudder his mouth sought hers again.

The entry of his tongue was an intimate invasion, and her knees turned to jelly beneath her. Plunging into her mouth, it took her breath away, and she clung to him helplessly as he plundered her sweetness.

'I did warn you,' he said against her ear, his arms the only support she had, and she burrowed instinctively against him.

'I'm not complaining, am I?' she got out jerkily, and with a sound of desperation he pulled her down on to the sofa.

With his mouth still silencing any protest she might have made, his hand slid beneath the loose T-shirt, and presently she felt his fingers fumbling with the fastening of her bra.

'Wait,' she said, lifting a trembling hand to loosen the clip between her breasts, and he sighed in satisfaction as his hand closed over one small mound.

'You're beautiful,' he groaned, burying his face between her breasts, and she shuddered uncontrollably. 'So beautiful,' he added, his thumb enticing one sensitised nipple to peak against his palm. 'And—I want you, here—and now.'

'I want you, too,' she told him unsteadily, and, even though she wasn't entirely sure what that admission actually meant, she knew she couldn't let him go.

'Oh, Rachel,' he muttered, climbing over her and cupping her flushed face between his palms. 'We shouldn't be doing this; you know that, don't you?'

'I know it's what I want,' she replied, intensely conscious of his straddled form, of the rough texture of the couch pillows at her back, and of Matthew's arousal, an unmistakable swelling against his tight jeans, only inches from her face...

'God!' he groaned, and with a tense deliberation he tugged the T-shirt up and over her head. The bra was easily disposed of, and then, as she lay beneath him, naked and exposed from the waist up, and achingly vulnerable, 'Am I a complete bastard?'

'I don't think so,' she breathed huskily. 'Oh, Matt—kiss me! *Please*...'

And he did. But his shirt buttons were digging into her breasts, and when she protested he brought her hands to the fastenings. 'You do it,' he said against her mouth, and with trembling fingers she loosened the shirt and then eased it off his shoulders, until he could shrug out of it. Then he came down to her again, and now the light covering of fine dark hair on his chest was a tantalising abrasion.

But it wasn't enough. Even in her innocence, she knew she wouldn't be satisfied until there were no clothes between them. She wanted to feel Matthew's legs against hers, his flanks, his thighs, the flat planes of his stomach—and his sex, that most of all.

Almost instinctively her hands sought the buckle of his belt, and he levered himself up on to his knees to make it easier for her. At the same time he unfastened the button at her waist and pressed the zip down to its fullest extent. His eyes narrowed when he saw the bikini briefs beneath, and he ran one finger from the low waistband down over the quivering core of her womanhood.

She shuddered then, her hands going automatically to stop him, and, aware of her inexperience, he unzipped his own trousers and pushed them down to his knees. Now only the thin silk of his briefs contained his maleness, and Rachel couldn't look at him any more.

'Relax,' he breathed, bending towards her, and she jerked uncontrollably when he took one taut nipple between his lips.

Immediately a knife-sharp wave of heat swept over her, and she shook helplessly beneath his hands. Dear God, what was he doing? She choked, opening her eyes. But the sight of him suckling at her breast sent another shaft of heat prickling down into her stomach, and from there to the moist place between her legs. The darkness of his head against her breast was a shattering image, and almost involuntarily her hands came up to cradle his head.

Meanwhile, she felt him easing her jeans and panties down her legs, and presently he shifted to remove his own pants. And now she could feel the burning length of him against her thigh, and his leg slid between hers, his knee nudging the quivering juncture of her legs.

'Good?' he murmured, his lips drifting down over her midriff to her navel, and when she felt his tongue laving her stomach she was unable to do anything more than nod. But when he would have parted her legs she uttered a choked protest, and with a regretful sigh he returned to her mouth. 'One thing at a time,' he reassured her gently, and then, with his tongue silencing the cry that flew to her lips, he eased himself into her. 'It's all right,' he whispered against her lips, as a latent sense of panic caused her to resist him at last. 'I love you,' he added, licking the treacherous tears from her cheek. 'And when people love one another, it's the most beautiful thing in the world.'

# CHAPTER EIGHT

AND it had been. Even though she had been half afraid she was going to make a fool of herself, that evening Rachel had discovered the true extent of her own sexuality. Of course, she acknowledged unwillingly now, Matthew had been a good teacher. Some might say an expert teacher, she appended bitterly. But, for whatever reason, he had been gentle with her, and although she had been totally inexperienced he had made it good for her.

Which was no mean feat, considering her initial reaction to his lovemaking, she conceded. For all she had wanted him so badly, the realisation had been not a little frightening. The feel of his powerful body lying dormant inside her had filled her with alarm, and, although at that moment she had had no real conception of what was involved, she had been half regretting her impulsiveness.

But Matthew had known how she was feeling, and instead of ravaging her, which he had confessed afterwards he had wanted to do, he had slowly restored her confidence. Allowing the palpitating nerves that surrounded him to subside, he let his mouth induce the same urgent needs she had been experiencing before he'd thrust himself upon her. Stroking and nuzzling her breasts, laving the nipples with his tongue, and sometimes taking the whole areola into his mouth, he gradually brought her to a trembling state of expectancy, and only then did he begin to move inside her.

She had thought it would be painful, but it wasn't. Her body was more than ready for his, and as he found his rhythm her muscles tightened convulsively around him. 'Oh, God,' she heard him whisper, as her hands clutched his broad shoulders, her nails digging into his damp skin. 'God,

Rachel, you are beautiful! Don't fight it, sweetheart. Come on—let it go…'

The memory of that moment, when their two bodies had simultaneously splintered into sexual fulfilment, still had the power to stir her, and Rachel moved restlessly between the silken sheets. No other man had ever even tempted her to test that perfection, and, although she had had friends, she had had no other lovers.

Naturally, their marriage had been the talk of the village, and the surrounding area. That Matthew Conroy, the eligible heir to the Conroy estate, should choose to take an eighteen-year-old receptionist as his wife had been little short of a scandal, and among the greatest perpetrators of the story had been Rachel's aunt herself.

But, in spite of everything, they had got married, and they had been happy—for a while at least. To begin with, Matthew had been very understanding about her final examinations, and her desire to continue with her job at Kirkstone Television. Her initial spell of helping out with the production of *Newsreel* had been extended when Lynn Turner had left to have her baby, and her aptitude had been such that Simon Motley had offered her a full-time job as an assistant researcher.

Of course, they had had problems, as all newly married couples did. The fact that Matthew's mother still lived at Rothmere had been a continual bone of contention, and Lady Olivia had lost no opportunity to criticise her daughter-in-law.

But, on the whole, they had ridden all the difficulties, their continuing delight in each other more than making up for other people's interference.

And it was this aspect of their relationship which had kept them together as long as they had been, Rachel reflected grimly. They had been so good together, and any problems they'd had had been quickly erased by the frantic heat of their lovemaking. They hadn't seemed able to get enough of one another, she remembered now. It hadn't even been unusual for Matthew to come to the television station at lunchtime, and lock both of them in the station director's office. So it was appropriate that when the break came it should involve the very substance of their feelings for one another. How could she ever forget the horror she had felt on discovering Matthew had been unfaithful to her? And with her own cousin, her own flesh and blood.

Of course, she had always known that Barbara had been jealous of her. After her marriage, her relationship with her erstwhile family had not improved, and visiting the vicarage had always been a traumatic occasion. Naturally, Matthew had usually accompanied her and, because her uncle had appreciated the gesture, she had never suggested otherwise. But it had been hard to ignore the way Barbara had behaved with her husband, aided and abetted by Aunt Maggie, whose resentment had coloured every word she spoke. But for Rachel, watching her cousin smile and flutter her eyelashes every time Matthew said anything even remotely amusing, it had been a nail-biting experience. And, although he had sometimes teased her that she was jealous, too, the maliciousness of Barbara's actions had inspired a nameless dread.

They had been married over two years, and Rachel had just been offered the chance to work in front of the cameras, when Matthew had decided it was time they started a family. The idea had come, Rachel knew, from a conversation Aunt Maggie had instigated on their last visit to the vicarage. Although her aunt could have had no desire for them to cement their relationship with the advent of a child, her comments had been unquestionably provocative. She had known, as well as everyone else, that Rachel was just beginning to make her mark at Kirkstone Television. Matthew had always been generous in his praise of his wife's accomplishments, and he had made no secret of the fact that she had been offered the chance to co-present the evening's features programme. However, even he had not been immune from sly aspersions cast on his masculinity, and Aunt Maggie's casual suggestion that perhaps Rachel's job was in compensation for not having children had been sufficiently barbed to stir his sensitivities.

And, even though he had to acknowledge that her aunt's remarks had been deliberately cruel, the notion behind them took root. So much so that they had their first really serious row over Rachel's refusal to even consider having a child, and when he flushed her contraceptive pills down the toilet she spent several nights in another room.

That particular argument blew over, of course, but it was not the last. The more popular Rachel became at the television studios, the more determined Matthew seemed to make her give it all up. Even though he knew she hadn't started taking the birth-control pill again after their reconciliation, he still persisted in goading her, and, although she discovered later that Aunt Maggie had been fuelling the fires of his anger, she couldn't have succeeded without his consent.

And, in all honesty, Rachel was not opposed to the idea of having a baby. What she was opposed to was Matthew's arrogant assumption that he could rule her life. Nevertheless, as month succeeded month and she didn't conceive, she had to face the possibility that perhaps she couldn't.

It was a traumatic time, she remembered unwillingly, and even her success as a television presenter couldn't possibly assuage her unhappiness. She went from being determined not to have a baby to wanting one desperately, and all without Matthew's sympathy, or knowledge.

It was then that Barbara started coming to the house to help Matthew. As a director of several other companies as well as Kirkstone Television, he was a busy man, and once again it had been Aunt Maggie's suggestion that Barbara should help out as part-time secretary. She had nothing else to do, having still not found a job, and Aunt Maggie said he would be doing her a service by giving her some real work experience. Of course, Matthew had Patrick Malloy to do most of his secretarial work, but there was no denying that another typist would be useful. In consequence, Rachel came home from work many evenings to find her husband and her cousin sharing an after-work drink in the library, and even though Lady Olivia didn't approve of the situation either there was nothing they could do.

For her part, Rachel's hands were tied. She could hardly ask Matthew to dismiss her cousin when there was nothing she could do to take her place. And she could hardly tell him she wanted a baby when it was becoming distressingly obvious that she couldn't have one. For, in spite of their increasing polarisation in daylight hours, at night her husband still came to her bed as regularly as ever. That aspect of their relationship was as satisfactory as it had ever been— although there were times, she knew, when Matthew despised himself for his need of her.

And then, one evening, she was late arriving home. Very late, she recalled bitterly, wondering if even then she could have saved her marriage. But by the time she arrived home, it was too late. The damage had been done. And nothing Matthew could say or do could persuade her to forgive him.

She used to drive herself home in those days, Matthew having taught her to drive soon after their marriage. He had even bought her a car—a sporty little Peugeot—to enable her to get about when he was unable to escort her.

She remembered that on the way home she had been thinking that perhaps tonight she might conceive. Lady Olivia was away, for once—a too infrequent occurrence— and she was anticipating them having the place to themselves with a genuine sense of excitement. The doctors she had consulted had all been of the opinion that she was trying too hard to have this baby, but they didn't understand what it meant to her. They didn't know she was in danger of losing the only man she would ever love. Maybe tonight she would succeed, she told herself eagerly. If she didn't, it wouldn't be her fault.

It was after ten when she parked the car at the side of

the house and entered the building. The sight of her uncle's car parked on the drive was daunting—it meant Barbara was still here—but she determined not to let that faze her. Entering the house, she went straight to the library, prepared to apologise herself, if necessary, for the delay in getting home. But there was no one there. Empty glasses stood on the cabinet, and an empty bottle of Scotch was rolled significantly under a chair, but the room itself was empty.

Her first thoughts, she remembered, were that they must have gone out, and although that idea wasn't appealing she could only blame herself. After all, she was invariably home by seven-thirty, and just because there had been an electrical failure at the studios, there was no reason why she shouldn't have phoned. But the situation between her and Matthew was so volatile at the moment that she had found excuses not to fuel his impatience, and it had never occurred to her that it might precipitate disaster.

Watkins was in the hall when she came out of the library, but when she asked him if he knew where Matthew was he was strangely reticent. But his eyes did turn guiltily to the ceiling above their heads, and with a growing sense of apprehension Rachel left him to run headlong up the stairs.

She had heard their voices before she reached the suite of rooms which she and Matthew shared. She remembered hearing Barbara's laughter, and Matthew's rueful chuckle, so that when she threw the door open she was half prepared for what confronted her.

But even then the reality was so much worse than the anticipation. Rachel had stared aghast at her half-naked husband, his chest bare, his trousers pooled around his ankles, and Barbara's hands hooked into the waistband of his briefs, caught in the act of pushing the black silk over his lean hips. Barbara herself was almost decent, although her unbuttoned blouse and mussed hair spoke of a greater intimacy. And, of all of them, she was the one with the least to lose, the one with the most to gain.

The tableau was imprinted on Rachel's mind for months

to come. How she had stood there, looking at them, without throwing up, was an achievement in itself. How could Matthew have done it? Had their relationship sunk to such an ebb that he could actually justify his actions? For there had been no shame, no contrition. Only a bland defiance in the face of her distress.

Of course, he had been drunk, she had realised that later. Not falling-down drunk, not incoherently intoxicated, but coldly, and calculatedly, immune to any recrimination. He had simply appeared not to care what she thought of him, and Barbara had burst into crocodile tears, with more than a hint of triumph.

There was no row then. That came the following morning, after Rachel had spent a sleepless night in a spare room. She had no idea how long Barbara had stayed, or indeed if she was still in the house, when she went downstairs before breakfast. But Matthew was waiting in the library for her, and the exchange that followed was just as horrible as she had anticipated.

What could she expect, he demanded, when it was obvious she thought more about her bloody job than him? Why should she complain if he found sympathy elsewhere? Their marriage was just a sham anyway; she had no intention of ever giving him a family.

There was more in the same vein—angry, bitter words that tore through Rachel's stand for independence, and found it wanting. She was just a shell, he told her, a miserable, useless thing, who held on to her puerile career because it was the only thing she was good at. Just because they were married there was no reason for her to think she was indispensable. If he wanted to have sex with someone else, he would do it, and to hell with her.

Rachel remembered him slamming out of the house after that, and her being scarcely able to climb the stairs again. But climb them she did, and she packed a suitcase with sufficient clothes to see her through the next couple of days before following him out of the house. She didn't take the car. She called a taxi. And only Watkins saw her go, a troubled, anxious figure.

The ironic thing was, Matthew came after her. She had never thought he would, but he did. It wasn't difficult for him to find the address of the holiday apartment she had temporarily leased in Penrith, and, once it became apparent that she wasn't coming back, he came to find her.

But it was too late. She refused to speak to him, locking herself behind closed doors and not answering his phone calls. Of course, it couldn't go on. Her work at the studios was suffering, and she knew that it was only a matter of time before she would be forced to leave the area.

Her uncle came to see her, too, but he had little more success. His assertion that Barbara was grief-stricken by what had happened was not quite believable, particularly when Barbara herself showed so little remorse. And when Aunt Maggie came to see her six weeks later to impart the news that Barbara was expecting a baby, Rachel didn't hesitate before seeking a divorce.

The days and weeks that followed were the worst kind of purgatory. But at least Matthew no longer pestered her. Evidently Barbara's news, combined with the divorce papers he had been served, had at last killed any lingering responsibility he felt towards her. And when Simon Motley offered to use his influence to find her a job in London Rachel jumped at the chance to leave this miserable period of her life behind.

But it was not quite over. A week after moving into the apartment that the London studios had found for her in Kensington, Rachel was taken ill in the night. Racked with pain, she could do nothing until morning, when she rang the studios and explained that she thought she ought to see a doctor. She was bleeding, and although she thought it might be her period she had never been so sick before.

The doctor was sympathetic, but unable to help her. It was too late. She was having a miscarriage, he told her gently. But, because she had waited so long before calling him, there was nothing he could do…

Of course, she had been shattered at the news, particularly so after everything that had gone before. For days and days she had been unable to do anything but cry, and, although the doctor reassured her that it was a perfectly natural reaction, she knew better.

It was just something else to blame herself for, and it took months, *years*, before she was able to get it into perspective. She knew it had been walking in on Barbara and her husband that had put all other considerations out of her head, but for a long while she continued to bear the burden for her baby's loss of life. It had been a little boy, they had told her, when she had asked, perfect in every way. Matthew's son. Perhaps the only thing that could have saved their marriage, and she hadn't even known.

That was when Justin had been such a comfort. Although their association had been brief up to that point, he had made her feel she had at least one friend in London. But it had been a while before she'd told him the full story, in all its ugly detail.

# CHAPTER NINE

RACHEL was out of bed and sitting by the window when there was a scuffled sound outside her door the next morning. She was feeling much better: not half as shaky as she had felt the previous day. But she was unwillingly coming to accept Dr Newman's opinion that it would be days at least before she was well enough to drive back to London, and although she was impatient there was nothing she could do.

Now, hearing the curious sound of rustling paper, she got up from her chair and walked, albeit a little unsteadily, across to the door and pulled it open.

Rosemary practically tumbled into the room. She had evidently been crouching down, probably looking through the keyhole, Rachel thought resignedly, and when she'd opened the door the little girl had lost her balance.

'We must stop meeting like this,' she remarked drily, as the child picked herself up off the floor and stuffed the bag of sweets she was holding into her jeans pocket. 'Did you want something?'

Rosemary's cheeks were pink, and for once she looked almost attractive. It was mostly her sallow complexion that gave her face such an unhealthy appearance, but now, with colour in her cheeks and her hair neatly combed into a tight braid, she appeared quite pretty.

'I came to see how you were,' she answered now, as Rachel made her way back to her chair. Rosemary watched her sink rather weakly on to the cushions, and then gave a rueful grimace. 'I s'pose it was my fault again that you cut your head on the rocks. I came to say I'm sorry. I'm sorry you got hurt.'

'Yes. So am I,' murmured Rachel, leaning her head back against the pillows behind her, and feeling ridiculously weary after her brief exertion. 'But don't worry, it wasn't your fault. Not really. I just—stumbled, that's all. It could have happened to anyone.'

Rosemary hesitated a moment, biting her lip, and then she turned and closed the door. 'Daddy was ever so worried about you,' she confided, leaving the door to approach the woman. 'I think he thought he had *killed* you,' she added dramatically. 'You were just lying there on the sand, not moving. And then I saw the blood, and he just flaked!'

'Flaked?' echoed Rachel wearily, half wishing the child would go so that she could close her eyes. But, having come to a dubious understanding with the little girl, she had no desire to resurrect her hostility. All Rosemary really needed was attention, and she wondered how long it was since either of her parents had given her any.

'You know,' Rosemary was saying now. 'He kind of— went all to pieces. Grandmama says it was because of the shock, but I think it was something else.'

'Do you?' Rachel sighed and met the little girl's gaze with wary eyes. There were times when Rosemary could be unnervingly perceptive, and she was half afraid of what she was about to reveal.

'Yes.' Rosemary paused, pulling the bag of sweets out of her pocket again, and offering one to Rachel. When she refused, Rosemary took a toffee for herself, and unwrapped it with the air of someone about to impart a state secret. 'I think my father was so upset because he likes you—'

'*Likes* me?'

'Yes. Oh, I know he seemed angry—'

'He didn't *seem* angry, Rosemary, he *was* angry,' Rachel informed her flatly. And then, after a moment, 'Mostly because you hadn't told anyone where you were going.'

'Oh, *that*!'

Rosemary was disparaging, but Rachel lifted her head.

'Yes, that,' she agreed, regarding the little girl reprovingly. 'You know that was naughty, don't you?'

'Well, no one's cared where I was before,' retorted the child, scuffing her shoe against the carpet. ''Cept Grandmama, sometimes.'

'Oh, Rosemary, that's not true!'

'It *is* true.' The little girl was adamant. 'Ask anyone. Mrs Moffat says I'm just allowed to run wild.'

And that was so adult a statement that Rachel had to believe she had heard it. Trying to ignore her own feelings, she said consolingly, 'Mrs Moffat was probably talking about—well, while your mother was ill. Obviously, she couldn't look after you then, and your father was very upset—'

'No.'

Rosemary pushed her hands into her pockets, and looked down at her feet, and Rachel sighed. 'No, what?' she prompted gently. 'No, Mummy couldn't look after you—?'

'No, she never looked after me,' mumbled Rosemary bitterly. 'She was always too busy to talk to me, and Daddy is never here.'

Rachel gasped. 'I'm sure you're wrong. About your mummy not caring about you, I mean. And—and your father is a busy man.'

Rosemary looked unconvinced. 'Anyway, Miss Seton took care of me,' she said. 'Until Daddy got rid of her and hired Agnetha.'

'Miss Seton?'

'She was nice.' The child's face relaxed, transforming her pale features. The resemblance to Matthew had never been more marked, and Rachel's stomach muscles tightened. 'I wanted her to stay, but Daddy said she was too old, and that I was too old to need a nursemaid.'

'I see.' The identity of Miss Seton resolved, Rachel breathed a little more easily.

'Anyway, I don't need anyone to look after me,' Rosemary asserted suddenly. 'I can look after myself. Better than you can, it seems to me. Why didn't you tell Daddy why you were chasing me?'

'Oh…' That was not so easy to answer, and Rachel lay back against her pillows rather tiredly. 'Let's say it's our secret,' she murmured. Then, 'Does he know you buy cigarettes at the village shop?'

'No.' Rosemary hunched her shoulders. 'But he knows about the cigarettes. Agnetha told him.'

'Agnetha?'

Rosemary nodded. 'She found them in my bedroom and split on me,' she answered sulkily. 'Daddy was furious. He says he's going to send me away to school because I'm so disobedient. I bet he used to smoke when he was my age. And I bet Grandpa didn't punish him!'

'I wouldn't be too sure about that, if I were you,' Rachel was saying rather drily when the bedroom door abruptly opened to admit the small yet imposing figure of Lady Olivia.

Rachel offered an inward groan at this unwelcome intrusion, and Rosemary adopted a defiant stance, as if this was the last place she was supposed to be. It probably was, acknowledged Rachel wearily. Matthew did not approve of her associating with his daughter, and she didn't suppose his mother did either.

'So this is where you are, Rosemary,' her grandmother observed now, her sharp eyes briefly shifting to Rachel's drawn features before returning to the child. 'I thought your father warned you about disobeying him again. Run along, at once. Agnetha is waiting. And no slipping out to the stables. Mr Ryan has orders not to let you near Marigold for at least a week.'

'Yes, Grandmama.'

Rosemary had little alternative but to submit, and, looking at Lady Olivia's grim features, Rachel couldn't help thinking she would have done the same. She hoped the old lady hadn't come here to cause trouble. Just at this moment, she didn't have the strength to defend herself.

Offering the child a rueful smile as she let herself out of the door, Rachel made a determined effort to gather her resources. She and Lady Olivia had had many confrontations in the past, but never had she felt less equipped to deal with another. The old lady mustn't guess that, though. She already possessed an overwhelming advantage.

'Well, Rachel,' she said now, as the door closed behind Rosemary. Slim and elegant in her simple but expensive grey dress, her almost white hair coiled into a knot on top of her head, Matthew's mother seated herself on the ottoman, crossing her ankles in true aristocratic fashion. 'Dr Newman tells me you're feeling a little better this morning.'

'Yes, I am.' Rachel's fingers curled defensively over her wrist. 'I'm sorry I'm being such a nuisance.'

'Hardly that.' Lady Olivia's inbred sense of courtesy did not allow for rudeness. And it would have been rude to imply that Rachel had chosen to be brought here. After all, she had been unconscious when Matthew had carried her into the house. 'However, you must admit this is an unusual situation.'

'Yes.' Rachel took a steadying breath. 'Well, you can be sure that as soon as I'm able to leave, I will.'

Lady Olivia made no answer to this, merely linked her somewhat gnarled hands together in her lap and allowed a pregnant silence. Then, apparently having some trouble marshalling her words, she remarked unexpectedly, 'You appear to have made a hit with Rosemary.'

'I wouldn't say that.' Rachel swallowed.

'I would.' Lady Olivia's eyes, so like Matthew's, speared her with a raking glance. 'She's not usually friendly with strangers.'

'No.' Rachel wondered how she was supposed to respond to that. 'Well, I suppose we have a lot in common.'

'You think so?' Lady Olivia frowned. 'I don't see the connection.'

*No, you wouldn't,* thought Rachel tersely, quelling the

urge to involve herself in Rosemary's affairs. 'My mother died when I was very young, too,' she compromised.

'Ah, yes.' The old lady inclined her head. 'But your circumstances were slightly different. And Barbara had been ill for quite some time.'

Now it was Rachel's turn to accept her words without answering. She was half afraid she might say something she would regret, and Matthew's mother was a past mistress at inducing the unwary comment.

'So—what were you and Rosemary talking about?' she asked at last, when it became evident that Rachel was not about to enlighten her uninvited. 'Forgive me, but I couldn't help overhearing you say that you wouldn't be too sure about something. What was that? Was she asking your advice?'

Rachel was tempted to tell her to mind her own business, but she didn't. All the same, only Matthew's mother would have dared to ask such a question, and Rachel could feel her hackles rising with well-remembered indignation. Only the suspicion that any prevarication on her part might bring some further punishment down on Rosemary's head forced her to bite her tongue.

'She's—concerned that her father may decide to send her away to boarding-school,' she replied, after a moment, and Lady Olivia frowned.

'But you don't think he will?' she queried tersely, and Rachel realised why she should interpret her remarks in that way.

'I really don't know what Matt's intentions are towards her,' she responded carefully. 'But I think he should be careful. She seems a very distrustful child.'

Lady Olivia sat up straighter. 'You think so, do you?'

Rachel's hesitation was barely perceptible. 'Yes.'

'And what would you know about it?' enquired the old lady sharply, and Rachel realised she had gone that little bit too far in expressing her opinion. 'It's not as if you know anything about children,' she added, her lined features taut with indignation. 'Are you suggesting I should trust your assessment of Rosemary's needs above that of my son?'

'No. No, of course not.' Rachel sighed now. 'It's just that—well, I got the impression that she feels—' She broke off at that point. She had been going to say 'neglected', but after Lady Olivia's reaction to her earlier words she stifled the criticism. Once again, she was compelled to remind herself that Rosemary's problems had nothing to do with her. Just because she felt some sympathy for the child, there was no reason to provoke Matthew's mother's antagonism towards herself.

'I hardly see how peddling claptrap to the masses equips you in child psychology,' the old lady declared bluntly. 'Why is it that women who consider child-bearing an outdated vocation nevertheless feel themselves capable of deciding what's best for other people's offspring?'

'I never said that.'

'But you do have doubts about the suitability of Rosemary's upbringing!'

'I—suspect—she may have had a raw deal, yes.' Rachel couldn't prevent the involuntary admission.

'A raw deal?' Lady Olivia's lip curled. 'But not half such a raw deal as you dealt her father, hmm? How dare you impugn his intentions when your own behaviour leaves so much to be desired?'

Rachel offered an inward groan. Getting into this kind of a confrontation with Matthew's mother had been something she had hoped to avoid. And in her present state of uncertainty she was definitely not equipped to deal with it.

'Forget what I said,' she murmured, wishing Nurse Douglas would appear to rescue her. 'As you say, it's nothing to do with me. How Matt chooses to educate his daughter is obviously not my concern.'

'No, it's not.' But Lady Olivia was not prepared to leave it there. Rachel suspected she had played right into the old lady's hands by offering an opinion, and resentments long since buried were rearing their ugly heads. 'It's ironic, don't you think, that the woman who refused to have my son's child should now be offering him advice?'

'I didn't—' The unwary words were almost spoken, and Rachel felt the hot colour rise into her cheeks.

'You didn't—what?' Matthew's mother was quick to note her heightened colour. 'You didn't offer him advice?' She paused. 'Or you didn't refuse to give him a child?' Her lips twisted. 'Oh, come now, Rachel, you can't expect anyone to believe that!'

'I don't care what you believe.' Rachel closed her eyes. 'Would you ask Nurse Douglas to come in, please? I'd like to get back into bed.'

Her aunt and uncle came to see her during the afternoon. By then, Rachel had had another nap and was feeling more ready to face a second wave of criticism. But in the event Matthew accompanied his in-laws into the room, and, evidently much to Aunt Maggie's chagrin, he stayed.

In consequence, the conversation was much less vindictive than it might have been. Even so, her aunt couldn't resist voicing a little of her resentment that Rachel should be usurping Matthew's hospitality.

'You have a perfectly good room at the vicarage, Rachel,' she declared, with barely suppressed irritation. 'There is no earthly need for you to impose yourself on—on—well, on the Conroys.'

'Ah, yes, but I wouldn't dream of putting you to such trouble,' Matthew essayed, before Rachel could answer. 'I know how much your husband depends upon you, and it wouldn't be fair to expect you to care for an invalid on top of everything else.'

'I—well…' Aunt Maggie was apparently lost for words. 'That may be so, but—'

'Matt does have a point, dear,' Geoffrey Barnes intoned, drawing a distinctly malevolent glare from his wife which, fortunately, only Rachel intercepted. 'It's very kind of you,

Matt. Very kind indeed. Maggie does too much; I'm always telling her that.'

'Geoff—'

'I hope I won't have to impose on anybody for much longer,' Rachel interposed quickly, feeling uncomfortably like the skeleton at the feast. 'Perhaps another couple of days—'

'We'll let the doctor decide that,' declared Matthew, his words successfully circumventing any alternative suggestion, and Rachel wondered why he was taking it upon himself to defend her. For he must know, as well as anyone, how her aunt must be feeling.

'I think that's the most sensible course,' her uncle approved, seemingly unaware of his wife's indignation. 'It's reassuring to know you're in good hands, my dear.'

'And you don't think the fact that Barbara has just died makes the situation just the the tiniest bit questionable?' persisted Aunt Maggie tensely. 'I mean—everyone knows who Rachel is—*was*!'

'Aunt Maggie—'

'I don't believe what anyone else thinks is of any consequence,' responded Matthew smoothly. 'And now, I think, we should allow Rachel to rest. That is what the doctor recommends, and I know you are as anxious as I am to see her restored to full health.'

It was tactically unassailable, and Rachel guessed that her aunt was wishing she had chosen some other method of making her point. But, in the circumstances, she was obliged to concede defeat, and Rachel breathed a sigh of relief as the door closed behind them. So much anger, so much bitterness, she thought wearily. Did no one feel any sympathy for her? After all, she wasn't the one who had been unfaithful.

She had insisted on getting up again to receive her visitors, but now she looked reluctantly towards the bed. Strong emotions were such a drain on her resources, and not one of her callers seemed to care about the fact. Even Rosemary had been an innocent source of turmoil. Why had she had to tell her that her father had been concerned about her, for heaven's sake? What could he possibly have said to make the little girl think he liked her? It was all too obscure and unbelievable, after the way he had behaved at the funeral. And she was too tired to make any sense of it anyway.

# CHAPTER TEN

RACHEL felt strong enough to put her clothes on the next day. It was amazing how much better she felt after a decent night's sleep, and her anxieties of the previous day seemed less of a problem this morning.

Dr Newman made his regular call as she was finishing her breakfast, sitting at the small table in the window embrasure, overlooking the lawned garden and the lake beyond. After examining her head, he pronounced himself satisfied with the progress she was making.

'The cut is healing nicely,' he said, accepting her offer of a cup of coffee, and seating himself opposite her at the linen-covered table. 'And you are definitely looking brighter. If this goes on, I may consider revising my estimate of two weeks, and say you might be able to return to work in ten days.'

'Ten days?' Rachel shook her head, remembering she had still to get in touch with Justin. She was not looking forward to making that phone call. After the way he had reacted when she'd asked for these four days, she had no illusions but that he would be furious, particularly when he found out where she was staying. Forcing a smile, she asked lightly, 'Is that your best offer?'

'I'm afraid so. And it's only a provisional prognosis.' The doctor regarded her curiously. 'You're very anxious to leave here, aren't you?'

Rachel looked down into the cup of coffee she was holding to avoid his shrewd gaze. 'I do have a job to do,' she reminded him evenly. 'And I presume you'll have no objections if I return to London in a couple of days.'

'If all goes well.' Dr Newman was evidently not prepared

to make any reckless pronouncements. 'Shall we say I'll consider the possibility towards the end of the week? Until then, I'm afraid, you'll have to accept your host's hospitality.'

'But you don't think there will be any complications?' she ventured.

'No.' The doctor inclined his head agreeably. 'But that doesn't mean there won't be any, so don't build your hopes too high. However, you can go outside, if you feel up to it. As long as you wrap up warmly, and don't do anything too energetic.'

Rachel gave him a guarded look. 'All right.'

'Good.' He finished his coffee and rose smoothly to his feet. 'And now, I'm afraid I must take my leave of you. Regrettably, Sundays are much like any other day in my profession.'

Rachel nodded. 'Thank you for coming.'

'It was my pleasure.' He gave her a rueful smile as he walked towards the door. 'Not all my patients are half so agreeable, believe me.'

His compliment compensated a little for the disappointment she had felt when he'd refused to be more specific about her leaving, and she was still considering what he had said when Nurse Douglas reappeared. She had left the room while Dr Newman had coffee with his patient, but now she came back to remove the breakfast dishes.

'By the way,' she said, tutting at the fact that Rachel had only eaten one slice of toast, 'Mr Conroy wants to see you. Shall I send him in?'

Rachel caught her breath. 'He's outside?'

'Not precisely, no.' Nurse Douglas looked a little disconcerted. 'He—I—we were talking downstairs, while you were with Dr Newman. Shall I ask him to come up?'

'Why not?' Rachel was surprised he had asked. Or perhaps it had just been an excuse to talk to Nurse Douglas, she reflected, bitter that she should even care. And, judging by the young nurse's attitude towards him, no real excuse was needed.

He came into the room, bringing a distinct smell of outdoors with him. In tight-fitting moleskin trousers, which were in turn pushed into knee-length boots, and a black leather jacket, he had evidently been riding, and she envied him his ability to appear indifferent to his responsibilities.

However, he seemed surprised to see that she was dressed, and she was ridiculously pleased that she had chosen to put on jeans and a loose cream thigh-length sweater. She had put the casual clothes into her case at the last minute, she remembered, and she wondered if she had had some premonition that she might need them. After all, she had not intended to spend more than one night at Rothside, whereas...

'You're looking much better,' he observed, after a pregnant pause, and she wondered if he was anticipating her departure as much as she was. 'How do you feel?'

'Much—better,' she conceded tersely, linking her hands together in her lap to prevent the automatic urge to touch the dressing that had replaced the bandage only that morning. 'Dr Newman says I should be able to leave in a couple of days.'

Matthew's mouth thinned. 'I understood Newman to say that he was going to review your condition towards the end of the week,' he declared. 'You must have misunderstood him.'

'Or you did,' Rachel flared unsteadily, refusing to be intimidated. 'Um—Nurse Douglas said you wanted to speak to me. Was there a reason, or was that just an excuse to browbeat me?'

'Browbeat you?' Matthew stared at her disbelievingly. 'How have I browbeaten you? All I've done is ask how you're feeling. I'm sorry. I didn't realise that constituted a threat!'

Rachel sighed, feeling a little silly now, and not liking it a bit. After all, he had provided her with the best of medical care, and it wasn't his fault that she was taking so long to recover.

'Look,' she said, forcing herself to look at him, even though she would have preferred to look anywhere than into his lean, taut face, 'I know how—intolerable—this situation is—'

'Intolerable to whom?'

Rachel caught her lower lip between her teeth. 'Well— to your mother for one,' she said unwillingly. 'And—Aunt Maggie—'

'Ah, yes. Aunt Maggie.' Matthew hooked the chair that Dr Newman had occupied earlier towards him, and, swinging it round, he set it in front of her. Then, straddling the seat so that his knee was barely inches from hers, he regarded her with a cynical gaze. 'You know, I might have expected some thanks for diverting your aunt, instead of being accused of God knows what ulterior motives!'

Rachel shifted uncomfortably. Now that he was on eye-level terms with her, it was far more difficult to maintain a composed expression, and when she did look away from his dark face she was made overwhelmingly aware of his powerful body, taut beneath the skin-tight trousers and sweat-shirt. His jacket had parted to reveal the leather belt that spanned his waist, and she could smell the heat that emanated from him, and the unforgettable scent of his skin...

'Anyway,' he was saying now, and she dragged her senses back from the brink of disaster, 'I didn't come to argue over Newman's diagnosis, and I knew better than to expect your gratitude for anything I might do. No. I came to tell you I've spoken to your editor in London, and he quite understands that you can't possibly return to work for another two weeks—'

'You've done what?' Rachel hardly let him finish, before jumping up from her seat and staring down at him with disbelieving eyes. 'You've spoken to Justin?'

'If that's Harcourt's name, I suppose so,' conceded Matthew drily, his lips tightening at her evident indignation.

'Look, calm down, will you? Someone had to tell him you wouldn't be back tomorrow, and how was I to know you'd be well enough to speak to him your—'

'How dare you?' Rachel was incensed. 'How dare you speak to Justin behind my back?'

'It wasn't behind your back,' said Matthew bleakly, his fingers tightening where they rested along the back of the chair. 'That's why I'm here, isn't it? To tell you that I've spoken to him.'

'You couldn't wait, could you?' Rachel was beside herself, although why she resented his interference so much, she couldn't quite have explained. Except that she had kept her life in London totally apart from Rothmere, and all it meant to her. 'You had to get involved in something that's nothing to do with you! I would have explained to Justin exactly what had happened. I would have told him where I was staying, and when I would be back.'

Matthew's face hardened, and, getting to his feet, he thrust the chair aside. 'And don't you think I was capable of doing the same?' he demanded, his tone reminding her that he had a temper, too. 'What's the matter? Is this— Justin—the new man in your life? Are you afraid I may have blown it by telling him you were with me?'

'I'm not *with* you,' Rachel retorted, frustrated by his ability to always take the upper hand. 'At least, not through choice. And my relationship with Justin is my affair, not yours. Just stay out of my life, Matt. I don't need you any more.'

'If you ever did,' muttered Matthew harshly, his eyes glittering like grey chips of granite. 'Except as a means of getting into television, of course. I mustn't forget that, must I?'

'You—bastard!'

Rachel, who had turned away from his hard, accusing face, swung back abruptly. Her balled fists itching to wipe the sarcastic expression from his narrow features, she overlooked the fact that there was a chair between them. Her knee struck the wood painfully, knocking it aside, and, instead of launching in at him with flailing fists, she stumbled and lost her balance, so that only his presence of mind and the swift support of his hands saved her from repeating the accident which had put her in this position. Strong fingers around her wrists stopped her from tumbling to the floor, but the force of her propulsion sent her thudding against his chest.

For a moment, she was too stunned by what had happened to move. Her face was pressed against the fleecy softness of his shirt, and his raw masculinity enveloped her with a strength that was far more than just physical. Then, as his arms closed around her, she was made aware of the whole length of his taut body, his thighs muscled and powerful, his hard flanks supporting her distinctly shaky legs.

'God, I thought you were going to crack your skull again,' he muttered roughly, his head bent so that his breath stirred the hairs at the side of her neck. 'Are you all right? Hell, I didn't mean to upset you.' The warm draught was like a caress. 'You shouldn't make me so mad. All I did was make a phone call!'

Rachel was trembling, and she couldn't stop it. But it wasn't just the shock that had robbed her of her control. It was Matthew, only Matthew, she knew perversely. Being held in his arms like this was both a heaven and a hell, and, no matter how she fought it, she couldn't deny her own response.

But, as if mistaking her involuntary submission, Matthew was already propelling her away from him. Holding her at arm's length, he forced her to look at him, and Rachel closed her eyes against the penetrating fire of his.

'Rachel,' he muttered, shaking her a little as she continued to evade his searching gaze. 'For God's sake, what's the matter? Do you feel sick? Faint? What?'

'I'm—all right,' she got out at last, endeavouring to free herself from his hands. Forced to open her eyes, she looked anywhere but into his face. 'It—it was just the shock, that's all. And—and I banged my knee.'

'You did? Where?' Releasing her, he dropped down on to his haunches in front of her, and to her dismay she felt his hands peeling up the leg of her jeans to expose the purpling skin. 'Hell,' he swore grimly, his fingers unbearably gentle as they probed the quivering bones, 'why do you persist in making me feel such a brute?' He tilted his head back to look up at her, and her heart palpitated at the look of naked frustration in his eyes. 'I thought I was doing you a favour, can you believe that? Instead, I've only made you hate me even more than you already did!'

'I—don't—hate you.' She could say that with all certainty. She wished to God she did. It would have been so much less painful. 'Honestly,' she added unsteadily, bending to roll down the leg of her jeans, and in so doing bringing her face within inches of Matthew's.

Afterwards, she realised that he had recognised the danger at the same moment she did. They both straightened together, and she thought his expression mirrored her own sudden sense of anguish, though there was no trace of it in his abrupt withdrawal.

'I'd better go,' he said, and his voice was almost formally detached. He picked up the chair which had caused the trouble, and deposited it back beside the table. 'Unfortunately, I can't do anything about the phone call, but there's nothing stopping you from ringing him again and putting him straight. I'll have Nurse Douglas fetch you the cordless phone—'

'Don't bother.' Rachel broke in before he had finished what he had to say. 'I—I'll speak to him later. When—when I know when I'm leaving.'

'As you wish.' Matthew made a gesture of indifference, and walked towards the door. 'I'll leave you now. If you want anything—anything at all—just ask Nurse Douglas.'

'Thank you.'

Rachel watched him let himself out of the door, and after it had closed behind him a feeling of total devastation gripped her. In the last few minutes she had run the gamut of her emotions, and she was left with the unpleasant realisation that only the strongest of these survived. And, in her case, it wasn't the contempt she had believed she would feel when she saw her ex-husband again…

Matthew reined in his mount on the lower slopes of Rothdale Pike. Running soothing hands over Saracen's neck, he surveyed the whole length of the lake, with the roofs of Rothside like stepping-stones below him. In spite of the early hour, there were already one or two white sails dotting the wide expanse of water, with a couple of windsurfers nearer at hand, riding the gentle waves.

'I don't think Marigold's very fit, Daddy!' exclaimed Rosemary, panting a little as she dug her heels into the pony's sides to urge her up the track to join her father.

'I think she's just short of exercise,' responded Matthew drily, reaching over to grasp the pony's bridle and pull her nearer. 'And remember, it could have been several more days before she got some air. I believe you were supposed to be grounded for a week.'

'Oh, it was Grandmama who said that—'

'*I* said it, too,' amended her father warningly. 'Which reminds me, you never did tell me where you got those cigarettes. Do you want to tell me now, or is it to remain a bone of contention between us?'

'Oh, Daddy!'

Rosemary sighed, and Matthew knew a moment's contrition. He hadn't meant to sound so severe, and he half wished he hadn't brought up the subject of the cigarettes—not this morning.

The decision to take his daughter riding had been a spur-of-the-moment thing. He wasn't at all sure why he had invited her to join him, except that it had something to do with what Rachel had said that morning he had caused her accident. And he *had* been the cause of it, he thought ruefully. Whatever she said, and however much he might justify to himself what had happened, the fact remained that if he had not lost his temper and pushed her she would not have fallen and injured her head.

Still, he had to admit that since that morning he had spent an awful lot of time considering what Rachel had said. He didn't want to admit it, but it was true—he did give little of his time to his daughter. Yet, while Barbara was alive, he had seldom felt a sense of guilt about it.

Perhaps if he had been able to feel that she really *was* his daughter he would have acted differently, he reflected now. Not that he had ever voiced his doubts to anyone else. Being accused of being incapable of siring a child was not something you discussed with anyone except your wife, particularly if she was the one who was making the accusation.

He shook his head. What a ruinous mess he had made of his life, he thought bitterly. How much different things might have been if he had done as his mother had wanted and married Cecily Bishop in the first place.

And yet, he and Rachel had been happy in those early days, before her career had become more important to her than he was. No one had been able to hurt them; they had been impregnable. But then the rows had begun, and his isolation had grown; and Barbara had seemed so sympathetic…

'What are you thinking about, Daddy?'

Rosemary's anxious voice dragged him back to the present, and the realisation that he had been indulging in maudlin retrospection. What did it matter now what had been said? Barbara was dead. Rosemary *was* his daughter. And, as Rachel had pointed out, she needed him if no one else did.

'Nothing,' he said now, forcing a tight smile to his lips. 'Come on, we'll ride down to the village, and get some ice-cream.

# CHAPTER ELEVEN

'SO, WHEN are you coming back?'

Justin's enquiry was pleasant enough, but Rachel sensed the controlled impatience behind the words. And why not? she asked herself unhappily. When she had come north, he had expected her to be away for only two days. Those two days had now stretched to a week, and she still could give him no real definition of when she would actually return.

'I'm sure you're managing to cope,' she ventured lightly, hoping to divert him, but Justin wasn't amused.

'Oh, we're managing to cope very well,' he replied nastily, clearing his throat. 'Perhaps you should be worrying about that. We may find we manage very well without you.'

Rachel sighed. 'It's not my fault that I'm stuck up here.'

'Well, it's certainly not mine,' retorted Justin. 'If you remember, I didn't want you to go in the first place. I knew something like this would happen. I knew Conroy would find some way to keep you there.'

'Oh, don't be ridiculous!' Rachel was impatient now. 'Matt isn't responsible for what happened. That is—well, he is, I suppose. If you want to be literal about it. But it was an accident! He didn't engineer it. Heavens, I could have fallen without anyone else being involved.'

'But Conroy was involved, wasn't he? However indirectly. And I have to tell you, I don't like his attitude. Were you too scared to ring and tell me what had happened? I'm telling you, he got a great deal of enjoyment out of giving me the news.'

'Oh, Justin.' Rachel's fingers tightened around the receiver. 'You know you're exaggerating. Matt only rang because he thought I wasn't up to it.' And when had she come to that conclusion? 'I intended phoning you myself. He beat me to it, that's all.'

'And have you stopped to ask yourself why?'

'I've told you why.' Rachel hated Justin in this mood. He could be so objectionable. She had seen him reduce some of the younger reporters and secretaries to tears at times, but it was a new experience for him to turn his bile on her. 'Anyway, I'm ringing you now, aren't I? What more can I do? You know I'll be back as quickly as I can.'

'Do I?' He didn't sound convinced. 'You still haven't told me when that's likely to be.'

'Because I don't know!' exclaimed Rachel in exasperation. 'But—well, I went outdoors yesterday for the first time, and the doctor thinks that in another week—'

Justin snorted. 'Another week?'

'That I should be well enough to drive back to town, at least.'

'But not to work?' The sarcasm was back, and Rachel shook her head.

'Not—immediately, perhaps. But in a couple of days—'

'So we can't expect you back in the office for at least another two weeks?'

'Well,' Rachel licked her dry lips, 'it's Tuesday today. Perhaps a week on Thursday, hmm?'

'What choice do I have?'

Justin sounded furious, and justifiably so, thought Rachel unwillingly. But there was no point in prevaricating. Unless she was prepared to override Dr Newman's advice and make her own arrangements, she was compelled to remain where she was.

'I'm sorry,' she murmured now, and she heard his angry intake of breath.

'So am I,' he conceded, without any sigh of compassion, and before she could say anything more he had slammed down his receiver.

Rachel was sliding the small aerial belonging to the cordless phone back into its socket when someone knocked at her door. Putting the phone down, she rose to her feet as the door was propelled inward, and then sank back into her seat when Rosemary's head appeared. 'Can I come in?'

'Can I stop you?' Rachel pushed the anxieties caused by her call to Justin aside, and smiled at the little girl. 'What do you want?' she asked, glancing towards the windows, where she could see the sun gleaming on the lake. 'Isn't it too nice a day to be indoors?'

'Not 'cording to Grandmama,' replied Rosemary, with a grimace, and Rachel frowned.

'Oh, but I thought—that is—Mrs Moffat said that your father took you riding the other morning.'

'Yes, he did. Yesterday,' Rosemary nodded. 'But—well, anyway, today he's gone off to Carlisle, and Grandmama says I have to do some reading.'

'Reading?' Rachel ran her tongue over her lower lip. 'But you do go to school, don't you?'

'In Rothside,' agreed Rosemary quickly. But then, with a grimace, she added, 'I don't know if I'll be going back, though. Daddy was awfully cross. And just when he was being nice, too.'

Rachel shook her head. 'Matt—I mean, your daddy was cross about you going to school?' She was confused.

'No!' Rosemary hunched her small shoulders. 'About the cigarettes. He found out, you see. Mrs Reed told him.'

'She did?' Rachel was surprised.

'Well, not on purpose!' exclaimed Rosemary impatiently, realising what she had said. 'It was yesterday, you see. Daddy suggested we should ride down to the village, and get some ice-cream.'

'When you were out riding?' Rachel probed, and the little girl expelled her breath in a noisy assent.

'How was I to know she would think he'd come to complain?' she asked frustratedly. 'I mean, Daddy never—ever—goes into the village stores. Mrs Moffat gets everything we want delivered.'

'I see.' Rachel was beginning to understand. 'And Mrs Reed spilled the beans, hmm?'

'Mmm.' Rosemary groaned. 'I s'pose it was me being with him, and Daddy asking her how Mr Reed was keeping. Mr Reed has bronc—broncy—a bad cough, and Daddy said he hoped he'd stopped smoking, because cigarettes make coughs worse.'

'And Mrs Reed thought he knew she had been supplying you with cigarettes.'

'I think so. Anyway, she got all flustered, and said she worried a lot about giving cigarettes to children, but that as he was such a good customer she didn't like to refuse.'

'The old—' Rachel had been about to say 'devil', but she managed to bite her tongue. 'So, what happened?'

Rosemary pulled a face. 'Well—Daddy was ever so polite. He didn't tell her he knew nothing about it, like I thought he would. He said he wouldn't send me to the shop for cigarettes ever again, and that he knew he could trust Mrs Reed not to say anything, because she might lose her licence if she did.'

'Neat.' Rachel couldn't prevent the wry smile that touched her lips at the little girl's words. So, Matthew had defended his daughter at last. And spiked Mrs Reed's guns into the bargain.

'That was then,' added Rosemary gloomily. 'But when we got home he was really angry. He said he had been having second thoughts about sending me to boarding-school—you know, like I told you before—but that if I was prepared to *steal* to defy him, perhaps he ought to think again.' She sniffed. 'I wasn't stealing really, was I? Mrs Reed knew what I was doing.'

Rachel hesitated. 'Yes. But you were asking her to put them on your father's account. He was paying for them, wasn't he? Not you.'

'Well, he buys me sweets and Colas all the time.'

'That's different, and you know it.'

Rosemary looked sulky. 'I thought you were my friend.'

'I am your friend. At least, I hope I am. But you have to admit, you were spending money that wasn't yours.'

Rosemary shrugged. 'Oh, well, it doesn't matter now,' she muttered moodily. 'He's hardly likely to give me a second chance.'

'I wouldn't say that.' Rachel regarded her gently. 'And don't say he, say Daddy. You're not going to get anywhere if you revert to being insolent.'

'What do you know about it?' Rosemary gave her a brooding look. 'You'll be leaving soon. Grandmama says so. She says that when you get back to London you'll soon forget all about me.'

'No, I won't.' Rachel knew a moment's irritation at the old lady who, deliberately or otherwise, was helping to give Rosemary such a complex. 'And don't expect the worst of everybody. Your father's had a difficult time, coping—coping with the funeral and everything. Maybe if you tried to understand his position, he'd find it easier to understand yours.'

'Do you think so?' Rosemary's face mirrored her uncertainty. 'He used to like me. At least, I thought he did. When I was little he used to play with me a lot. He even taught me to ride. But for ages now he's always been too busy when I've asked him to go riding with me, and he never takes me to see Auntie Helen and Uncle Gerry like he used to do before.'

'Helen and Gerald,' echoed Rachel softly, remembering Matthew's sister and her husband with some affection. They had not exactly been close friends when she was married to Matthew, but at least they hadn't turned against her when the marriage fell apart.

'Do you know them?' asked Rosemary at once, and Rachel instantly regretted her involuntary admission.

'I—used to,' she conceded, unwilling to explain exactly how she knew them. 'Um—you know, it's such a lovely morning, I think I might go for a walk. Do you want to come with me?'

Rosemary's small face brightened, and then grew doubt-ful again. 'Well—I'm supposed to stay indoors today,' she admitted slowly. 'Daddy said—'

'I would welcome your company,' put in Rachel tempt-ingly, deciding that, no matter what Matthew thought, as long as she was here at Rothmere she would do what she could to make Rosemary's life a little more exciting. It didn't sound as if she had any fun in the normal course of events, and while Barbara's illness must have accounted for part of the problem it was by no means the whole solution. Something had gone wrong here, something more than the trauma created when one member of a family develops a terminal disease. Not that Rachel expected to find out ex-actly what that problem was, that wasn't her concern. But if by befriending the child she could help her and her father to understand one another better, then surely it was worth the effort?

'Well…' Rosemary was faltering. 'Perhaps if you *need* somebody to come with you…'

'Oh, I do.' Rachel smiled. 'How about if you show me your pony, hmm? The walk to and from the stables should be just about right.'

It was a good morning, and Rachel, just as much as Rosemary, enjoyed the outing. Meeting Jim Ryan again was quite an experience, and if the old Irishman thought it was odd that she and the child who had caused the break-up of her marriage should seem such good friends, he kept his opinion to himself. Instead, he expressed his pleasure at see-ing her again, and asked how she was feeling after suffering such an accident.

'Sure, and you won't be wanting Jessica saddled this morning, will you?' he added ruefully. 'Not that she's used much these days anyway. But Mr Matt wouldn't have me get rid of her. You know, I think he's got some affection for the beast.'

Of course, Rosemary was curious to know when Rachel had ridden the old chestnut mare, but she managed to divert the girl by asking to see the other horses in the stables. Particularly the black stallion Matthew had been riding the afternoon they had met on Rothdale Pike. That proud animal, which Rosemary told her was named Saracen, snorted a little nervously when they approached his stall, and Jim Ryan was on hand to advise caution.

'Ah, but he's a fine creature, so he is,' Ryan nodded, dodging the stallion's nodding head. 'But I think he has an aversion to the ladies. Now, watch out, Rosie, his teeth are sharp.'

They walked back to the house in time for lunch, and to Rachel's relief—and Rosemary's too, no doubt—they didn't meet anyone on the way.

'We'll have to do this again,' Rachel said lightly, as they parted at the foot of the stairs, and the little girl nodded eagerly.

'Tomorrow?' she suggested, and Rachel made a gesture of assent.

'Why not?' she agreed, starting up the stairs towards her room. 'Come and see me after breakfast. That is, if your father has no objections.'

Rosemary's expression was eloquent of her feelings, and Rachel guessed they were both thinking the same thing. No one could be sure what Matthew's reaction might be, and if Lady Olivia found out Rachel had no doubt that she would object, very strongly.

The next morning, Dr Newman told her he was dismissing Nurse Douglas. 'Not that I want you to infer from this that I consider you completely recovered,' he added swiftly. 'But, in the circumstances, I don't believe her presence is warranted, particularly as Mr Conroy's staff are more than capable of providing the necessary care.'

'I see.' Rachel's tongue circled her upper lip. 'But—couldn't I return to the vicarage, then?'

'I wouldn't advise it.' The doctor was concerned. 'My dear Mrs Conroy, my reasons for letting Nurse Douglas go are as I have stated: because you are being adequately cared for here. I can hardly endorse your returning to your uncle's home, when by his own admission his wife has more than enough to do already.'

Rachel hesitated, wondering who had told him that. She could guess, but what she couldn't understand was why Matthew seemed to be compelling her to stay. Even so, she couldn't deny it was something of a relief not to have to face the prospect of meeting Aunt Maggie's recriminations until she felt stronger.

Meanwhile, her friendship with Rosemary blossomed. In spite of the fact that Matthew, and his mother, were unaware of the relationship, Rachel couldn't find it in her heart to send the little girl away. Besides, she consoled her conscience, they were doing no harm. And if her company made this transitionary period easier for the child, surely no one should complain?

In consequence, she became accustomed to Rosemary's appearing in her room every morning, ready and willing to escort her new-found friend on expeditions about the estate. She didn't know what Rosemary told Agnetha, or where the au pair thought she was. But for Rachel herself they were voyages of rediscovery, as she became reacquainted with the memories of her past.

Of course, there was a bittersweet quality to her memories, and it wasn't always easy to dissociate them from the feelings she had shared with Matthew. But she knew she might never have another chance to explore the sometimes painfully familiar woods and gardens of Rothmere, and she drank in the sights and sounds she saw like a prisoner who was soon to be cut off from them forever.

The weather had continued to be warm and dry, as if making its own contribution to her recovery, and she and Rosemary spent a lot of time down at the lake. Rachel half wished they could take one of the small dinghies they found in the boat-house out on to the water, but it was years since she had sailed with Matthew, and she dared not take that responsibility.

However, it was appropriate that when Matthew found them it should be down at the jetty. They were sitting on the wooden boards, legs dangling over the water, trailing a line that Jim Ryan had given them in the hope that they might catch something. Not that it was likely, of course, and they had already agreed that if they did by some miracle catch a fish they would throw it back, but it was sufficiently absorbing an occupation for them not to be aware of anyone's approach until they felt the vibration of his footsteps on the planks.

'Um—Daddy!' exclaimed Rosemary in some alarm, scrambling to her feet with alacrity. 'What are you doing here? Grandmama said—'

She broke off at that point, belatedly realising how incriminating her words had been, and Rachel sighed. Until that moment she had remained where she was, refusing to allow Matthew's appearance to panic her into a display of the trepidation she was feeling, but now she felt obliged to get to her feet. It was her fault that Rosemary was here, and she was the one to be blamed.

'And what did Grandmama say?' Matthew was asking now, his lean frame propped against the wall of the boat-house, and Rachel's prepared response faltered in the face of the indulgence of his tone. He didn't look angry, she thought doubtfully, and he didn't sound angry. But could she trust his expression after the way he had behaved before?

'I—well—she said you had an—an appointment in—in town,' Rosemary stammered in reply. 'I—I have been doing some reading, honestly. Only—only Rachel needed some company, and—and I offered to show her around.'

'I see.'

Matthew's arms were folded, and he inclined his head, as if considering her explanation. He was dressed more formally today, Rachel noticed unwillingly. His dark blue suit of fine wool accentuated the width of his broad shoulders, and the narrow trousers enhanced his height and the muscled length of his legs. He looked as if he was indeed equipped for a business meeting in the city, and she wondered what had brought him here, so far off his usual route.

'I should say that what Rosemary says is true,' Rachel offered now, as the pregnant silence stretched. 'She—I—we have spent some time together. I'm sorry, if you don't approve, but I have been grateful for her company.'

'Did I say I didn't approve?' Matthew countered, lifting his head and looking at her with cool, appraising eyes.

'No, but…' Rachel thrust her hands into the back pockets of her jeans to hide their trembling uncertainty. 'I can't imagine any other reason why you might have come looking for us. Did—did Mr Ryan tell you where we were?'

Matthew regarded her steadily for a moment, and then he straightened and pushed his own hands into the pockets of his jacket. 'I didn't need anyone to tell me where you were,' he replied, turning his attention to the water. 'I've known what was going on for several days—'

'You have?' Rosemary interrupted them, her eyes wide. 'Did Grandmama—'

'As far as I know, your grandmother still thinks you spend every morning reading with Agnetha,' retorted Matthew flatly. 'But if you think *she* was prepared to take the responsibility for your absence, you're very much mistaken.'

Rosemary's jaw dropped. 'Agnetha told you?'

'Who else?'

'The mean thing—'

'It *is* her job,' replied Matthew reprovingly. 'Look, don't blame Agnetha. I didn't stop you, did I? You're still here.'

Rachel moistened her dry lips. 'Does that mean you have no objections to Rosemary and I spending time together, then?' she asked evenly. 'You must appreciate this is quite a surprise, after—after—'

'After the way I behaved before, I know.' Matthew's mouth thinned. 'But I had plenty of time to regret my actions, didn't I? And, contrary to popular belief, I don't get any pleasure out of hur'ing people.'

Their eyes met, and held, and this time it was Rachel who looked away. 'Well,' she said evenly, 'that's all right, then, isn't it?' She gave the little girl an encouraging look. 'Because we've become good friends, haven't we?'

Rosemary smiled. 'Yes. Yes, that's right, Daddy,' she agreed eagerly, obviously relieved at this unexpected turn of events. 'So you won't tell Grandmama, will you? I mean, she doesn't like Rachel, and she'd never understand.'

Matthew turned to his daughter. 'Did she say that? Grandmama, I mean. That she didn't like Rachel?' His eyes were intent.

'Well...' Rosemary looked a little uneasy now. 'Maybe not, exactly. But it's obvious, isn't it? You should hear the way she speaks to her!'

Rachel looked surprised now, and a frown drew Matthew's eyebrows together. 'What did you say?' he exclaimed. 'What have you heard your grandmother say that I haven't?'

Rosemary's face turned red. 'Not a lot,' she said, evidently regretting her impulsive outburst, but her father was not prepared to leave it there.

'Come on,' he invited, his tone hardening as he spoke. 'I'm waiting to hear how this revelation came about.'

'Oh, Daddy.' Rosemary looked utterly deflated now, and although Rachel felt sorry for her there was little she could do. 'It was just something I overheard Grandmama say when she went to visit Rachel when she was ill. You know how—how *cold* Grandmama can be.'

'I still don't understand how you heard what was said between Rachel and your grandmother,' replied Matthew tersely. 'Were you there?'

'No.' Rosemary hunched her shoulders. 'Not exactly.'

'What does that mean?'

'Oh, Daddy!'

'Rosemary.'

'Oh, all right.' She flung her hands out in front of her. 'I heard what she said as I was leaving.'

'You mean you eavesdropped outside the door,' amended her father shrewdly. 'Isn't that right? Isn't that what you did?'

'Lady Olivia was talking before Rosemary left the room,' Rachel put in quickly, trying to remember exactly what Matthew's mother had said. She had certainly brought up the subject of Rachel's not being prepared to have her son's baby, and she hoped Rosemary hadn't heard this, or, if she had, that she hadn't understood it.

Matthew's attention shifted. 'So,' he said, making an evident effort to control his impatience, 'you agree with Rosemary's assessment of my mother's attitude?'

'I didn't say that.' Rachel sighed. How quick he was to jump to conclusions. 'Matthew, you know as well as I do that your mother didn't want me here. If the child's picked that up, too, can you blame her?'

Matthew looked as if he was about to say something scathing, and then seemed to change his mind. With an obvious effort, he forced himself to relax, and both Rachel and Rosemary breathed a little more easily as he turned once more to rest his shoulder against the boat-house. 'OK,' he said, staring out across the water. 'I won't tell my mother what's been going on—'

'Oh, Daddy! *Thank you!*'

Without waiting for him to finish, Rosemary covered the space between them and wrapped her thin arms around his waist. And, looking at Matthew over his daughter's head, Rachel thought he was as surprised as she was at this unexpected display. Evidently embraces of this kind were not a common thing between them.

But Matthew's initial response was in the same spirit at least, even if the verbal response that followed was not what Rosemary had expected. His arms automatically closed about his daughter, hugging her to him warmly, and, watching them together, Rachel knew a treacherous feeling of envy. He should still have been her husband, and this should have been *their* daughter, she reflected bitterly, unable to tear her eyes away. Or their *son*, she amended, as remembrance knifed inside her.

'I want *you* to tell her.'

Matthew's words brought her abruptly back to the present, and she blinked a little confusedly herself as Rosemary uttered a disbelieving cry. 'You don't mean that!'

'I do.' Matthew held her, as she would have pulled away from him. 'I want you to tell Grandmama that you and Rachel are friends, and that I have no objections to your spending your free time with her.'

Rosemary's instinctive denial faltered. 'You mean you'll tell her you knew about what was going on?'

'I mean I won't tell her I didn't,' amended Matthew drily. 'But in future I want you to come to me if you have any— problem with Grandmama. I want us—you and me—to be like a family again.'

Rosemary's lips quivered. 'Do you mean that?'

'I've just said so, haven't I?'

'And—and what about—' she was obviously loath to say it, but she eventually got the words out '—going to boarding-school?'

Matthew looked across at Rachel, holding her eyes as he spoke. 'It's early days yet,' he said. 'We'll see how you behave over the next couple of months. I may revise my opinion and send you to a girl's day-school I know in Keswick. It's where your cousin Lucy goes, and she seems to like it.'

Rosemary gulped. 'And would I be a day girl, too?'

'If you behave yourself, I don't see why not,' replied her father, looking down at her now. 'But only if I hear no more reports of naughtiness from Agnetha. Or your grandmother either, if it comes to that.'

'You won't.' Rosemary was almost speechless. She caught back a sob. 'Can I go and tell Mrs Moffat?'

'Why not?'

Matthew smiled, and after another swift hug Rosemary released herself. 'Did you hear that?' she asked, turning to Rachel as she brushed an errant tear from her cheek. 'I'm going to go to Lucy's school. Daddy's not going to send me to boarding-school, after all.'

'That's wonderful news,' said Rachel warmly, despising herself for envying the child. If only her problems could be as easily solved as Rosemary's. Unfortunately, she didn't have anyone fighting on her side—least of all Matthew.

# CHAPTER TWELVE

THERE was a distinct silence after Rosemary left them, and Rachel turned to watch the child's skipping departure to avoid Matthew's subjective gaze. She supposed she ought to have accompanied her, but Rosemary was obviously eager to get back to the house, and Rachel would have been an unnecessary encumbrance. All the same, it was difficult to know what to say now, and although she wanted to express her approbation at his decision she doubted he would be interested in hearing it.

'You approve, I take it,' he said at last, and now she was compelled to turn and face him.

'Of course,' she replied, lifting her shoulders in an expressive gesture. 'It's—it's what she needed; your—your belief in her.'

Matthew inclined his head. 'You think I didn't believe in her before, is that it?'

Rachel sighed. 'I don't know. I only know that—well, you didn't seem to have a lot of time for her be—before.'

'Before what?' Matthew moved nearer to her. 'Before Barbara died? Or before you came here?'

Rachel stood her ground. 'I don't flatter myself that my coming here had anything to do with it,' she declared, meeting his gaze with an effort. 'Maybe—maybe Barbara's illness obscured—'

'Barbara's illness didn't obscure anything,' retorted Matthew tautly. 'You could say it clarified a lot of things.' He didn't explain what he meant by this, but went on, 'My—relationship with Rosemary was in trouble long before Barbara was taken ill.' He shook his head. 'I'd almost forgotten what it was like to have a daughter.'

'You're very lucky to have her.' Rachel took a steadying breath. 'She's a very loyal little girl.'

'Do you think so?' Matthew seemed to be considering this. He took another step towards her. 'But you didn't like her much when you first met her, did you?'

Rachel sighed, and glanced behind her, grimacing at the dark expanse of water only a couple of feet away at the end of the jetty. Of all places to conduct a conversation, this must be the most unsuitable, she thought frustratedly. With Matthew between her and the shore, she was virtually his prisoner.

'Look, I've revised my opinion,' she said, edging alongside the boat-house. 'And I really am glad you've changed your mind about a boarding-school. I—I'm sure Barbara would have approved—'

'Barbara didn't give a damn what happened to Rosemary,' Matthew retorted harshly, putting out his arm and successfully blocking her exit. 'I thought you'd have realised that. Or did you think I was totally to blame for her irresponsibility?'

Rachel caught her breath. He was so close, and she wondered if he was aware of how much she was aware of him. He couldn't be, or he wouldn't be behaving like this, she thought unsteadily. Not after the way he had repelled any emotion between them the last time he had seen her. As she had wanted him to do, she reminded herself starkly. Dear God, just because the warmth and scent of his lean body was shudderingly familiar, there was no reason for her to lose sight of all reality…

'Will you let me pass?' she said now, forgetting for the moment that he had asked her a question, and he expelled a heavy breath.

'What's the matter?' he asked. 'Don't you want to believe that I'm not the unfeeling monster you've always painted me? Does it put a grain of doubt in your mind if I remind you that you were the one who used to tell me that Barbara could be both devious and self-motivating?'

'Stop it!' Rachel was forced to look up at him now, and she shivered at the look of weary resignation in his eyes. 'Barbara's been dead only three weeks! How can you talk about her like this?'

'Quite easily,' he said flatly, using his free hand to tuck a silken strand of honey-blonde hair behind her ear. His hand lingered against her flesh, and it was all she could do not to tilt her head against the hard brush of his fingers. 'You see, I never loved Barbara, and she certainly didn't love me. What I could give her, perhaps, but nothing else—'

'Don't!' Rachel pushed his hand away and tried to duck under his arm. But his arm dropped as she did, and instead of escaping him she was backed up against the warm wood of the boat-house wall. 'Matthew, you're going to regret this!'

'I regret it already,' he retorted, looking down at her with impassioned eyes. 'But I have to go to Geneva this afternoon, and I'm very much afraid you'll be gone by the time I get back.'

Rachel swallowed. 'You're going to be away for a few days?'

'Until next Tuesday or Wednesday, at the least,' he agreed, capturing her chin between his fingers. 'And while I was succeeding in convincing myself that I could let you leave here without making a fool of myself for a second time, I find that now there's an actual deadline to our separation I can't do it.'

'Matthew—'

'No, listen to me,' he muttered, bending his head and putting his mouth against the side of her neck. 'I want you to know I don't blame you for what happened—'

*'Blame me?'*

The terrible inertia that had been stealing over her at the touch of his lips was abruptly banished. That he should actually believe that she might welcome his advances was bad enough, but to suggest that she might blame herself for what had happened in the past was mortifying.

'Yes,' he was intoning now, his hand at her nape causing unwanted ripples of sensuality to invade her spine. 'For years I have blamed you. For years I swore that if I ever saw you again, I'd kill you! But although you might believe you can control your mind, you can never completely control your senses, and as soon as I saw you again I knew I'd been fooling myself all along—'

'Let go of me!' With a concerted effort, Rachel tore herself away from him, putting an arm's length between them, and staring at him with angry, disbelieving eyes. 'Don't touch me! Do you hear me? Don't you ever lay a hand on me again!' She caught back a sob. 'You say you don't blame me! My God, am I supposed to be grateful for that? What have you got to blame me for, that's what I'd like to know! I didn't do anything. *You did!* Do you need me to remind you what you did? Do you want me to tell you how I felt when I found you and Barbara—*my own cousin!*— together?'

Matthew's mouth was grim, but his emotions were still in command. Lunging forward, he grasped her wrist, and before she could formulate any resistance he had hauled her unceremoniously towards him. Her breasts, loose beneath the thin silk of her shirt, were crushed against his chest, and her legs bumped against his thighs. His breath was hot on her forehead as he wound the arm he had hold of behind her back, and, apparently uncaring that he might be hurting her, he trapped her effectively against him.

'You don't think before you speak, do you?' he snarled, glaring down at her. 'You never would listen to reason. You wouldn't even give me a hearing, before you ran away to London—'

'I didn't run away,' she got out painfully, but he obviously didn't believe her.

'I used to come and sit outside that apartment you took in Penrith, did you know that? Waiting for you to come out. But you never did, did you? At least, not while I was there.

You were too scared to meet me face to face. Too scared to even pick up the telephone!'

'I wasn't scared,' she protested, wondering if he was aware that he was almost breaking her arm. Dear God, if he didn't let her go soon she was going to faint, and she had no wish to give him that satisfaction.

'What would you call it then?' he demanded now, and she took a gulping breath.

'How about—disgusted?' she choked, dredging up the last of her strength. 'Tell me, how long had it been going on before I found out? Barbara was already three months pregnant when I went away, which means that it has to have been—'

Her release was as sudden as her capture had been. One moment Matthew was holding her in a biting embrace, and the next he had uttered a savage interjection and let her go. So unexpectedly, indeed, that she was forced to clutch at him to save herself from falling off the jetty. Her fingers clawed desperately at his chest, tearing open the buttons of his shirt and finding purchase on the cloth. And, in so doing, the backs of her fingers came into contact with the warm skin of his midriff. But as soon as she felt his flesh against hers she dragged her hand away.

'What did you say?'

The violence of Matthew's tone was a welcome distraction to the wilful madness of her thoughts. Even though her shoulder was still stinging, as blood surged back into the tortured muscles, the sensuality of his warm body was a potent attraction. For a moment—for a heart-wrenching moment—she had known an almost uncontrollable impulse to go on touching him, and all the pain and anguish that lay between them had melted in the heat of that temptation. But it was only a physical aberration, she knew, born of her own frustrated emotions. And of her instinctive response to Matthew's sexuality...

'*What did you say?*'

She came to her senses a second time to find him staring

at her with raw impatience. Evidently, he had repeated his question, and she had to blink away a certain incoherence as she struggled to remember what he meant.

'I—don't—know—'

'Barbara!' Matthew prompted grimly. 'You said Barbara was pregnant when you went away. Who told you that?'

Rachel blinked again. 'What do you mean? Who told me? It was a fact, wasn't it? What does it matter who—?'

'Because it wasn't true,' said Matthew savagely.

'Don't be stupid—'

'Don't you dare tell me not to be stupid!' he retorted angrily. 'For heaven's sake, Rachel, Barbara wasn't pregnant when you went away! Rosemary was born almost a year after the divorce! I want to know who told you Barbara was pregnant. Was it Barbara? God, I have to know the truth!'

Rachel backed away from him along the jetty, trying desperately to come to terms with what she had heard. 'But— Rosemary's ten years old,' she protested unsteadily, but Matthew shook his head.

'She's nine!' he told her flatly. 'Ask her how old she is, and she'll tell you.'

Rachel swallowed. 'Why should I believe you?'

'Don't be ridiculous! What would be the point of lying? You could easily find out when Rosemary was born. The records are there for everyone to see.'

Rachel put a trembling hand to her temple. 'But you did—you did—sleep with her, didn't you?' she got out unsteadily.

Matthew's nostrils flared. 'Yes.'

Rachel caught her breath. 'Oh, God!'

Matthew's mouth twisted. 'Don't you want to know *when*? Or *why*?'

Rachel shook her head. 'No—'

'Well, by God, you're going to,' declared Matthew harshly, going after her. 'And if you run away this time, I'll go straight to your aunt and uncle and tell them how Barbara lied to get what she wanted.'

Rachel, who had reached the path that led up through a copse of trees, budding now with blossom, halted uncertainly. Then, even though all she really wanted to do was escape to the unguarded sanctuary of her room, she turned back.

'It—wasn't Barbara,' she admitted painfully. 'I—Aunt Maggie told me that Barbara was pregnant.'

'Good God!' Matthew made a sound that was a mixture of anger and anguish. 'And you believed her?'

'Why shouldn't I?' retorted Rachel swiftly. 'By your own admission, you and Barbara had been having an affair—'

'Not an *affair*!' Matthew shrugged off his jacket and thrust it roughly over his shoulder. 'Rachel, believe it or not, that night you—you found us, as you put it, was the first time we had ever—touched.'

'Oh, Matt, please—'

'Goddammit, it's the truth!' he swore angrily. 'And you had only yourself to blame! Or you would have, if you could see further than that selfish bloody nose of yours!'

'How dare you?'

'I dare, because it's the truth,' he stated. 'All right. You didn't want to have a baby. I was coming to terms with that—'

'Were you?'

'All right, I had my faults, too, but I was never deceitful—'

'Oh, Matt!'

'Never deceitful with you.'

Rachel shook her head. 'I don't know what you mean.'

'I think you do.'

'No, I don't.'

'All right,' he said again. 'When—when we had that first row, and I flushed the pills you were taking down the toilet, I thought you'd at least have *told* me if you'd started taking them again.'

Rachel stared at him uncomprehendingly. 'Yes. I would have.'

'But you didn't, did you?'

'Didn't what?'

'Tell me, dammit! You let me go on hoping that you might get pregnant, when all the time you were popping pills like there was no tomorrow!'

'That's not true!'

'It is true.'

Rachel caught her breath. 'It's not! I'm telling you now, I've never—I've never taken a contraceptive pill since—since you disposed of them.'

Matthew studied her grimly. 'Wait a minute. Let me backtrack a minute. Are you saying you've never knowingly tried to prevent a pregnancy since I destroyed your prescription?'

'That's right.' Rachel was trembling. *If he only knew,* she thought achingly, thinking of that still little body that had been taken from her...

'And—Maggie told you Barbara was pregnant?'

Rachel bent her head. 'Yes.'

'God!' Matthew rammed the heel of his hand hard against his forehead. 'So we both believed what we were told.'

Rachel licked her lips before looking up at him again. 'Not entirely,' she said unevenly. 'Don't forget, I had the evidence of my own eyes.'

'And so did I,' muttered Matthew savagely, scuffing his booted foot against the wooden piles of the jetty. 'That night you found us together, Barbara had shown me a half-used strip of contraceptive pills. She took them out of the drawer beside your bed.'

Rachel's lips parted. 'But—they weren't mine!'

'I didn't know that.'

Rachel stared at him in horror. 'But why didn't you ask me?'

'I was going to,' he declared bitterly. 'Only, if you remember, I never got the chance.'

Rachel tried to think. 'But when I found you—'

'I was stoned out of my mind!' exclaimed Matthew wearily. 'I don't know how much I drank that night. I don't remember too much of the night at all, after Barbara's revelation.' He expelled a heavy breath. 'I remember her saying what a pity it was that you seemed to care more about your career than me. I remember that. And I remember her mentioning that as long as you were taking the Pill you weren't likely to conceive, and I also remember arguing with her about it.'

'Oh, Matt.'

He frowned. 'Anyway, I know earlier in the evening we went upstairs to look in the drawer of the bedside cabinet, and the foil strip *was* there.'

'But she could have put it there at any time,' cried Rachel.

'I'm beginning to realise that now, but then—'

'You got drunk?'

'I suppose so. We went back to the library, and I remember my glass always seeming to be full, and Barbara sympathising with me, and smiling at me, and telling me how she would never do such a thing.'

Rachel felt sick. Even after all this time, his words still had the power to distress her.

'And when I came home?'

'I don't know.' He raked his hair back with a hand that was not quite steady. 'I suppose she must have suggested that I ought to be in bed and offered to help me undress.'

'Do you mean—?' Rachel could hardly say the words. 'Do you mean you hadn't slept together before I found you?'

'I don't think so.'

'You don't *think* so?'

'All right, then, *no*. We hadn't.' He shook his head. 'I doubt if I was capable of it.'

'That's some consolation, I suppose.' Rachel was bitter.

'Well, goddammit, if I had I'd have considered myself justified!' he replied unevenly. 'Rachel, I've never loved anyone as I loved you, and when I found out—*thought* I'd found out—that you'd been cheating on me—'

'You let Barbara offer you consolation!'

'Not until after you left,' Matthew countered harshly, and Rachel shivered.

'Left Rothmere?'

'Left *Penrith*,' corrected Matthew, with a scowl. 'That's how I know Barbara couldn't have been pregnant when you went away. But the night you went to London I decided I had nothing left to lose.'

'But why *Barbara*? Did you—did you *love* her?'

'Not love, no. I was grateful to her, I suppose, for exposing your duplicity, or what I thought was your duplicity, anyway. And she was there. And, dammit, I wanted to hurt you as you had hurt me!'

'Oh, Matt!'

'So now you know,' he muttered, coming closer to her. 'Does it make a difference?'

Rachel couldn't take it all in. She couldn't believe that everything that had happened could have pivoted on a lie— two lies, if she accepted that Barbara had tricked Matthew with what must have been her own contraceptive pills.

She looked up at Matthew, and her heart bled. Was it true? Had he really believed she had been lying to him? And why not, when she had been equally as eager to believe that he was having an affair with her cousin?

'Rachel…'

He put out his hand towards her, but she avoided his touch. However much she wanted to believe him, she had to have a little time to assimilate all she had learned, and what it might mean. And first of all she wanted to speak to Aunt Maggie. If what Matthew had said was true, then she had an awful lot to answer for.

'What's wrong?' he demanded now, his frustration plain, and her heart went out to him.

'Just—give me a little time to get used to the idea,' she begged, and, unable to resist the temptation, she put her hand on his sleeve. The flesh beneath the fine silk was taut and pulsing with life, and she knew an urge to bend her head and brush her lips against his warm skin.

'God—Rachel!' he groaned, as aware as she was of the chemistry between them, but the remembrance of Barbara, and what she had done to both of them, was a compelling deterrent. 'Look,' he added harshly, 'you know I don't have a lot of time. I'm leaving in—' he cast a swift look at his watch '—about half an hour. I wish I could postpone the trip now, but perhaps it's a blessing in disguise. By the time I get back, you'll have had time to decide what you want to do. At least promise me you'll stay until I get back. I need your assurance that you won't run out on me again.'

Rachel moistened her lips. 'All right.'

Matthew expelled a heavy sigh. 'You mean that?'

'Yes.' Rachel looked down at her hand on his sleeve, and then, throwing caution to the wind, she leant forward and kissed his cheek. 'Have a good journey,' she whispered. 'Take care.'


It was late in the afternoon when Rachel arrived at the vicarage. It had been difficult to get away from Rothmere without attracting undue attention, and she would have preferred no one to know where she was going. As it was, she had had to prevail on the old butler's kindness to enable her to borrow one of the estate's vehicles, but at least the mud-spattered Land Rover he had provided had not aroused the curiosity Matthew's Range Rover might have done.

In spite of the extreme tension she was feeling, driving again had not been a hazard. Indeed, she was amazed at her own resilience, after the body-blow of Matthew's revelations. She suspected the shock of what she had learned hadn't really hit her yet, and that the courage it was taking to come and confront her aunt was being sustained by the artificial amount of adrenalin in her system; but it had to be done. There was no way she could dismiss what Matthew had told her and look only to the future. If they were to have any future at all, she had to dispose of the skeletons of the past, and unless she saw Aunt Maggie face to face she would never know the truth.

Her aunt was in the sitting-room. Too late, Rachel remembered that the Young Wives had their regular weekly meeting at the vicarage on Friday afternoons, and the sound of perhaps a dozen female voices jarred her determination. But, after making no attempt to disguise her entry into the house, she was obliged to show her face, and she steeled herself against the stares that accompanied her appearance.

'Why—Rachel!' Her aunt's tone was at once surprised and wary. 'You should have let us know you were coming.'

'Yes.' But Rachel knew that was the last thing she would have done. She had wanted to catch her aunt unawares, and unprepared, but now the older woman was having plenty of time to consider why her niece had appeared.

'Why don't you sit down and join us?' Aunt Maggie invited, struggling to behave as the vicar's wife should. 'Girls, you all know my niece, Rachel Barnes, don't you? She came for dear Barbara's funeral, and, unfortunately, she had an accident while she was playing with Rosemary.'

That was hardly accurate, but Rachel was relieved not to have to go into further details. She acknowledged the ripple of restrained sympathy—some of it from girls she and Barbara used to go to school with—with polite gratitude, and then, excusing herself from the gathering, she offered to make some tea.

'That won't be necessary,' said her aunt swiftly, nodding at the cups on the table in front of them. 'We've had tea, haven't we, girls? I'm sure we'd all prefer to hear about the exciting job you have in London, instead. Rachel's an assistant producer, aren't you, dear? Very career-minded, our Rachel. Always was.' She met her niece's eyes. 'Always will be.'

'I wouldn't bank on that, if I were you,' said Rachel, equally as smoothly, and she saw her aunt's jaw sag for a moment.

But the aberration was brief, and Maggie quickly recovered. 'Well, I'm sure you know your own business best,' she remarked evenly. 'But it's a pity we can't all be as happy as Barbara and Matthew used to be. Poor Barbara! I don't know how Matt's going to manage without her. He's been totally devastated since she died.'

There was another murmur of sympathy from the women gathered in the room, and Rachel felt her nails digging painfully into her palms. With a few words, her aunt had altered the whole atmosphere of the meeting, and there was no doubt at all that the change had been deliberate.

However, not all the women present had regarded Barbara as the saint her mother was implying she had been, and one of them, Gillian Wyatt, got abruptly to her feet.

'I think it's time we were leaving,' she said, breaking up the meeting. 'It's obvious that Rachel would like to speak to her aunt alone, and it is nearly four o'clock. Time we were getting home and making ourselves useful to our husbands.'

'Oh, but I'm sure Rachel—' began Maggie urgently, but already two or three of the others were on their feet.

'Gill's right,' said Nancy Cullen, buttoning her cardigan. 'I know you're too polite to ask us to leave, but I'm sure you'd like to have a quiet word with your visitor. After all, it's been too long since Rachel visited the valley. We should see you more often, Rachel. It's not that far from London to Rothside.'

Rachel was quite touched by the way so many of the women took it upon themselves to wish her well as they were leaving. She had thought she would be regarded as the pariah in their midst, but it seemed that in this respect also she had been wrong. No one appeared to blame her for what had happened, or, if they did, they were prepared to keep their thoughts to themselves.

But when she and her aunt were alone she met an entirely different reaction. Maggie was grim and aggressive, and obviously of the opinion that the best method of defence was attack.

'Well?' she said, coming back into the sitting-room, where Rachel had been waiting while she said goodbye to her guests. 'What do you want? I hope you're not going to ask me if you can stay.'

'I'm not.' Rachel pushed her hands into the pockets of her jeans, and endeavoured to take control of the conversation. 'As a matter of fact, I don't want anything from you but some answers. Like, for instance, why you told me Barbara was pregnant when she wasn't.'

Maggie's thin face blanched. 'I beg your pardon?'

'You heard what I said, Aunt Maggie. Why did you tell me Barbara was pregnant—?'

'What are you talking about?' The older woman was blustering now. 'Why did I tell you Barbara was pregnant? I told you because she *was* pregnant, that's why. She and Matt—well, you know as well as I do what happened—'

'I know what *you* told me happened,' retorted Rachel harshly, and Maggie took a step back.

'What do you mean?'

'Oh, don't pretend you don't understand, Aunt Maggie. You understand very well. Only you never expected I would hear the truth, did you? You knew I was so upset over what I'd seen—what I *thought* I'd seen—that I'd believe anything. *Anything!*'

Her aunt swallowed. 'I don't know what this is all about, I really don't. Coming here, shouting about me lying to you. I haven't lied to you. Why should I?'

'Because you gambled that I'd believe you,' said Rachel tremulously. 'You guessed that if Barbara came to me with that story, I'd have been suspicious. That I might have asked Matt about it. But you—you knew I'd never expect you to *lie!*'

'And I didn't.' Her aunt stared at her with resentful eyes. 'How dare you even suggest such a thing? Just because

Matt's a widower now, and you think you might have some chance of rekindling the past. You're getting older. You're beginning to regret what you lost—'

'Oh, I regret it, all right,' choked Rachel bitterly. 'And Matt does, too. He told me.'

'Matt told you—?' For a moment, Maggie was nonplussed. However she had thought Rachel might have learned of the deception, she had evidently not expected it to have been from him.

'Yes, Matt,' said Rachel contemptuously, pursuing her objective. 'He told me the truth. The whole truth. How he had nothing to do with Barbara in a sexual way until I left the district. That Barbara couldn't possibly have been pregnant, and that Rosemary isn't *ten* years old, she's *nine*!'

Maggie blinked, and Rachel could almost find it in her heart to feel sorry for her. It must have been hard to justify the lies she had told to herself, even if they had been to help Barbara. And, although she had never liked Rachel, surely she had not hated her enough to do what she had done without coercion?

But even as these thoughts superimposed themselves upon her consciousness, her aunt spoke again. 'You're a fool, Rachel,' she said scornfully, and Rachel could sense the returning confidence in her voice. 'Matt's told you the truth, has he? He's told you that Barbara wasn't expecting his child when you went away, and you believed him because Rosie is only nine years old!' She gave a harsh laugh. 'He didn't tell you about the miscarriage she had, I suppose? He didn't tell you that Barbara lost their first baby only weeks before it was due!'

'That's not true!'

Rachel's response was instinctive, born of the desire to silence her aunt's accusing voice, but Maggie was not finished.

'It is true,' she retorted. 'And if you don't believe me,

ask your uncle. He wouldn't lie to you, would he? Not
Uncle Geoff! Not the man who gave you a home at the
expense of his own family!'

# CHAPTER THIRTEEN

'You've got a visitor, Rachel.' Alan Maxwell stopped beside her desk and quirked a mocking eyebrow in her direction. 'Does Justin know you've been investigating the aristocracy for this new lifestyles format he's creating?'

'What?' Rachel lifted her head wearily, not really in the mood for her young colleague's provocation. She had a mountain of work to get through before the airing of that evening's programme, and with Justin breathing down her neck every five minutes she was in no state to indulge in verbal sparring with the man who wanted her job.

'I said—does Justin know—?'

'Yes, I heard that.' Rachel endeavoured not to let her tension show. It wouldn't do to give Alan another reason to complain to Justin that she simply wasn't doing her job. 'You mentioned something about the—aristocracy?'

'That's right.' Alan jerked his head towards one of the empty studios. 'I've put her in there. You'd better go and sort it out before she really sets the station by its ears.'

Rachel put down her pen. 'Sort who out?' she asked evenly.

'She calls herself Lady Olivia—Conroy. Funny that. I never realised before. It's the same name as yours.'

Rachel felt as if all the blood were draining out of her body. Lady Olivia? Here? Her hands curled convulsively on the desk in front of her. What was Lady Olivia Conroy doing in London? And why had she come to see her? What possible reason could have brought her here?

'Are you all right?'

Even Alan, uncaring of her feelings as he usually was, had noticed her pallor, and Rachel made a determined effort to allay his curiosity. If he went to Justin now and told him that Matthew's mother had come here to see her, who knew what further catastrophe that might precipitate?

As it was, she and Justin were barely on speaking terms, his reaction to her return to work four months ago very much tempered by her present lack of any enthusiasm. He had no sympathy with her, she knew, and she had never attempted to explain what had happened at Rothside to him. But she had no doubt that he had guessed that Matt was at least in part to blame for her loss of co-ordination, and it was only their long association that was preventing him from replacing her.

But it was incredibly difficult to apply herself to anything at the moment, and she was seriously thinking of giving up her job at the television station and finding something less demanding to employ her time. Where once she had looked forward to coming to work, now she loathed even getting out of bed in the mornings, and her whole life seemed empty and without any point.

She had believed that she couldn't feel any worse than she had when she'd first come to London ten years ago, but that had been proved to be as untrue as everything else. Wounds that had at least partially healed did not take kindly to being opened again, and, although once she would have said that Matthew couldn't hurt her any more, now she recognised this for the fiction it was.

She should have left well alone, she thought bitterly. No matter how convincing Matthew's words had sounded, she should never have attempted to verify the past. It should have been enough that he had *told* her his side of the story. Without her aunt's involvement, they could have been happy.

Or could they? For weeks after her return to London Rachel had asked herself that question without coming up with any satisfactory answer. If she had not approached Aunt Maggie, would the woman have let them be happy?

Or would she have chosen to wait until they had a child of their own before exposing Matthew for the liar he was?

In any event, she had not waited to find out. Once Uncle Geoff had conceded, albeit a little bemusedly, that Barbara had indeed lost a baby before Rosemary was born, Rachel had only wanted to escape. She had been sorry to leave Rosemary, particularly as she had been unable to tell the little girl when, or even *if*, they would ever see one another again. But it was imperative that she get away before Matthew returned from Geneva, and although she had wondered if he might come after her, as he had done before, she had heard nothing more from him.

And now this. Her stomach quivered at the thought of Matthew's mother sitting in the empty studio, waiting to speak to her. And for what purpose? What earthly reason could have brought Lady Olivia to London? Rachel knew the old lady had friends in town, but she couldn't believe that this was just another social call. She and Lady Olivia didn't have—had never had—that kind of an association.

'Do you want me to get rid of her?' Belatedly, Alan showed an unexpected compassion. Perhaps even he could see how unnerved his news had made her, and the stark pain in the eyes she raised to his face made him shift a little uncomfortably. 'I can tell her you're too busy,' he offered. 'I could even tell her you're not here. Why don't you take an early lunch? It's cold outside, but the sun is warm.'

'No.' Rachel looked down at the papers on her desk again and shook her head. 'No, it's all right. I'll see her,' she said, sliding back her chair and getting to her feet on legs that were distinctly shaky. 'But—thanks for the offer. I'll do the same for you some time.'

Alan looked as if he half regretted his leniency, but he said no more as she ran a nervous hand over her hair and checked that there were no specks of lint on her skirt. The dark green velvet suit she was wearing unfortunately enhanced her pallor, and she thought how haggard she looked when she caught a glimpse of her reflection in the swing glass doors.

Lady Olivia was not *sitting* waiting for her. When Rachel entered the small studio, which was used for recording interviews for their radio channel, she found the old lady standing stiffly by the windows, staring out on to the roofs below with a definite air of tension. But she turned when she heard the door open, and her knuckles tightened perceptibly on the bag she held in her hands.

Rachel squared her shoulders, unconsciously adopting a defensive stance. But she could still think of no good reason why Lady Olivia should be here, and she automatically anticipated the worst.

'Good morning,' she said, her words tight, her features schooled and impassive. 'I understand you wish to see me.'

Lady Olivia regarded her silently for several seconds, and then, as if no longer capable of maintaining her indifference, her shoulders sagged. 'May I sit down?'

'Of course.' Rachel shook off a sense of unreality, and nodded towards a chair. 'Please.' She paused as the old lady took the seat. 'Can I get you some coffee?'

'Perhaps. Later,' said Matthew's mother, fingers that were not quite steady loosening the buttons of her tweed jacket. 'There.' She sighed. 'That's better. I was beginning to think you had refused to see me.'

Rachel could feel the sense of unreality returning, and frowned. 'I beg your pardon?'

'I said, I was beginning to think you had refused to see me.' Lady Olivia's thin lips parted in a faint smile. 'But you always were a polite child, weren't you, Rachel? Even if people were not always polite to you.'

Rachel wondered if she had been working too hard, and that this little scene was simply a figment of her imagination. Perhaps she was dreaming, she thought. Perhaps she would wake up soon and discover she was late for work again. Justin had already complained about her tardy time-keeping. He had even asked her if she was trying to get him to sack her...

'I know I must be the last person you expected to see.' Lady Olivia's voice came again, as if from a distance, and Rachel struggled to concentrate on what she was saying. 'I must admit, six months ago, I would have agreed with you. But circumstances alter cases, as they say, and I find my son's happiness is more important than my pride.'

Rachel stared at her. 'I'm afraid I—'

'You don't know what I'm talking about, do you?' Lady Olivia didn't wait for her to shake her head before continuing, 'No, well, I dare say that's not so surprising. I haven't exactly welcomed you to Rothmere in the past.'

'Lady Olivia—'

'Please, won't you sit down, too? What I have to say will not take long, but I find myself faltering these days, and with you standing over me like this—'

Rachel expelled a breath. 'Did Matthew send you here?' she asked abruptly, without any emotion, a possible excuse for the old lady's being here suddenly occurring to her. 'Because if he did—'

'Matt doesn't know I'm here,' the old lady replied wearily. 'You have my word on that. Indeed, I would go so far as to say that he would be furious if he knew. But, unhappily, that is not likely, and—'

'*Unhappily?*'

'Yes. Oh—' Lady Olivia spread her hands '—won't you sit down, Rachel? I can't go on looking up at you like this. It makes my head swim, and I have to keep my senses.'

Rachel hesitated a moment, and then, reluctantly, drew forward another of the leather-based chairs and subsided into it. 'All right,' she said. 'I'm sitting. What is it you want to tell me?'

Lady Olivia's fingers smoothed the fabric of her skirt, pleated the wool repeatedly, and then, just as Rachel was on the verge of springing frustratedly to her feet again, she said, 'I want you to come back to Rothmere.'

'*What?*' Rachel felt a surge of adrenalin coursing through her veins, and how she prevented herself from thrusting back the chair and walking out of the studio, she never knew. 'You're not serious?'

'I am serious.' Lady Olivia lifted her head and looked at her now. 'Matt needs you, Rachel. Rosemary needs you, too, I think. And *I* need you.' Her lips twisted. 'Oh, don't look like that, I've not entirely lost my reason. What I'm saying is, I need you because Matt needs you. If you don't come back, I'm very much afraid I'll lose him.'

Rachel blinked. 'Lose him?' she echoed. 'What do you mean, lose him?'

Lady Olivia heaved a sigh. 'Well—ever since the accident, he's been drinking—'

'Accident?' Rachel's mouth dried. 'What accident?'

'Rosemary's accident. But you know about that.'

'No, I don't.'

'You don't know she had a fall from Saracen?'

'No!' Rachel was horrified. 'How could I?'

'But—well, didn't your uncle write and tell you—?'

'No one wrote to me,' Rachel cut in swiftly. 'What happened? Is she all right? Good lord, *Saracen*! That's her father's horse, isn't it?' She remembered the huge black stallion with awful apprehension.

'Yes, that's right.' Lady Olivia shook her head. 'The little idiot should never have got on its back. But when Matthew came home and found you'd gone back to London, he became totally unapproachable, and I suppose Rosemary was trying to attract his attention.'

'Oh, God!' Rachel felt sick. 'Was she—was she badly hurt?'

'Fortunately not badly.' Lady Olivia grimaced. 'She had cuts and bruises, of course, and like you she had some concussion. But I'm afraid her ruse—if that's what it was—to get Matt's attention backfired. If anything, since the accident he's been even more withdrawn, and when Malloy told me how much he was drinking—'

Rachel's hands clenched. 'What makes you think I can do anything to help him?' she asked, fighting the instinctive urge to throw common sense aside and go and see Matthew for herself.

'Who else is there?' replied Lady Olivia bitterly. 'It was you he always wanted. He would never listen to anyone else.'

'How can you say that?' Rachel couldn't prevent the uncontrollable retort. 'He lied to me—'

'When? When did he lie to you?' Lady Olivia stared at her fiercely. 'If he told you he never loved Barbara, then it's the truth. He's not lying. After the first few months, their marriage was just a sham. If it hadn't been for Rosemary…' Her voice trailed away, and she fumbled in her handbag for a tissue as Rachel took several steadying breaths.

'It wasn't that,' she said at last, realising she at least owed it to this woman to be honest. 'I don't know if Matt ever loved Barbara. He was certainly attracted to her—'

'Not until you went away,' the old lady asserted swiftly. 'You didn't really believe he had been unfaithful to you, did you? My God, that night he found out you had been cheating him, he was too drunk to—well, you know what I mean.'

Rachel's features felt frozen. 'Is that what he told you?'

'Eventually,' agreed Lady Olivia. 'After I confronted him with it. Mrs Moffat found the bottles the following morning. It wasn't until later that I found out Barbara had been involved.'

Rachel got up now, unable to sit still any longer. 'I—wasn't cheating on him,' she said at last, walking to the windows and rubbing her elbows with nervous hands. 'Barbara—I think Barbara made that up to cause trouble between us. In any event, she achieved her objective, didn't she? And picked up the pieces into the bargain.'

Lady Olivia caught her breath. 'Are you saying you were not opposed to having a baby?'

'No. Yes. Oh, in the beginning I was, but afterwards...'
Rachel shook her head. 'All I'm saying is, they weren't my
pills that Barbara showed Matt. They must have been hers.'

'And when did you learn all this?'

'Matt told me,' said Rachel dully. 'The day before I left
Rothmere.'

'And it didn't mean anything to you?'

Rachel swung round. 'Of course it meant something to
me. But it wasn't enough.'

Lady Olivia lifted her thin shoulders. 'I hoped—I had
hoped—that you still cared for my son.'

'It's a little late for that, isn't it?'

'I'm beginning to think it is.' The old lady looked
drained.

'In any case,' Rachel couldn't let it alone, 'even if I did
still care about Matt, I couldn't live with a liar.'

'You said that before.' Lady Olivia blinked. 'In what way
did Matt lie to you? I've told you he didn't love Barbara—'

'And I've said it wasn't that.'

'Then what was it?'

Rachel was trembling now, but she couldn't help it.
'He—he told me Barbara wasn't pregnant when I left
Penrith.'

'She wasn't.' Lady Olivia frowned.

'She was.'

'No.' Lady Olivia shook her head. 'I can assure you—'

'If you're going to say that Rosemary is only nine years
old, I already know that. But Barbara had a miscarriage,
didn't she?'

'Well—yes—'

'There you are, then.' Even now, the confirmation made
her feel sick.

'But it was after they were married, my dear. And the
foetus was barely two months old.'

'No!' Rachel couldn't believe it. She *wouldn't* believe it.
Her uncle had endorsed everything Aunt Maggie had said,
and he wouldn't have lied to her.

'I'm afraid it's yes.'

'It can't be.' Rachel shook her head.

But what had Aunt Maggie said exactly? she asked herself desperately. How had she phrased the question? She had asked Uncle Geoff, on Rachel's behalf, whether it was true that Barbara had been pregnant before her marriage, and Uncle Geoff had said yes. And then she had gone on to ask whether Barbara had had a miscarriage, and—and—Rachel put an unsteady hand to her head. And—she had jumped to the obvious conclusion, just as Aunt Maggie had known she would.

She must have groaned, because Lady Olivia got up then, and came to put an anxious hand on her arm. 'Are you all right, Rachel?' she asked, her tone concerned, and Rachel knew an overwhelming urge to confide in the old lady.

'I—I—when Aunt Maggie told me Barbara had had a miscarriage, she said it had happened just—weeks before the baby was due.'

'Good lord!' Lady Olivia was astounded. 'But—why did you believe her? Did she offer you any proof?'

Rachel shook her head. 'No. No, she didn't. But she did ask Uncle Geoff to confirm it, and—and he did.'

'That the baby was only weeks from being due?' Lady Olivia looked aghast. 'I always thought Geoffrey Barnes was a foolish man, but I never thought he would betray his calling.'

'No. No, he didn't.' Rachel struggled to get some order into her words. 'But, you see, Matt hadn't told me about the miscarriage—'

'Because it wasn't important.'

'It was to me.' Rachel bent her head. 'Anyway, when—when Uncle Geoff agreed that Barbara had lost a baby, I didn't pursue it. It—it was enough, don't you see? As—as Aunt Maggie knew it would be.'

'That woman!' There was a wealth of dislike in Lady Olivia's voice. 'How your uncle has lived with her all these years, I'll never know.'

Rachel shook her head. 'I have to think—'

'Yes. Yes, I understand that.' Lady Olivia nodded now, and then, as another thought struck her, she added, 'There is one other point I think you should consider.'

'Yes?' Rachel was wary.

'Well,' said Lady Olivia, with the air of one who has just discovered something everyone else has overlooked, 'you might ask yourself how Barbara could have got pregnant at that point if she herself was using those pills you spoke about.'

# CHAPTER FOURTEEN

IT WAS dark by the time she reached Rothmere, and the doubts Rachel had been nurturing during the latter part of the journey flourished anew as she turned between the familiar stone gateposts.

Although the roads had not been particularly busy once she had passed the Birmingham interchange, it had been after four o'clock before she could get away, and even then she had had to leave her apartment in some disorder. She had packed one suitcase, only to discover it was filled with shoes and underwear, so that she was obliged to tip everything out on to her bed and start again. But at that time her brain had simply not been functioning on any level beyond the basic one of getting to Matthew, and she guessed that if Lady Olivia had had any idea of the state she was in she would not have agreed to spend the night in London.

Justin had recognised defeat when he saw it, although he had, characteristically, been the one to kindle her misgivings. 'What makes you think Conroy will want you back, after you were so obviously willing to believe the worst of him?' he enquired, voicing thoughts Rachel would have preferred to leave unquestioned. 'After all, it isn't the first time you've walked out on him, is it? You might just find he's not prepared to take you back.'

Of course, he had been right, but at that time she had still been convinced that what she was doing was right. Now she was not so sure, and her hands clenched convulsively around the wheel of her car as she drove rather erratically towards the house.

It was a chilly September evening, and when she stepped out of the car the wind off the lake penetrated the folds of the cape she had wrapped around her. She had not stopped to change, and she was still wearing the dark green velvet suit she had worn to the studios, although now she felt dishevelled, and tired from the journey.

There were few lights visible in the house, and she wondered what she would do if Matthew was not at home. Lady Olivia had assured her that he seldom went out these days, but that was not to say he was a hermit. He could easily have decided to spend the night with some friends after his mother had left for London. Particularly as Lady Olivia had dropped Rosemary off at her daughter's on her way to see Rachel, and had explained that Agnetha had long since returned to Sweden.

Watkins answered her tentative ring, his old eyes widening at the sight of her. 'Why—Mrs Conroy!' he exclaimed, and Rachel managed a warm smile for his uncomplicated welcome. 'This is a pleasant surprise. Does Mr Matthew know you're coming?'

Rachel's smile faltered. 'No. No, he doesn't,' she admitted, glancing anxiously beyond him. 'Um—he is in, isn't he? I—I haven't made a wasted journey?'

'No. No, of course not.' But as Watkins stepped back to let her into the hall, his face mirrored his uncertainty. 'It's just that—well, Mrs Conroy, if he's not expecting you...'

Rachel could guess what he was thinking. If what Lady Olivia had confided was true, Matthew was seldom sober after six o'clock, and poor Watkins would be dreading the prospect of approaching him.

'It's all right,' she said now, patting the old man on the arm. 'You don't have to announce me. Is he in the library?' And at Watkins' nod, 'OK. Just leave it to me. I'll take the responsibility.'

'But Miss Rachel—'

Watkins evidently felt it was his duty to warn her what she might find, but Rachel shook her head. 'Don't worry,' she said firmly. 'If he throws me out, you can come and pick up the pieces.' She forced a light laugh. 'Honestly, it'll be all right. Lady Olivia knows I'm here.'

'Does she?'

The voice was harsh, but painfully familiar, and Rachel's brief spurt of humour expired. Although she had not thought she and Watkins were speaking loud enough to be overheard by anyone, Matthew's hearing was apparently sharper than she had thought. While she had been struggling to reassure the butler, he had wrenched open the library door, and now he stood regarding them with wary speculation.

Rachel had thought she was prepared for anything. Ever since her doubts about coming here had begun to plague her, she had played every possible scenario she could think of in her mind. Anger, resentment, bitterness, remorse. Anxious as she was, she had nevertheless believed that she could cope with any situation. She had even steeled herself to face his possible rejection. But what she had not anticipated was the shock that his appearance would generate. Even four months ago she had not been faced with anything like this.

For Matthew looked *ill*. There was no other word to describe him, and for the first time she realised why Lady Olivia had been desperate enough to come to London. The old lady had not been exaggerating when she had expressed her fears of losing her son. Looking at him now, Rachel could hardly believe that she had contributed to this change.

He was so thin, she thought worriedly, noticing how his clothes hung on him. There didn't appear to be any flesh on him anywhere, and his face was gaunt and shadowed with beard, his eyes red-rimmed and hollow.

'I said—does she?' he repeated now, supporting himself with one hand against the frame of the library door. 'I wondered where the old girl had gone.' His lips twisted. 'Where is she? I want to tell her exactly what I think of her!'

'Matt…'

Rachel glanced awkwardly at Watkins, but evidently Matthew had no qualms about involving the old butler in the proceedings. 'You can show—Miss Barnes out again,

Watkins,' he stated, ignoring Rachel's tentative greeting. 'And, in future, you'd better ask me before inviting—*undesirables* into the house.'

'Oh, Mr Matt—'

'It's all right, Watkins.' Rachel realised she had to take charge of the situation before it got completely out of hand. 'I can show myself out, if necessary. You go and get on with your supper—'

'Don't you tell my staff what to do!' snarled Matthew, swaying a little as he pushed himself away from the door, and Rachel could smell the alcohol on his breath. 'You—get out of here right now. *Right now!*'

It took some doing, but Rachel turned her back on him and spoke once again to the butler. 'Go on, Watkins,' she directed, giving him an encouraging look. 'And tell Mrs Moffat we'd like some coffee, please. Black coffee. For two.'

'You've got a bloody nerve!' roared Matthew, as Watkins took one look at his employer and then hurried off to do Rachel's bidding. 'Coming here uninvited, giving your orders. Who the hell do you think you are?'

'I'm the woman who loves you,' said Rachel steadily, nodding towards the lamplit room behind him. 'Now, do we go into the library and talk about it? Or would you rather we conducted our conversation out here, with an uninvited audience?'

Matthew's mouth went slack. 'What did you say?' he muttered. And then, as if convinced he had misunderstood what she had said, he shook his head a little blankly. 'No,' he added. 'Don't tell me. I don't want to know. I just want you to get out of here. I don't need anybody's pity, least of all yours.'

'It's not pity,' said Rachel quietly. 'Look, can't we just talk about this in private? I have come quite a long way.'

Matthew's mouth hardened. 'No one asked you to.' He scowled. 'I didn't ask you to, anyway.'

'I know that.' Rachel took a steadying breath. 'Please.'

'Please what?'

'Please can we go into the library and talk about this?'

'There's nothing to talk about.' Matthew's hand came up to support himself again as he almost lost his balance, and he rested his forehead on the muscled length of his forearm. 'God, Rachel, haven't you done enough? Did you have to do what the old lady asked you? God knows, you've never done it before.'

Rachel sighed. 'If I'd known you were in this state—'

'Yes? Yes?' He lifted his head sardonically. 'What would you have done? Come rushing back here to console me?' He grimaced. 'Like you did when Rosemary almost broke her neck?'

Rachel shook her head. 'I didn't know about Rosemary's accident—'

'And you professed to care about her,' he muttered, not listening to what she had to say. 'You know, you had her fooled, just like you fooled me. I really thought we were beginning to get somewhere before I went away. And then what happened? I come back, and find you've gone—just as you did before.' He groaned. 'God, I wanted to kill you!'

'Matt, I didn't know,' she insisted fiercely, and now he did hear her.

'Didn't know? Didn't know what? That I was crazy about you? That I'd always been crazy about you? Of course you did—'

He was talking in the past tense, and Rachel felt helpless. 'Rosemary's accident,' she cut in desperately. 'Matt, I didn't know she had had an accident. No one—no one told me.'

Matthew frowned, obviously trying to concentrate on what she was saying. 'You mean—Barnes never wrote and told you?'

'No.'

Matthew looked savage for a moment, but then he lifted his shoulders in an indifferent gesture. 'Oh, well,' he said carelessly, 'it's par for the course, isn't it? It's probably just as well. If you'd come back just then, I probably would have strangled you.'

'Oh, Matt!' Rachel heaved a deep breath. 'I know I've been stupid. I know you have every reason to be angry with me. But I did have my reasons, and if you'd only listen to me I could explain. After all, you didn't try to get in touch with me again, did you? How do you know I didn't think it was because you regretted what you had said?'

Matthew stared at her for a long moment, and then he licked his dry lips. 'I need a drink,' he said, lurching back into the library, and Rachel took the opportunity to follow him. Closing the door behind her, she moved quickly to put herself between him and the tray of bottles on the bureau.

'You don't need a drink,' she declared, resisting the angry aggression in his eyes. 'Don't you see? We have to talk to one another.'

'What about?'

'Us.'

'There is no "us",' he said flatly. 'Not any more.'

'Yes, there is.' Rachel refused to be daunted. 'Unless you're telling me you don't want me any more. Is that what you're saying?' She held her breath. 'Well? Is it?'

He turned away from her then, running unsteady hands through the tangled darkness of his hair, and her heart went out to him. He looked so lost and troubled, and she badly wanted to put her arms around him. But her courage was not that strong, no matter what Lady Olivia had said.

'You wouldn't be here if it weren't for my mother,' he muttered, after a long pause. 'You walked out of here of your own free will. Nothing's changed.'

'Yes, it has.' Rachel caught her lower lip between her teeth. 'Didn't you ever ask yourself why I might have gone away?'

Matthew's lips twisted. 'Oh, yes,' he said harshly. 'Yes, I asked myself that. But there was no answer, was there? I'd told you my side of the story, but evidently it wasn't enough, was it?'

'Yes. Yes, it was.' Rachel took a steadying breath. 'But that wasn't the end of it.'

'What do you mean?'

'I mean…' Rachel knew there was no easy way to explain her reasons for seeing her aunt. 'Oh, Matt, I don't know why I did it, but—I went to see Aunt Maggie the afternoon you left for Geneva.'

'So?'

Matthew was unperturbed, and if Rachel had needed any further proof that he was innocent of any deception his attitude would have convinced her. But that didn't make her own task any easier.

'I had to see her,' she said at last. 'I know you may think it was foolish, but I wanted to confront her with her own lies. For so many years, I had believed everything she told me—' She broke off as the irony of that truth gripped her yet again. 'I was sure that this time I had the upper hand, and I wanted to tell her that, in spite of everything, we were going to get back together.'

'And?'

Matthew's eyes were almost sober now, and Rachel wondered how she could ever have disbelieved him.

'Well,' she said jerkily, 'it didn't work out the way I expected.'

'No?'

'No.' Rachel groaned. 'Oh, Matt, she said—she said Barbara had had a miscarriage—'

'She did.'

'I know that now. But Aunt Maggie said it was the baby she had been carrying when I left Penrith.'

Matthew blinked. 'But I told you, I hadn't touched Barbara before you left for London.'

'I know. I know.' Rachel could feel the hot tears pricking at the backs of her eyes. 'But—don't you see? She said you were the one who had been lying, not her. And—and—'

'You believed her.' Matthew's voice was harsh.

Rachel bent her head. 'Yes.'

'Why?'

'Oh, God, I don't know.' Rachel sniffed. 'I suppose I still couldn't believe she had been lying all these years.'

'But you believed I could?'

'No. Yes. Oh, I don't know. I've told you. I didn't know who to believe.'

'Even after I had told you about the pills!'

'I know.' Rachel felt terrible. 'I have no excuse for what I did, and actually your mother pointed out that if they were Barbara's pills then she couldn't possibly have got pregnant, even if—'

'Even if I had made love to her?' Matthew finished coldly. 'My God, you have some opinion of me, don't you? Even now.'

'No. *No!*' Rachel covered her face with her hands. 'You don't understand. So much had happened in so short a time, and I couldn't take it in—'

'You couldn't believe me.' Matthew sounded furious now. 'Hell, and you think that by coming here now you can ignore the past?'

Rachel's hands dropped to her throat. 'I—did think that,' she admitted huskily, clutching the frogged fastening of the cape. 'But—perhaps I was wrong—'

'You were!' he snarled, stepping closer to her, so that she could see the raw fury in his face. 'You bloody were,' he added. 'What do you think I am? Some kind of emotional tap, that can be turned on and off at will? Well, it's too late. Much too late. I don't need you, Rachel. I don't need anyone.'

Rachel couldn't take any more. A sob catching in her throat, she brushed past him and almost ran towards the door. She had to get away, she thought despairingly, before she humiliated herself utterly by bursting into tears in front of him. This was not one of the scenarios she had envisaged, and, no matter what Lady Olivia expected of her, she had to get out of there.

His hand embedded in the swirling mass of her hair arrested her, and she almost screamed at the pain he inflicted. 'Wait,' he muttered savagely, pressing his other hand flat against the door, preventing her from opening it, even had she had the strength to do so. 'Wait,' he said again, and now she felt his breath hot against the back of her neck. 'Damn you, Rachel, don't you walk out on me again.'

As his hand in her hair eased its pressure, Rachel turned so that her back was against the door and looked up at him through tear-filled eyes. 'I thought that was what you wanted,' she protested, and he uttered a defeated groan.

'Well, it's not,' he said thickly, his tone a mixture of hunger and frustration. 'I was always a fool where you were concerned. God, Rachel, why did you come here? Was it just because my mother asked you to, or did you really want to see me?'

'I really wanted to see you,' she assured him huskily, as his fingers disentangled themselves from the silky strands that were as reluctant to release him as she was. 'If I'd only never gone to see Aunt Maggie, none of this would have happened. I should have waited. I should have waited until you came back, and we could have gone to see her together.'

Matthew rested his forehead against hers. 'And now?'

She took a trembling breath. 'That's up to you.'

'Is it?' His fingers slid down her neck to the scented hollow of her throat. 'Is it really?' His thumbs probed the sensitive contours of her ears. 'And if I believe you, will you promise not to run out on me again without at least listening to my side of the story?'

'Yes. Oh, yes.' Rachel put up her hands to cover his, shaking her head against the hot tears that refused to be denied.

'Oh, love…'

His voice was hoarse as he lowered his mouth to hers, and she quivered uncontrollably as his warm lips rubbed gently against her yielding flesh. It was so long since he had kissed her, and the memories came flooding back. But, with infinite tenderness, Matthew licked away the treacherous tears that overspilled her eyes, and when his mouth returned to hers again there was a definite urgency to his kiss.

Keeping his mouth on hers, his hands found the lapels of her cape, parting the cloth so that when he rested his body against hers she was able to feel the heat of his lean frame.

'God, I can't believe this,' he muttered, cupping her face in his hands and gazing down at her with eyes that were both dark and pain-filled. 'Are you sure you know what you're doing? I won't let you go away again, you know. If you—if you stay here now, it's for good!'

The persistent rap at the door behind them was unnerving, but belatedly Rachel remembered she had ordered coffee for both of them.

'Um—Mrs Moffat,' she breathed, reluctantly trying to push him away from her, and with a supreme effort Matthew used the door on either side of her head to gain his balance.

'As you say,' he said, with the precise enunciation of someone who is not quite in control of himself, and as he moved away Rachel turned to open the door.

Mrs Moffat took in the scene she had interrupted with shrewd eyes, but if she was surprised to see Rachel she kept that particular observation to herself.

'This room smells like a brewery,' she declared bravely, bustling in to put the tray of coffee on the table, before opening a window to allow the cold night air into the library. 'And you must be tired, Miss Rachel,' she added, turning to her with a tight smile. 'I suggest you go and freshen up, and I'll have a nice little supper waiting for both of you when you come down.'

'That won't be necessary—' began Matthew, but Rachel overrode his denial.

'That would be lovely, Mrs Moffat,' she averred, avoiding her ex-husband's impatient gaze. 'I'm sure Matt could do with freshening up, too.'

'I'm sure he could,' agreed Mrs Moffat, taking advantage of Rachel's presence to voice thoughts she would otherwise never have dreamed of articulating. She looked at her employer with wary eyes. 'Is—er—is that all right, Mr Matt?'

'Why ask me?' enquired Matthew tersely, pouring himself a cup of black coffee and raising it grimly to his lips. 'Mrs—*Miss* Rachel appears to be giving the orders around here.'

Rachel sighed. 'Matt—'

'No. You go ahead,' he declared harshly, putting his empty cup back on the tray. 'As you both seem to think I'm in need of some immediate restoration, I'd better go and do something about it.'

'Matt—'

But he was already walking out of the room, albeit a little unsteadily, and, meeting Mrs Moffat's eyes, Rachel decided to let him go. They had plenty of time…

'Are you staying, Miss Rachel?'

Mrs Moffat's question brought her eyes back to the elderly housekeeper, and, putting her own thoughts aside for the moment, Rachel inclined her head. 'I hope so.'

'Well—thank goodness for that.' Mrs Moffat was relieved. 'Now perhaps things can go back to normal around here.'

Rachel smiled. 'Thank you.'

'Don't thank me. Just don't—change your mind again, will you?' exclaimed the housekeeper fervently. 'I don't think Mr Matt could stand it.'

After Mrs Moffat had gone to prepare the supper she had suggested, Rachel forced herself to drink a cup of coffee before going out to her car to rescue the suitcase she had left there earlier. Then she climbed the stairs to the first landing, turning instinctively towards the room she had occupied just four months ago. She had left here feeling so betrayed, she remembered, shivering. She must never let that happen again.

Evidently, Mrs Moffat had sent up one of the maids to turn down the bed, and lamplight glowed on creamy silk pillowcases and a pale lemon quilted duvet. Obviously, the housekeeper had not been prepared to speculate as to where Rachel might be spending the night, and the room was warm and welcoming.

Setting her suitcase on the ottoman at the foot of the bed, Rachel took off her cape and laid it over the arm of a chair. Outside, an owl swooped over the house, and she heard distinctly its eerie call as she peeled off the velvet jacket of her suit, and the olive-coloured blouse beneath. The skirt slid easily over her hips. Matthew was not the only one who had lost weight, she reflected, and, catching a glimpse of her reflection in the mirrors of the dressing-table, she wondered if he had noticed.

And where was he? she wondered, extracting a deep red dressing-gown from her case, and wrapping its silken folds about her. She had thought he might have been here, waiting for her, but evidently he had gone to his own suite of rooms.

She hesitated only a moment before opening her door again, and making her way along the corridor to where Matthew's apartments were situated. In spite of all that had gone before, she was still nervous, and it took every ounce of courage she had to open the door to his sitting-room and step inside.

Closing the door again, she leaned back against it, and as she did so she heard the sound of running water. Obviously he was taking a shower, and, although her instincts urged her to go through the bedroom and into the bathroom, there were some things she just could not do. It had been ten years, after all, she reminded herself unsteadily. And just because she was swamped with painful memories, there was no reason to suppose Matthew felt the same.

All the same, she could not remain glued to the bedroom door, and, taking a deep breath, she stepped away from the supporting panels. Matthew's rooms, *the rooms they had once shared*, had changed, too. Whereas, when they had lived together, there had been some feminine influence in their design, now they were almost starkly masculine, and she wondered why Barbara had never imprinted her personality upon them.

But thinking about Barbara was still too painful to bear, and instead she moved on, through the plain gold and brown austerity of his sitting-room, to his bedroom door.

Like the sitting-room, the bedroom was decorated in shades of beige and brown, the only splash of colour the multicoloured pattern of the quilt that covered the enormous king-sized bed. It was the bed they had chosen together when they'd first got married, and thinking of him sharing *that* with Barbara was almost unbearable.

She was standing there, staring at the bed, when Matthew appeared in the bathroom doorway. Evidently he had not heard her come into his apartments, and his eyes met hers with obvious wariness, before the awareness of his own lack of covering caused him to step back.

'Don't—don't go!' exclaimed Rachel hastily, her eyes shifting from his face, and the light covering of dark hair on his chest, to the flat planes of his stomach, where more hair arrowed down to his sex. It was the first time she had seen Matthew naked for so long, and although he was painfully thin he was still the most beautiful man she had ever seen. 'Oh, Matt,' she breathed, as his body shifted revealingly beneath her eyes. 'I love you. I love you so much.'

She covered the space between them in milliseconds, and when his arm closed around her, imprisoning her against his hard body, she knew a marvellous feeling of homecoming. Winding her arms about his waist, she pressed herself against him, and his hardening body fitted naturally against the yielding softness of hers.

'I want you,' he groaned, his tongue sliding between her lips to ravage the trembling contours of her mouth. 'God—you don't know how much!'

'I have some idea,' she breathed huskily, slipping her hand between them and touching his throbbing hardness. 'Oh, Matt, make love to me, *please*! I need you. I need you so much.'

The quilt that covered the bed was soft and cool against her bare back as Matthew knelt over her. The red silk dressing-gown had been discarded on to the warm beige carpet, and Matthew was gaining a certain amount of satisfaction from divesting her of the remaining items of her clothing. She had not been wearing a bra, but she was still wearing lacy bikini briefs, and gossamer-fine black tights, and, although Matthew was as eager as she was to consummate their loveplay, as he peeled her tights off her legs he followed them with his lips.

'Soft—so soft,' he breathed unsteadily, finding the sensitive skin of her inner thigh and probing the soft curls at the junction of her legs. 'Dear lord, Rachel, this is not going to be a prolonged seduction, I'm afraid. I need you now. This minute! Oh, God, you're so beautiful! How have I ever lived without this—?'

Rachel flinched a little as he slid into her. It had been so long. But it was a marvellous feeling, knowing his body was joined to hers once again, and she wound her arms around his neck to bring him closer, arching her hips up to his.

It was over almost too soon, although the pulsating heat that shook her body long after Matthew had collapsed on top of her kept her on a high of ecstasy for many mindless minutes. She hadn't forgotten Matthew, but she had forgotten the perfection of their lovemaking, and when he would have drawn away she wrapped her legs around him, and kept him where he was.

'Do you have any idea what you're doing to me?' he groaned, burying his face between her breasts, and as he swelled inside her she uttered a contented giggle.

'I have a pretty good idea,' she breathed, and as he levered himself up on his elbows to look down at her she laved one of his hard nipples with her tongue.

'You said we had to talk,' he reminded her thickly, finding the parted sweetness of her mouth, but Rachel didn't want to talk right then.

'Later,' she whispered, her nails digging possessively into his narrow buttocks. 'Mmm, Matt, do that again! I love it…'

Evidently, Mrs Moffat had decided against reminding them that she was preparing supper. A couple of hours later, Rachel opened her eyes to find Matthew propped up on one elbow looking down at her, and it was obvious the thought of food was the last thing on his mind, too.

'You're the only woman I know who looks just as good asleep as awake,' he murmured, lowering his head to caress her lips with his tongue, and although Rachel didn't much care for the comparison she decided to be charitable.

'You've had a lot of experience, I suppose,' she ventured, trying to make light of it, but her pain was not as easy to hide as she had thought.

'Not a lot, no,' Matthew replied gently, understanding her feelings. 'And since you came back into my life, there's been no one else.'

Rachel moistened her dry lips. 'Was there—before?'

'When Barbara was alive, you mean?' Matthew's lips twisted. 'Some, I guess. As I told you before, Barbara and I did not have a real marriage.'

'Not—not ever?'

'Oh…' Matthew groaned and rolled on to his back, raising his arm to shade his eyes against the warm glow from the lamp on the table beside the bed. 'Well, we had a sexual relationship for a while. But it didn't work out. That's the simple answer, at least.'

'And the unsimple one?'

'God!' Matthew ran weary fingers through the tumbled thickness of his hair. 'We had so many problems. Once my initial desire to hurt you was blunted, it was easy to see the holes in our relationship. We had nothing in common, for a start. Barbara liked travelling, spending money on expensive clothes and jewels, going to parties! I didn't. And she hated being pregnant. I'm pretty sure that was why she lost the first baby. But she knew that two miscarriages would look pretty suspicious, and I suppose she was prepared to do anything to secure her position. But, once she was pregnant again, things went from bad to worse. We used to row all the time, and she told me she had only married me because—well, because she was jealous of you.'

'She hated me, you mean.' Rachel shivered. 'Oh, Matt.'

She turned her face into his chest, and pressed her lips against the hair-roughened skin. His skin smelt warm and musky, and when she touched him with her tongue he tasted sharply masculine.

He shuddered under her caressing lips, but he had to go on. 'After Rosemary was born, she hardly saw her mother. Barbara was never there. I suspected there were other men, but I didn't care. I had no desire to start divorce proceedings, and maybe run the risk of Barbara's getting custody of Rosemary. But even that wasn't enough.'

'What do you mean?'

Matthew heaved a sigh. 'I don't know why she did it now. Maybe she already knew she was ill, and it was her way of taking her revenge. In any event, she evidently resented the love I had for our daughter, because when Rosemary was six years old she told me that I wasn't the child's father.'

'No!' Rachel blinked and sat up. 'Why would she do that?'

'Perhaps it was the truth.'

'No!' Rachel was adamant. 'She was lying.'

'Was she?'

'Of course she was.' Rachel shifted, and Matthew's eyes darkened as the lamplight glinted on her small breasts, swollen and erect from his lovemaking. 'Rosemary's your daughter. How could you doubt it?'

'Well—' Matthew expelled a breath '—lately, I have come to the conclusion that you might be right. But for months—years, even—I couldn't be certain.'

'Oh, Matt!'

'Well, you have to admit, *we* were married for almost four years, and we never had any children—'

'You know why.' Rachel stared at him helplessly. 'Besides—'

'In any case, Barbara accused me of being incapable of siring a child, and you don't know what that does to a man.'

'Oh, God!'

Rachel was horrified, but now she could understand so much. Not least, why Matthew and his daughter had been so estranged.

'I guess it was her way of hurting me. And I tried not to let it affect my feelings for Rosemary, but it did,' he muttered heavily. 'Until—until you came back—'

'Me?'

'Yes, you.' Matthew closed his eyes for a moment. 'I think it was seeing you two together; realising what I had lost. I know I was jealous, at first. Jealous of you, and jealous of Rosemary. It was only when you had that fall, and I thought I'd killed you, that I realised what was wrong. I realised, too, that it didn't really matter whether Rosemary was my child or not. She thought she was, and that was all that mattered.'

Rachel shook her head, leaning over him so that the pointed tips of her breasts were brushing his chest. 'She *is* your daughter,' she told him huskily. 'Anyone can see that.' She caught her breath. 'Why else do you think she's so provoking?'

Matthew's hand behind her head brought her mouth to his. 'So long as I provoke you,' he said unsteadily.

'Oh, you do,' she breathed, smoothing her thumbs across his cheeks. Then she shook her head again. 'Poor Barbara! You know, I can almost feel sorry for her now.'

'You're very charitable.'

'Yes—well, I'm very lucky,' said Rachel shakily. 'After all, I've got both of you, haven't I? You and Rosemary.'

Matthew bit his lip. 'And if we don't have any more children, you won't mind?'

'But we *will*!' Rachel sighed, and then she added softly, 'I wasn't going to tell you this. Not yet, at any rate. But—

I had a miscarriage, too. Just—just a few days after I arrived in London.'

Matthew stared at her then, his eyes wide and comprehending. 'Our child!' he muttered disbelievingly. 'Oh, God! Our child!'

'Our son, actually,' she admitted, the memory of that awful occasion still having the power to bring the tears to her eyes. Determinedly, she blinked them away. 'But we'll have others. If—if it's what you want.'

'If it's what I want?' he groaned, rolling over so that she was imprisoned beneath him. 'God, you know what I want. But is it what you want? Downstairs—downstairs, I told you it was all—or nothing, and I thought you looked pretty relieved when Mrs Moffat interrupted us.'

'Did you?' Rachel's lips twisted now. 'Oh, darling, if I looked relieved when Mrs Moffat interrupted us it was probably because I was in danger of tearing your clothes off there and then, and somehow I don't think your housekeeper would have approved.'

Matthew buried his face in her neck. 'And—Harcourt?' he muttered, as if he was dreading her answer and didn't want to see her face when she made it.

'He's found a replacement,' whispered Rachel gently. 'A young man called Alan Maxwell. I can assure you, he's much more to Justin's taste than I ever was.'

Matthew lifted his head to look at her. 'Are you serious?'

'Do I look serious?' she asked, touching his mouth with her fingers, and he caressed each one with his lips.

'You look—beautiful,' he told her huskily. 'The most beautiful woman I have ever known.' He paused. 'You won't mind living here again, will you? I mean—' He broke off. 'I know it must have unhappy associations.'

Rachel shook her head. 'Not now. Not now that we're together again.' She took a breath. 'Did—did you redecorate these rooms after Barbara died?'

'Barbara never shared these rooms,' said Matthew roughly. 'That was one betrayal I couldn't make. We—slept in one of the other bedrooms. While we were sleeping together, that is. Long before she told me about Rosemary, I had moved back in here.'

Rachel couldn't deny the overwhelming feeling of relief she knew right then. She pitied Barbara, and she was sorry she was dead. But she was glad that Matthew had kept their love inviolate.

'About Rosemary,' she ventured now, 'do you think she will mind if—if I come to live here?'

'If you marry me, you mean,' Matthew corrected her softly. 'Let's have no more misunderstandings. I love you, and I want you to be my wife. And you know Rosemary will be delighted. She's very fond of you.'

'Honestly?'

'Honestly,' he assured her. 'And from now on that's going to be the only thing between us. Agreed?'

'Agreed,' she conceded, somewhat unsteadily. And there didn't seem a lot more to say...

**Carole Mortimer** says: 'I was born in England, the youngest of three children—I have two older brothers. I started writing in 1978, and have now written over 90 books for Mills & Boon®. I have four sons, Matthew, Joshua, Timothy and Peter, and a Bearded Collie dog called Merlyn. I'm in a very happy relationship with Peter senior; we're best friends as well as lovers, which is probably the best recipe for a successful relationship. We live on the Isle of Man.'

**Look out for THE UNWILLING MISTRESS
by Carole Mortimer
in Mills & Boon Modern Romance™, March 2004.**

# *LOVERS IN THE AFTERNOON*

**by**

**C**AROLE **M**ORTIMER

For
John, Matthew
and Joshua

# CHAPTER ONE

WHAT was this man *doing* in her bed!

Dear God, it wasn't even her bed but his, she remembered now. She had been introduced to him at his office only that afternoon, and five hours later here she was in his bed!

She looked down at the man sleeping so peacefully at her side, one strong arm flung back across the pillow as he lay on his back, dark hair silvered with grey, all of his body deeply tanned, from a holiday he had taken in Acapulco he had told her over dinner. And she was well aware of the beauty of all that body, had touched every inch of it, from the broad shoulders, muscled chest with its covering of brown-grey hair, taut flat waist, powerfully built thighs, down long supple legs. The black silk sheet was pushed back to his waist now to reveal the strength of his chest and arms, the thick dark hair disappearing in a vee past his navel and down.

Her gaze returned quickly to his face. It was a strong, powerful face even in sleep, a wide intelligent forehead, widely defined eyebrows, beneath the long-lashed lids were eyes of a piercing grey, a long straight nose, firm uncompromising mouth, and a jaw that was firm as he slept. He was one of the most attractive men she had ever seen, or was ever likely to see, and she had spent most of the evening here in this bed with him, the first man to make love to her since her separation from her husband eight months ago.

But why did it have to be Adam Faulkner, rich industrialist, sixteen years her senior at thirty-nine, and her most recent client with the interior designing company she worked for!

She had gone to work so innocently this morning, had got out of bed at her usual seven-thirty, fed the fish and cat, warned the cat not to eat the fish while she was out all day, got her usual breakfast of dry toast and black coffee, both of which she consumed on her way to the shower as she usually did, applied the light make-up to her heart-shaped face and ever-sparkling green eyes, styled her feathered red-brown hair into its usual mass of uncontrolled lengths to her shoulders before donning the tailored blue suit and lighter blue blouse that made her hair look more red than brown, the white camisole beneath the blouse clearly the only covering to her unconfined breasts.

She had gone down to the underground car-park to her dilapidated VW, sworn at if for the usual ten minutes before it deigned to start. She had then emerged out into the usual helter-skelter of traffic that was London in the rush-hour, dodging the other sea-soned drivers as she drove to her office at Stevenson Interiors, cursing the fact that she needed to take the car at all, but the reliable London underground system went nowhere near her flat or the office. Yes, it had been a pretty usual day up to that point in time.

Her breathless entrance on to the sixth floor that housed the employees of Stevenson Interiors, after be-ing stuck in the lift for fifteen minutes was also usual; the lift broke down at least once a week, and Leonie was usually in it when it did. It would have been *unusual* if she weren't!

"The lift again?" Betty, the young, attractive receptionist, asked ruefully.

"Yes," her sigh was resigned. "One of these days I'm going to fool it and take the stairs."

"All twelve flights?" Betty's eyes widened.

Leonie grimaced, running controlling fingers through her flyaway hair. "That would be a little drastic, wouldn't it?" she conceded wryly.

Betty handed her her messages. "In your state of physical *un*fitness it could be suicide!"

"Thanks!" She skimmed through the pieces of paper she had been given, dismissing all of them as unimportant before pushing them into her navy blue clutch-bag. "What's on the agenda for today?" she looked at Betty with her usual open expression.

"The staff meeting at nine o'clock?"

"Nine—! Oh Lord," Leonie groaned, already fifteen minutes late for the meeting David had warned all employees *not* to be late for. "Maybe if I just crept into the back of the room…?" she said hopefully.

"David would notice you if you crept in on your hands and knees and stood hidden for the whole meeting," Betty told her derisively.

The other woman was right, of course. David had picked her out for his individual attention from the moment he had employed her six months ago, and although she occasionally agreed to have dinner with him she made sure it was only occasionally, not wanting any serious involvement, even if David was one of the nicest men she had ever known. An unsuccessful marriage had a way of souring you to the idea of another permanent relationship. Besides, David had little patience with the way things just seemed to happen to her, believing she should be able to have some control over the accidents that just seemed to occur whenever she was around. She remembered another man, her husband, who had also found these accidents irritating, and she didn't need that criticism in her life a second time. She could handle these "incidents" left to her own devices, she didn't need some man, no matter how nice he was, constantly criticising her.

"I'll creep in anyway." She narrowly missed walking into the pot-plant that seemed to be following her about the room. "What do you feed this on?" She looked up at the huge tree-like plant in horror. "It's taking over reception, if not the world!"

"A little love and conversation do seem to have done the trick," Betty acknowledged proudly. "Now shouldn't you be getting to the staff meeting?"

David's office was crowded to capacity as she squeezed into the back of the room, but nevertheless his reproachful gaze spotted her instantly, although he didn't falter in his flow of how well the company was doing, of how good new contracts were coming their way every day.

Leonie yawned boredly, wishing she had been stuck in the lift even longer than she had been, receiving another censorious glare from David as she did, plastering a look of interest on to her face that she had perfected during her marriage, while her thoughts wandered to the Harrison lounge she had just completed, as pleased with the result as the elderly couple had been. She always felt a sense of immense satisfaction whenever she completed a job, knew she was good at what she did, that she was at last a success at something. Although some people would have her believe differently.

"Leonie, did you hear me?"

She looked up with a start at David's impatiently

spoken question, blushing guiltily as she realised she was the cynosure of all eyes. "Er—"

"Steady," Gary warned as he stood at her side, deftly catching the papers she had knocked off the top of the filing cabinet as she jumped guiltily, grateful to the man who had taken her under his experienced wing from the day she came to work here.

Her blush deepened at the sympathetic ripple of laughter that filled the room; everyone knew of her habit of knocking and walking into things. "Of course I heard you, David," she answered awkwardly, her gaze guilelessly innocent as she looked at him steadily.

"Then you don't mind staying for a few minutes after the others have gone back to their offices?" he took pity on her, knowing very well that she hadn't been listening to a word he said.

"Er—no, of course not," she replaced the papers on the filing cabinet that Gary had caught for her, wondering what she was guilty of now, feeling like the disobedient child that had been asked to stay in after school. It couldn't be her lack of attention to what was being said that was at fault, she never did that anyway, and David knew it.

She moved to sit on the edge of his desk as the others filed out to go back to work. "Good meeting, David," she complimented brightly.

"And how would you know one way or the other?" he sighed, looking up at her, a tall loose-limbed man with wild blond hair that refused to be tamed despite being kept cut close to his head, the rest of his appearance neat to precision point. He was only twenty-eight, had built his interior designing business up from a two-room, three-man operation to the point where he had a dozen people working for

him. And Leonie knew she was lucky to be one of
them, that Stevenson Interiors was one of the most
successful businesses in its field, and that it was all
due to David's drive and initiative.

She grimaced. "Would it help if I were to say I'm
sorry?" she cajoled.

"You always are," David said without rancour. "I
wanted to talk to you about Thompson Electronics."

A frown marred her creamy brow. "Has something
gone wrong? I thought they were pleased with the
work I did for them. I don't understand—"

"Calm down, Leonie," he ordered impatiently at
her impassioned outburst. "They were pleased, they
*are* pleased, which is why the new President of the
company wants you to personally design the decor
for his own office suite."

"He does?" she gasped.

"Don't look so surprised," David mocked. "It was
a good piece of work. Even I would never have
thought of using that particular shade of pink—indeed
any shade of pink, in a group of offices."

"It was the brown that off-set the femininity of it.
You see I had—"

"You don't have to convince me of anything,
Leonie," he drawled. "Or them either. You just have
to get yourself over there at four o'clock this afternoon to discuss the details."

She was still relatively new at her job, and tried to
make every design she did a work of art, something
personal; she was more than pleased to know that
someone else had seen and appreciated some of her
completed work enough to ask for her personally. It
was the first time it had happened.

"Mrs Carlson will be expecting you," David continued. "She phoned and made the appointment first

thing this morning. And she'll introduce you to the President then.''

''Ronald Reagan?''

He gave a patiently humouring sigh. ''Where do you get your sense of humour from?''

She grinned at him. ''It's what keeps my world going.''

David frowned at the underlying seriousness beneath her words. Except for the friendly, and often loony façade she presented to everyone here, he knew little about the real Leonie Grant. Her employee's file said she had been married but was now separated from her husband, but she never spoke of the marriage or the man she had been married to, her openness often seeming to hide a wealth of pain and disillusionment.

But it never showed, and Leonie found as much humour in her clumsiness as everyone else did, able to laugh at herself and the things that happened to her.

His mouth quirked into a smile. ''I have to admit that when Mrs Carlson said the President would expect you at four o'clock the same thought crossed my mind!''

''Naughty, David,'' she shook her head reprovingly, her eyes glowing deeply green.

For a moment they shared a smile of mutual humour, and then David shook his head ruefully. ''Try not to be late for the meeting,'' he advised. ''From the way Mrs Carlson was acting he sounds pretty awesome.''

Leonie grimaced. ''Are you sure you want to send me, I could walk in, trip over a matchstick, and end up sliding across his desk into his lap!''

''He asked for you specifically.'' But David

frowned as he mentally envisaged the scene she had just described. ''I'll take the risk,'' he said without enthusiasm.

''Sure?''

''No,'' he answered with complete honesty. ''But short of lying to the man I don't know what else I can do. Just try not to be late,'' he warned again.

And she did try, she tried very hard, but it seemed the fates were against her from the start. She caught her tights on the door as she got into her VW, drove around for another ten minutes trying to find somewhere to park so she could buy some new ones, getting back to the car just in time to personally accept her parking ticket from the traffic warden, making a mad dash to find somewhere to change her tights, laddering that pair too in her haste, although it was high enough up her leg not to show. By this time she in no way resembled the coolly smart young woman who had left Stevenson Interiors in plenty of time to reach Thompson Electronics by four o'clock. It was already five to four, and she was hot and sticky from her exertions with the tights, her make-up needing some repair, her hair having lost its glowing bounce in the heat of the day. She was already going to be a few minutes late; taking time to refresh her make-up and brush her hair wasn't going to make that much difference now.

It was ten minutes past four when she entered the Thompson building, her slim briefcase in her hand, and except for the fact that she was late, looking like a self-contained young executive. Ten minutes wasn't so bad, she could blame that on the traffic. She certainly didn't intend going into the story of the ripped tights as her excuse, or the parking ticket either! It was—

Oh no, she just didn't believe this, it couldn't be happening to her! But she knew that it was as the smooth-running lift made a terrible grinding noise and shuddered to a halt somewhere between the eighth and ninth floors. She was stuck in a lift for the second time that day! And as usual she was alone. She was always alone when the damned things broke down, never had anyone to help calm the panic that she felt. This was a large lift, not like the one at Stevenson Interiors, but she would still rather be on the other side of those steel doors. Oh well, at least the floor was carpeted if she had to spend any amount of time here, so she could be comfortable. But it wasn't likely that she would be here for long, this was a big and busy building, someone was sure to realise sooner or later that one of the lifts was stuck between floors. And she hoped it was sooner!

She sank to the floor after pressing the emergency button, knowing from experience that people rarely took notice of that bell. God, what a day it had been, worse than her usual string of mishaps. If she didn't know better she would think— But no, she wouldn't even think about him. God, this was a hell of a place to start thinking of the disastrous effect her husband had had on her, his disapproval of almost everything she did making her more nervous, and consequently more klutzy, than ever.

She determinedly opened her briefcase, going through the fabric book she had brought with her, wondering what sort of colour scheme the President of the company would favour. She had thought of a few ideas, but basically she just wanted to hear what his tastes were.

She became so engrossed in matching paints and fabrics, the books strewn over the floor, that for some time she managed to forget she was marooned in a lift eight-and-a-half floors up. It was almost five-thirty when she heard the sound of banging from above, a voice that sounded strangely hollow calling down that the lift would be working shortly.

Leonie stood up, her legs stiff from where she had been sitting on the floor for over an hour, losing her balance as the lift began moving almost immediately, jerking for several feet before moving smoothly, Leonie flung about in the confined space, falling to the ground in a sprawled heap as it shuddered to a halt and the door miraculously creaked slowly open.

The first thing Leonie saw from her floor-level view was a pair of well-shod feet, the man's black shoes made of a soft leather, a meticulous crease down the centre of the grey trouser legs. Before she could raise her gaze any further Mrs Carlson was rushing into the lift to help her to her feet, the black shoes and grey-covered legs turning away.

''Bring her into my office as soon as you've helped her tidy up,'' ordered a curt male voice.

Leonie turned sharply to look at the man as the other woman fussed around her, but all she saw was the back of the man's head as he entered a room at the end of the corridor.

''Have you been in here long?'' The middle-aged woman helped her pick up her sample books from the floor, a tall capable woman who had been secretary to the last President of the company for over twenty years. Leonie had met her when she worked here last, and although the other woman tried to be distant and authoritative, her warm brown eyes belied the role.

Leonie liked the other woman, but she wasn't sure she liked anyone seeing her sprawled on the floor in that undignified way. ''An hour or so,'' she dismissed distractedly, pushing the books into her briefcase, anxious to get out of the lift.

Stella Carlson followed her out into the corridor. "In all the years I've worked here I've never known any of the lifts break down before," she shook her head.

Leonie grimaced, brushing her skirt down. "I have a strange effect on lifts."

"Really?" the other woman frowned. "Well as long as you're all right now…?"

"Fine," she nodded dismissively. "I'm too late for my meeting, so perhaps you could explain the reason for my delay to your boss and I could make another appointment for tomorrow?"

"Didn't you hear, you're to go in as soon as you feel able to."

She thought of the man with the black shoes and grey trousers. "*That* was the new President of the company?" she dreaded the answer, although she knew what it was going to be.

"Yes," Mrs Carlson confirmed.

Oh David, Leonie mentally groaned, I didn't trip and slide across his desk into his lap, but I did lie sprawled at his feet on the floor of a lift that *never* broke down! David would never understand, things like this just didn't happen to him. They didn't happen to *any* normal person!

"Now seems as good a time as any," she said dully, knowing her dignity was past redemption. "I'm sure I've delayed you long enough already."

"Not at all," the other woman assured her as they walked side by side down the corridor. "Things have been a little—hectic, here the last few weeks."

The new boss was obviously giving the employees a shake-up, Leonie thought ruefully, her humour leav-

ing her as she realised she would probably be in for
the same treatment. After all, if she hadn't been ten
minutes late in the first place she wouldn't have been
in the lift when it broke down. Or would she? As she
had told Mrs Carlson, she had a strange effect on lifts.
She had a strange effect on most inanimate objects,
things just seemed to happen to them whenever she
was around.

She smoothed her skirt down as Mrs Carlson
knocked on the office door, unaware of the fact that
her hair was sadly in need of brushing after her fall,
that the fullness of her mouth was bare of lipgloss
where she had chewed on her lips as she looked
through the sample books. Not that she would have
worried too much about it if she had known; she
couldn't possibly make a worse impression than she
had as she grovelled about the lift floor!

Mrs Carlson opened the door after the terse instruction from within for them to enter. ''Miss Grant, sir,''
she introduced quietly.

Leonie stared at the man seated behind the desk,
the man that belonged to the black shoes and grey
legs, the rest of the dark grey suit as impressive, the
waistcoat taut across his flat stomach, the tailored material of the jacket stretched across widely powerful
shoulders, the white shirt beneath the suit making his
skin look very dark.

But it was his face that held her attention, a harshly
attractive face, his chin firm and square, the sensuality
of his mouth firmly controlled, his nose long and
straight, ice-grey eyes narrowed on her beneath darkly
jutting brows, silver threading the darkness of his hair
at his temples and over his ears. Anyone who was in
the least familiar with the business world would recognise Adam Faulkner from his photographs in the

newspapers, one of the most successful—and richest—men in England today. He was also—

"Miss Grant," he stood up in fluid movements, the coldness instantly gone from his eyes, his voice warm and friendly, his hand enveloping hers in a grip that was pleasantly warm, not too firm and not too loose; the exactly right handshake for a businessman to instil confidence in the person he was dealing with.

But why he should waste his time on such a gesture with her was beyond her, she was—

"I hope your unfortunate delay in our lift hasn't disturbed you too much," he continued smoothly, releasing her hand slowly, leaving the imprint of his touch against her flesh.

Leonie was stunned at his obvious concern. "I—I have that effect on lifts," she mumbled the same lame excuse she had given Mrs Carlson, conscious of the other woman still standing in the room with them.

Dark brows rose questioningly. "That sort of thing happens to you often?"

Colour heightened her cheeks. "Yes," she bit out. "Look, I don't think—"

"Don't worry, I'm not expecting you to conduct our business meeting after your ordeal in the lift," he assured her. "I suggest we make another appointment for tomorrow," he looked at Mrs Carlson for confirmation. "Some time in the afternoon," he instructed as she left the room to consult his appointment book.

"Please, I—"

"Please sit down, Miss Grant," Adam Faulkner instructed when he saw how pale she had become. "Let me get you a drink. Would you like tea or coffee, or perhaps something stronger?" He pressed a button on his desk to reveal an extensive array of drinks in the cabinet situated behind Leonie.

Leonie just kept staring at him, too numb to even answer.

"Something stronger, I think," he nodded derisively at her lack of response, striding across the room to pour her some whisky into a glass. "Drink it down," he instructed her firmly as she made no effort to take the glass from his lean fingers.

She took the glass, swallowing without tasting, reaction definitely setting in.

Adam Faulkner moved to sit on the edge of his desk in front of her, dangerously close, the warmth of his maleness seeming to reach out and engulf her. "Terrible experience, getting caught in a stationary lift." He took the empty glass from her unresisting fingers, seeming satisfied that she had drunk it as instructed. "I've been caught in several myself in the past," he added dryly. "Although not lately."

"It's my second time today," Leonie mumbled dully, feeling the alcohol in her bloodstream, remembering too late that she hadn't had any lunch, that the piece of dry toast she had eaten for breakfast wasn't enough to stop the effect the whisky was having on her. That was all she needed to complete her day, to be roaring drunk in front of this man! "The one at work has always been unreliable," she added in defence of her clumsiness in getting stuck in two lifts that had broken down.

"Maybe you have too much electricity in your body," Adam Faulkner suggested softly. "And it has an adverse effect on other electrical things."

She looked up at him sharply, and then wished she hadn't as a wave of dizziness swept over her. She was going to get up out of this chair to make a dignified exit and fall flat on her face, just to *prove* what an idiot she was! If this man weren't already aware of that!

"Maybe," she nodded, swallowing in an effort to clear her head, having a terrible urge to start giggling. In one part of her brain she could logically reason that she had little to giggle about, and in another she just wanted to start laughing and never stop. There was so much about this situation that was funny.

"Miss Grant?"

She frowned up at him. "Why do you keep calling me that?"

He shrugged. "It's your name, isn't it?"

"Leonie Grant, yes," she nodded in exaggerated movements. "I—Hic. I—Hic. Oh *no*," she groaned her humiliation as her loud hiccups filled the room. She really was making a fool out of herself—more so than usual, if that were possible! She should never have got out of bed today, should have buried her head beneath the bedclothes and stayed there until fate decided to be kind to her again. If it ever did, she groaned as she hiccuped again.

"Maybe the whisky was a bad idea," Adam said in amusement, going over to the bar to pour her a glass of water.

Leonie gave him a look that spoke volumes before swallowing the water, almost choking as a hiccup caught her mid-swallow, spitting water everywhere, including over one black leather shoe as Adam Faulkner's leg swung in front of her as he once again sat on the edge of his desk. "Oh dear," she began to mop at the shoe with tissue from her bag, becoming even more agitated when several pieces of the tissue stuck to the wet surface.

She closed her eyes, wishing the scene would evaporate, that she would find it had all been a bad dream.

But when she opened her eyes again the black shoe dotted with delicate yellow tissue was still there, and the man wearing the shoe was beginning to chuckle. Leonie looked up at him dazedly, liking the warmth in his eyes, the way they crinkled at the corners as he laughed, a dimple appearing in one lean cheek, his teeth very white and even against his tanned skin.

Mrs Carlson entered the room after the briefest knock, breaking the moment of intimacy. ''I've checked your appointment book, Mr Faulkner, and you're free at twelve o'clock or three o'clock.''

''Twelve o'clock, I think,'' he still smiled. ''Then Miss Grant and I can go out to lunch afterwards.''

''Oh but I—''

''Book a table, would you?'' He cut across Leonie's protest, smiling at his secretary, much to her obvious surprise. ''My usual place. And you may as well leave for the evening now, Miss Grant and I are just going to dinner.''

''Er—yes, Mr Faulkner.'' The older woman gave Leonie a curious look, seeming to give a mental shrug before leaving the room.

''She's wondering why you could possibly want to take me to dinner,'' Leonie sighed, wondering the same thing herself. But at least the suggestion had stopped her hiccups!

Adam stood up after dusting the tissue from his shoe. ''It's the least I can do after your ordeal in the lift.''

''But that was my fault—''

''Nonsense,'' he humoured.

Leonie blinked at the determination in his face. ''Why should you want to take me out to dinner?''

''Miss Grant—''

''Will you stop calling me that!''

Would you prefer Leonie?'' he queried softly, locking his desk drawers and picking up his briefcase in preparation for leaving for the evening.

''Yes,'' she snapped.

''Then you must call me Adam,'' he invited huskily.

''I'm well aware of your name,'' she bit out impatiently. The whisky may have gone to her head but she wasn't that drunk! And she had no idea why this man should want to take her out to dinner, they—

''Then please use it,'' he urged, as his hand on her elbow brought her to her feet.

Leonie swayed slightly, falling against him, flinching away from the hard warmth of his body. ''Please, I don't want to go out to dinner,'' she protested as he propelled her from the room at his side, the top floor of the building strangely in silence, Mrs Carlson having followed his instruction and left for the evening, the other employees having left some time ago.

Adam didn't release her arm. ''When did you last eat?'' he asked pointedly as she swayed again.

''I had some toast for breakfast this morning. I need to diet,'' she defended heatedly as the grey eyes looked her over disapprovingly.

''You're too thin,'' he stated bluntly.

''I'm a size ten,'' she told him proudly.

''Definitely too thin,'' he repeated arrogantly. ''I happen to be one of those men who prefers his woman to have some meat on her bones.''

His woman? *His* woman! Just who did he think he was? ''I happen to like being thin,'' she told him irritably.

He arched dark brows. ''Do you also like starving to death?'' he drawled.

It was her weakness for good food that had pushed

her up to a size fourteen in the past, and she had no intention of giving in to that weakness again, not when it had taken so much effort to lose the excess weight. "I'll survive," she muttered.

"Will you be okay in the lift now that it's working properly?" Adam asked as the lift doors opened to them invitingly.

"I'll be fine," she dismissed his concern. "Although the way today is going so far it could break down on us again," she said ruefully.

Adam smiled down at her as they were confined in the lift together. "I can't think of anyone I would rather be stuck in the lift with," he said throatily.

Leonie gave him a sharp look, expecting sarcasm but finding only warm invitation in the dark grey eyes. He was flirting with her, actually *flirting* with her!

"Pity," he drawled as they arrived safely on the ground floor, stepping into the carpeted reception area, nodding to the man on night security, guiding Leonie to the parking area, opening the passenger door of the sporty BMW for her, the top to the pale blue car back in the heat of the day. He took her briefcase from her and threw it in the back with his own before climbing in next to her, starting the engine with a roar. "Would you like the top up or down?" he enquired politely.

She touched her hair ruefully. "I think it's beyond redemption, so down, please."

Adam glanced at her as he drove the car towards the exit. "You have beautiful hair."

Leonie tensed at the unexpected compliment, her breath held in her throat.

"The style suits you," he added softly.

The tension left her in a relieved sigh. "Thank you."

Conversation was virtually impossible as they drove to the restaurant, although the fresh air did clear Leonie's head somewhat, giving her time to wonder what she was doing on her way to dinner with this man. She should have been more assertive in her refusal, shouldn't have allowed herself to be manoeuvred in this way. And yet she knew she was curious, couldn't think what possible reason Adam had for wanting to take her out to dinner. And his tolerance with the mishaps that just seemed to happen to her was too good to last!

She had been to the restaurant before that he took her to, but it had been a year ago, and hopefully no one would remember that she was the woman who had tripped on her way back from powdering her nose and pushed some poor unfortunate diner's face into his dinner!

"Good evening, Mr Faulkner," the maitre d' greeted warmly, his eyes widening warily as he saw his companion. "Madam," he greeted stiffly.

He remembered her! It had been over a year ago now, and this man still remembered her. He probably didn't have many people who came here and assaulted another diner for no reason!

"Do we have to eat here?" she demanded of Adam in desperation as they followed the other man to their table.

His brows rose. "You don't like the restaurant? Or perhaps the French cuisine isn't to your liking?"

"I love it," she sighed. "I just don't feel—comfortable here, that's all," she mumbled.

"Thanks, Henri," Adam dismissed the other man, pulling out her chair for her himself. "Just relax,

Leonie.'' His hands were warm on her shoulders as he leant forward to speak softly in her ear, his breath gently ruffling her hair.

She felt strangely bereft when he removed his hands and went to sit opposite her, their table in a quietly intimate part of the restaurant. As the waiter poured the wine that had been waiting for them, she could feel the tingling of danger along her spine, wary of this romantic setting, wary of this game. Adam was playing with her.

''Adam—''

''Try the wine,'' he urged huskily.

''When are we going to discuss the work on your office suite?'' she asked determinedly.

''Tomorrow. Before lunch.''

''About lunch—''

''Don't worry, I'm sure you'll like the restaurant I've chosen for us,'' he sipped his own wine. ''Please try it,'' he encouraged throatily.

She sighed her impatience, ignoring the glass of wine. ''Why are you doing this?''

''This?'' he prompted softly.

She shrugged. ''The charm, the restaurant, dinner, the wine. Why, Adam? And don't say to atone for the lift breaking down with me in it because I won't believe you.''

''You're right,'' he nodded, perfectly relaxed as he leant back in his chair, dismissing the waiter as he arrived to take their order. ''I had this table booked for us tonight before I even realised you were stuck in the lift.''

''Why?''

''Don't you usually go out for business meals with your prospective clients?''

"Of course," she sighed. "But it's usually lunch, and so far we haven't discussed any business."

"We will," he promised. "Tomorrow."

"Why not now?"

He shrugged at the determination in her face. "Maybe after we've eaten," he compromised.

This time he didn't wave the waiter away when he came to take their order, and with the arrival of their first and consequent courses there wasn't a lot of time for conversation. And by the time they got to the coffee stage of their meal Leonie had to admit that she didn't give a damn if they ever discussed business, feeling numb from the head down, the wine one of her favourites, her glass constantly refilled as soon as she had taken a few sips, the food as delicious as she remembered, forgetting her diet for this one night.

"You look like a well-fed cat," Adam eyed her appreciatively.

"I feel like a *very* relaxed one, if you know what I mean," she smiled happily.

He grinned. "I know exactly what you mean."

He was so handsome, so ruggedly good looking, that he made her senses spin. Or was that the wine? No, she was sure it was him. And he had been so patient with her when she knocked a glass of wine all over the table, had dismissed the anxious waiter to mop up the surplus liquid himself, had got down on the floor and helped her pick up the contents of her handbag when she accidentally opened it up the wrong way and it all fell out, had even chuckled a little when she knocked the waiter's arm and ended up with a potato in her lap. Yes, he had been very charming.

"Shall we go?" he suggested throatily as she smiled dreamily at him.

''Why not?'' She stood up, narrowly avoiding another table as she turned too suddenly. ''I never go back to the same place twice if I can avoid it,'' she assured him happily.

''It must be difficult finding new restaurants,'' he smiled, a smile that oozed sensuality.

''I rarely eat out,'' she dismissed. ''It's safer that way, for other diners, I mean,'' she explained as they went outside, surprised to see it was already dark, a glance at her watch telling her it was almost ten o'clock. They had been in the restaurant hours!

His mouth quirked. ''I noticed you have a tendency to—well, to—''

''Drop things, knock things, bump into things,'' she finished obligingly. ''My husband found it very irritating,'' she added challengingly.

''Really?'' Adam sounded non-committal.

''Yes. He— Where are we going?'' she frowned as she realised they were in a part of London she didn't know very well, the exclusive residential area.

''My apartment.''

Leonie blinked as they entered the underground car-park. ''You live here?'' she frowned.

''Since my separation,'' he nodded, coming round to open her door for her.

Things were happening too fast, much too fast she realised as they entered the spacious apartment, barely having time to notice its elegant comfort before Adam swept her into his arms, his eyes glittering darkly with desire.

''I've wanted to do this ever since the lift doors opened and I saw you grovelling about on the floor,'' he announced raggedly before his mouth claimed hers.

She wanted to ask him what he found so romantic

about a woman making a fool of herself, but the magic of his kiss put all other thoughts from her mind, drawing her into him with the sensuous movement of his mouth, his arms beneath the jacket of her suit, his hands warm through the thin material of her blouse and camisole, his thighs hardening against her as his hands moved down to cup her buttocks and pull her into him.

The effects of the brandy and wine miraculously disappeared to be replaced by something equally as heady, sexual pleasure. She had heard all the old clichés about women who were no longer married, had scorned the idea of falling into that sexual trap herself knowing how little pleasure she had found in her marriage bed, and yet she knew that she wanted Adam. And he wanted her, there could be no doubting that.

Her lips parted beneath the assault of his tongue, knowing it was merely a facsimile of the lovemaking they really wanted, Leonie feeling filled and possessed by that moist warmth, drawing him deeper into her as she returned the attack.

Adam's breathing was ragged as he pulled away to kiss her throat, peeling the jacket expertly from her shoulders, throwing it to one side, beginning to release the buttons to her blouse, his hands sure in their movements, although they trembled slightly with anticipation.

It was this slight crack in his supreme self-confidence that encouraged Leonie to do some undressing of her own, his own jacket joining hers on the floor, his waistcoat quickly following, her fingers hesitating at the buttons of his shirt.

"Please," he encouraged achingly.

Her own hands shook as she revealed the muscled smoothness of his chest, the dark hair there silvered

with grey. He was beautiful without the trappings of
the successful businessman, wearing only tailored
trousers now, his arousal barely contained.

"Leonie!" His mouth captured hers again as she
caressed his bared chest, moving fiercely against her,
pulling her into him as the tip of her tongue tentatively caressed his lips.

They left a trail of clothes to the bedroom, both
naked by the time they lay down together on the bed
still kissing, Adam's hands at her breasts making her
gasp with pleasure, the nipples hardening and aching,
asking for the tug of his mouth. They didn't have to
wait long.

Leonie didn't stop to question her complete lack of
inhibitions, inhibitions that had made her marriage
such an agony, only knowing that this man, with his
gentle caresses, held the key to her sensuality in his
hands.

Adam kissed every inch of her body, found pleasure in the secret places no other man had ever
known, making her tremble uncontrollably as his
tongue rasped the length of her spine to her nape,
quivers of excitement making her arch back into him
as he homed in on the sensitive flesh there.

She lost all lucidity as Adam's caresses brought her
again and again to the edge of a fulfilment she had
never known, as he always pulled her back from the
edge before she could reach the pinnacle she craved,
her movements beneath him becoming more and
more desperate as he refused to let her escape him
even for a second.

"Please, Adam. Please!" Her eyes were wild as
she looked up at him.

"*You* take me," he encouraged raggedly, his eyes
black with desire.

"What—?" But she understood what he meant even as he pulled her above him, going to him eagerly, gasping as he lowered her on to him, filling her in every way possible before bringing her mouth down to his.

It was so right that it should be this way, that he should allow her the freedom to be the one to choose their pleasure, a pleasure she had never known during her marriage.

She was heady with delight, kissing the dampness of his salt-tasting shoulders and throat, quivering her own satisfaction as he groaned at the invasion of her tongue, feeling his movements quicken beneath her as he could hold back no longer, the hardness of him stroking her own desire until she felt the explosion begin in the depths of her being, beginning to shake as the warm aching pleasure ripped through her whole body in a climactic holocaust.

"My beautiful Leonie," Adam gasped as he reached the summit of his own pleasure, exploding in a warmth of warm moistness. "I knew it could be this way between us!"

And it hadn't stopped there, their strength and desire returning within minutes, their second lovemaking even more intense than the first, the pleasure seeming never-ending.

Leonie looked again at the face of the man who slept beside her, wondering what on earth she had done. Oh God, what had she done!

He stirred slightly as she moved from beneath the curve of his arm, her movements stilling until she realised he was still sleeping. She blushed as she found her clothes scattered in a disorganised path from the bedroom to the lounge; she had never been so carried away by passion before. She hastily began to dress.

"What do you think you're doing?"

She balked only slightly in the movement of pulling the camisole over her head. "What does it look like I'm doing?" she said sourly; at least he had had the decency to put on a brown towelling robe before following her from the bedroom!

"Isn't it usual to spend the whole night in circumstances like these?" he drawled, his dark hair still tousled, his jaw in need of a shave now. "I didn't expect you to go sneaking off while I was asleep!"

"I wasn't sneaking off," she told him resentfully. "And there's nothing *usual* about these circumstances!" She tucked her blouse into the waistband of her skirt.

"I want you to stay the night."

She shot him an angry glare, resentful that he could look so at ease, his hands thrust casually into the pockets of his robe, his stance relaxed. "Why?"

His mouth twisted. "I'm sure I've just shown you two very good reasons why."

"Sex!"

"And what's wrong with that?" He arched dark brows.

"Nothing, you know I enjoyed it," she snapped, knowing it would be useless to deny it, brushing her hair with angry movements, whether at Adam or herself she wasn't sure.

"So stay," he encouraged softly.

"I can't, Adam," she sighed impatiently. "I don't know what game you've been playing with me this evening—"

"A game you were quite happy to go along with," he reminded gently.

She shook her head in self-condemnation. "It seemed the easy way out at the time, so much easier for me to be Leonie Grant and you to be Adam Faulkner," she said shakily.

He shrugged broad shoulders. "Why not, that's who we are."

"Because until our divorce becomes final I'm still officially Leonie Faulkner, your wife, and you're my husband!"

"And now I'm your lover," he gave a slow smile of satisfaction. "It was your idea, Leonie, you're the one that said we shouldn't have married each other but just have been lovers. And after tonight that's exactly what we're going to be!"

# CHAPTER TWO

SHE vividly remembered shouting those words at Adam before she had walked out on him and their marriage eight months ago, remembered everything about her disaster of a marriage to this man. And she didn't intend becoming involved with him again in *any way*.

She was fully dressed now, straightening the collar of her jacket. "Tonight was a mistake—"

"I have another name for it," Adam drawled.

Her eyes flashed her resentment. "I'm well aware of the fact that you planned what happened—"

"Don't pretend you didn't want it, too," he warned her softly.

She blushed at the truth of that; from the moment she had seen him seated across the desk from her at the Thompson building her senses had become alive with wanting him. And the fact that he had acted as if it were the first time they had ever met had added to the excitement. But she had a feeling, knowing Adam as she did, a much less charming and relaxed Adam, that he had realised exactly what effect his behaviour was having on her, that it had been effected to get the response from her she had refused to give him during their marriage.

"It was certainly better than anything we ever shared during our marriage," she snapped waspishly, waiting for the angry explosion she had come to expect from him when they discussed the failure of the physical side of their marriage.

"I agree." Once again he disconcerted her; he had been doing it all evening, from the time she had discovered that her estranged husband was the new President of Thompson Electronics, during dinner when he had had such patience with her "accidents", to the infinite care and gentleness he had shown her during their lovemaking. "You were right," he continued lightly. "We're much better as lovers than as husband and wife."

"We are not lovers!" She looked around desperately for her handbag so that she might get out of here. "I've left my handbag in the restaurant," she finally groaned in realisation. "And that damned man—"

"Henri," Adam put in softly, his mouth quirked with amusement.

"He already thinks I'm some sort of escapee from a lunatic asylum." She hadn't missed his covert glances in her direction during the evening. "I just can't go back there," she shuddered.

"You don't have to—"

"And I don't need any of your high-handed interference either," she cut in rudely. "Why should one more visit to that place bother me!" she told herself defiantly.

"Because it does," Adam soothed. "And there's no need to torture yourself with the thought of having to do it; your handbag is in my car."

Her eyes widened. "Are you sure?"

"Very," he replied with satisfaction. "You were so eager to get up here that you left it next to your seat."

"I was not eager to get up here," she defended indignantly.

"Maybe I should rephrase that," he said thoughtfully. "*I* was so eager to get you up here that I didn't give you a chance to think of such mundane things as a handbag. Better?" he quirked dark brows in amusement.

It was that amusement that confused her; there had been little to laugh about during their marriage, Adam always so grim. But no one knew the deviousness of his mind as well as she did, and she wasn't fooled by this charm for a moment.

"What are you up to, Adam?" she demanded impatiently. "Why are you doing this?"

He strolled across the room to her side, his movements gracefully masculine, as they always were. "I want a lover, Leonie," he told her softly, only inches away from her as he stood with his hands thrust into the pockets of his robe. "I want *you.*"

She shook her head. "You had me for a year, and it was a disaster," she recalled bitterly.

Adam nodded in acknowledgment of that fact. "Nevertheless, I want you."

"You've only just got rid of me!" she reminded desperately.

"Of the marriage, not you, Leonie."

"It's the same thing!"

"No," he smiled gently. "We both found the marriage stifling, the sort of relationship I'm suggesting—"

"With me as your mistress!" she scorned.

"Lover," he insisted. "We would be lovers."

"No!"

"Why not?" his eyes had narrowed, although he remained outwardly relaxed.

"I don't want a lover!"

His mouth quirked. "You just proved, very effectively, that you do."

Colour heightened her cheeks. "That was sex—"

"The best sex we ever had, admit it," he encouraged.

She drew in a ragged breath. "Yes."

"And as I said before, what's wrong with that?"

She sighed her exasperation. "You just don't understand—"

"I understand perfectly," he cut in soothingly. "This has all come as a bit of a shock to you—"

"That has to be the understatement of the decade!"

Adam chuckled, at once looking younger. "Poor Leonie," he smiled. "What's shocking you the most, the fact that we found such pleasure in bed together for the first time, or the fact that I want it to continue?"

She couldn't deny that she was surprised at the amount of pleasure she had known with Adam tonight, a pleasure she had known beyond all doubt that he felt too, his responses open and complete. Their sex-life during their marriage, as with everything else during that year, had been a disaster. Adam had been so experienced that in her innocence she had felt inadequate, and she had resented the way he had tried to control her body, her responses automatic and emotionless, refusing to be dominated by him. But the lovemaking they had shared tonight hadn't been restricted by any of that resentment, had been uninhibited. But that Adam should want such a relationship to continue she couldn't accept, not when the breakdown of the marriage and subsequent separation had been such a traumatic experience for her. They simply couldn't pretend they were two people they weren't.

"The first shocks me," she replied coolly. "The second surprises me. Do you honestly not remember what it was like between us, the bitterness, the pain of knowing we were all wrong for each other from the start?"

"As a married couple, not as lovers," he insisted forcefully.

"Have you forgotten what *that* was like between us?"

"Didn't this evening prove that it doesn't have to be that way?" he reasoned.

"I'm still the same person, Adam," she told him with a sigh. "I'm still sixteen years younger than you are, with the same inexperience—no matter what happened here tonight," she added pointedly. "I'm still the same klutzy person I was when we were married—"

"That's a new name for it," he laughed softly.

"I read it in a book somewhere," she dismissed impatiently. "It seemed to suit me perfectly."

"It does," he nodded, still smiling, his eyes a warm grey, crinkled at the corners.

"Don't you remember how angry all those "incidents" used to make you!"

"You're right, I was intolerant—"

"You're missing my point, Adam," she said frustratedly. "It would take a saint to put up with all the things that happen to me in one day—and that's one thing I know you aren't!"

"Have I been angry tonight at all?"

"That was only *one* night," she sighed her impatience. "It would drive you insane—it *did* drive you insane, on a regular basis."

"Haven't you heard, lovers are more tolerant?"

"Adam!"

"Leonie?"

She glowered at him. "You aren't listening to a word I've been saying."

"Of course I am," he placated. "You're young and klutzy." He smiled. "I really like that word, it describes you exactly." He sobered. "As a husband I was rigid and intolerant, lousy at making love to you. As a lover I will be generous and understanding—and very good in bed."

"In your experience," she snapped waspishly.

He raised dark brows. "You sound jealous, Leonie."

She felt the heat in her cheeks. "I most certainly am not!"

"It's all right if you are." His arms came about her as he moulded her body to his. "From a wife it would sound shrewish, from a lover it sounds possessive. I like that," he stated with satisfaction.

That wasn't all he liked from the feel of his body pressed so intimately against hers, aroused for the third time tonight. Leonie couldn't pretend not to be shocked by this evidence of his renewed desire; their sex life had deteriorated so badly at the end of their marriage that it was an effort for them to make love once a week; Adam had never wanted her *three* times in one night before!

"Adam, please stop this." She pulled agitatedly away from him as her own body quivered in reaction to his. "You've had your fun—"

"It was mutual," he drawled confidently.

"Not that sort of fun!" she snapped. "God, I can't believe this is really you proposing this preposterous arrangement! Have you thought of the consequences of your actions?"

"I already know you're on the pill to regulate your periods." He dismissed the idea of pregnancy.

"Not those consequences!" It was embarrassing how intimately this man knew the workings, and malfunctions, of her body! "We both have families, Adam, have you thought of their reactions to the relationship you're suggesting?"

"My father and your sister." The amused glow to his eyes left for the first time that evening. "I'm thirty-nine and you're twenty-three, do you really think either of us needs their permission?" he ground out.

"Your father hates me." She deliberately didn't mention her sister's feelings towards Adam, although she was sure they were both aware of those feelings; it had been one of the reasons their marriage had proved such a failure.

"My father doesn't understand you," Adam corrected gravely.

"There's nothing to understand," she dismissed scornfully. "I am what you see. A little more accident-prone around you and your father, but otherwise I'm a open book."

"Then a few of the pages must have got stuck together, because I never felt that I knew you completely either!" He gave a deep sigh. "I don't intend to argue about the past with you now, Leonie."

"Lovers don't argue?" she mocked.

His mouth quirked. "Only when they know it will take them back to bed to make up." He took her back in his arms, his mouth claiming hers.

Her lips parted of their own volition, allowing access to the thrust of his tongue, trembling as desire claimed her, clinging to the broad width of his shoulders as she swayed weakly against him.

"Stay tonight, Leonie," he urged against the creamy warmth of her throat.

She was tempted, God how she was tempted. But she couldn't do it. It had taken her eight months to put herself back together after the devastation of loving this man; she couldn't leave herself open to that sort of pain again.

"No, Adam." She pushed away from him, breathing hard, knowing by his own ragged breathing that he was as aroused as she was. "There's something else lovers can do," she told him tautly. "They can end the relationship at any time; I'm ending it." She turned on her heel.

"Where are you going?" Adam asked softly.

"Home!" She didn't even turn.

"How?" his gentle question halted her. "Your car is still at Thompson Electronics, your keys to the car are in your handbag, your money, too, in case you were thinking of taking a taxi home, and your bag is in *my* car downstairs," he reminded softly.

She had done it again! "So much for my grand exit," she said dully as she turned around.

His smile was sympathetic. "It really was very good."

"Don't humour me, Adam," she snapped.

"Lovers—"

"We are not lovers!" she bit out between clenched teeth. "And we never will be. Now if you'll give me your car keys for a few minutes I'll go down and get my bag."

"No."

"You can't keep me here by force, Adam!" There was an edge of desperation to her voice.

"I don't intend to," he soothed. "I'm going to get dressed and drive you home."

"My car—"

"Will be locked into the car park by this time of night," he pointed out.

She looked at her wristwatch; it was after midnight! "If you will just let me get my bag I can get a taxi home."

Adam shook his head. "I can't let you do that this late at night."

"That doesn't sound possessive, Adam, it sounds autocratic," she taunted him.

He smiled. "It's concern for your welfare," he mocked. "Lovers are like that," he told her softly before going back into the bedroom.

Leonie stared after him frustratedly; she should have known that today was going to end as disastrously as it had begun. She should also have known Adam would have something to do with it, had felt a premonition of his presence while waiting to be rescued from the lift, her clumsiness always more pronounced whenever he was around.

She had been too stunned, too conscious of Mrs Carlson's presence, to do any other than follow Adam's lead of it being their first meeting when the other woman introduced them in his office. And once she recovered from the shock of seeing him again after all this time she was too intrigued by his behaviour to do any other than go along with the pretence. And as she had admitted to him, it was easier too. But the pleasant atmosphere of their evening together had seduced her into doing something she would rather forget, something that she wouldn't allow to be repeated, her reaction to Adam totally unexpected, given their history together.

Her breath caught in her throat as Adam returned to the room, the business suit replaced with a fitted black shirt and black cords. Adam *never* dressed this casually!

"Changing your image, Adam?" she taunted to hide her reaction to him.

"Like it?" he smiled, not fooled by her attitude for a minute.

She more than liked it, she wanted him again! It was ridiculous when she had been married to this man for a year, when they had been separated for over eight months, to feel the same instantaneous flood of emotion towards him as she had when she first met him almost two years ago. And yet looking at him now she did feel it, her mouth dry, her palms damp.

"You look very handsome," she told him primly. "Now could we please leave?"

"Certainly." He picked up his car keys.

"Lovers are obliging too, are they?" She couldn't resist taunting as she preceded him out of the apartment and into the lift.

"Any time," he said suggestively, his body pressed up against the back of hers. "Just say the word," he encouraged throatily.

She frowned her irritation, moving gratefully away from him as they walked over to the car, their footsteps sounding loud in the black stillness of the night. Adam proved to be right about her bag, it lay on the floor of the car as he opened the door for her to get in.

"You can pick your car up tomorrow," Adam suggested during the drive to her home, the car roof up now in the cool of the night.

"Tomorrow?" she frowned.

"When you come for our meeting," he nodded.

Her eyes widened. "You don't seriously expect me to still come to that?"

He glanced at her, his brows raised. "Of course."

"But I— Wasn't that just a set-up?" she frowned.

"I wanted to see you again," he acknowledged. "And it seemed a good way to arrange it in view of the way *you've* felt about seeing me again, but I do also want my office decorated."

"Not by me," she shook her head determinedly, quivering at the thought of having to see this man on a day to day basis in connection with her work.

"By you," he said firmly.

"No!"

"Yes," he insisted softly. "I really was impressed by your work on the lower floor."

"Adam—"

"Yes, Leonie?"

She drew her breath in sharply at his tolerant tone. "I am not going to work for you," she told him stubbornly.

"Yes, you are," he nodded confidently.

"You can't force me!"

"I wouldn't even attempt it," he assured her mildly. "But I think you might find it a little awkward explaining to your boss, David isn't it, the reason you won't work for me."

"You wouldn't make me do that?" she groaned.

Adam shrugged. "I don't see what else you can do."

"But David has plenty of other designers, much more capable ones than me!"

"I don't want them," he stated calmly. "I want you."

"Please don't involve my career in this, Adam," she pleaded desperately.

"All I want is my office decorated, is that too much to ask?"

His innocence infuriated her! "You aren't just asking *anyone* to do it, I was your *wife!*"

His expression softened into a reminiscent smile. "I'm not likely to forget that."

"But I've been trying to!" She was twisted round in her seat as she tried to reason with him. "I've put my life back together, made the career for myself that I gave up when I married you. I am not about to let you jeopardise that."

"But I don't want to." He shrugged broad shoulders.

"You're forcing me into a situation I don't want. You deliberately sought me out for this job, didn't you," she accused.

He nodded. "I bought the company because I knew you had worked there once."

"You—you did *what?*" she gasped.

"Well, I had to have a valid reason for seeing you, I knew you would flatly refuse to go anywhere where you knew I would be." He shrugged. "So I bought Thompson Electronics."

It was an example of the arrogance she had always associated with him in the past; if he wanted something then he went out and bought it. He had once bought her with that same wealth and self-confidence that had blinded her to how wrong they were for each other.

"Then you wasted your money," she told him tautly. "Because nothing would induce me to work for you."

"I didn't waste my money, the company is a very profitable one," he announced calmly. "And I don't intend to induce you into doing anything; surely you're adult enough that you could design something for my office suite without letting personalities enter into it?'' he raised dark brows.

"It isn't a question of that," she said stiffly. "I just don't want to work for you. Wasn't one member of my family enough for you?" she added disgustedly.

"You mean Liz?"

"Who else?" she scorned.

"Liz was the best personal assistant I ever had."

She had been a little too "personal" as far as Leonie was concerned! They had met because of her sister's relationship with Adam, and they had parted for the same reason. "Look, I'll talk to David tomorrow," she told him tautly. "I'm sure he'll be only too glad to send someone else over to work with you."

"I don't want anyone else," Adam said flatly. "I wondered about you and him for a while, you know," he added softly.

She looked over at him with startled eyes. "David and I?"

"Mm," he nodded.

Her mouth tightened resentfully. "And what stopped you wondering?" she snapped.

He shrugged. "Your dates were too occasional for them to be anything more than placating the boss who has designs on you," he dismissed.

Leonie's eyes widened. "You've been having me watched!" she realised disbelievingly.

"You are my wife—"

"Was," she corrected tightly. "We're legally separated, and once the appropriate time has elapsed our divorce will be finalised."

"I was just seeing if we couldn't speed up the proceedings," he explained.

Leonie blinked at him for several timeless minutes,

unable to believe what she was hearing. "Are you trying to say you were after evidence of adultery against me?" she said with disbelief.

Adam shrugged. "I thought you might feel more comfortable about our new arrangement if we were already divorced. I knew that I couldn't wait three years for you."

"I'm sorry I couldn't oblige!" Somehow the knowledge that he had done such a thing hurt her unbearably. God knows she had enough evidence of adultery against *him!* But she had chosen not to subject any of them to the embarrassing ordeal of revealing their personal lives in public. Knowing that Adam had considered doing it to her made her angry.

"Maybe I should have had *you* followed," she glared at him.

"Oh, I've been living very quietly since you left me," he dismissed.

"Quietly doesn't necessarily mean alone," she snapped.

"In this case it does."

And she knew the reason for that; Liz had continued to stay with her husband Nick. "Look, we're getting away from the subject," Leonie sighed. "You'll have to have someone else do your work for you."

"No."

"Adam, I will not be bullied by you into doing something I don't want to do."

He held up his hand defensively. "Have I tried to bully you? Did I bully you into anything tonight?" he added throatily.

Her mouth tightened. Tonight had been incredible, there was no denying that, and plenty of women would be only too agreeable to the sort of noncommittal relationship Adam was now offering her.

But not her. She had made a fool of herself over this man once, she wasn't going to do it again.

"Admit it was everything you thought it could be," he encouraged softly. "No complications of marriage, other people, just you and me making beautiful love together."

Just talking about the experience made her body tingle. "But it couldn't stay that way indefinitely," she reasoned impatiently. "Sooner or later one of us would expect more—"

"Not me," Adam assured her with finality. "I've tried being married to you; it didn't work out."

She swallowed down the pain his casual admission of their year together caused. It *hadn't* worked out, she would be the first to admit that, but to hear Adam talk so casually about the commitment they had made caused a constriction in her chest, as if someone had physically struck her.

"You?"

"Sorry?" she frowned as she realised she had missed what he had said next.

"You wouldn't want more either," he shook his head. "After all, you were the one that ended the marriage in the first place."

"Someone had to make that decision," she bit out abruptly.

"Oh don't worry, I'm glad that you did." He shrugged. "I'm just not husband material."

She hadn't thought about that at the time, although perhaps she ought to have done, Adam was already thirty-seven, had had several serious relationships, and even more that weren't serious, and before meeting her he had shown no inclination to marry any of those women, had enjoyed his freedom to the full. It was difficult enough for any man of thirty-seven to suddenly accept the changes marriage made to his life, to a man like Adam, who could have his pick of women no matter what his marital status, it was impossible. And she hadn't known about Liz then either.

"You think you would do better as a lover?" she derided.

"Haven't I?" he quirked dark brows.

She put a hand up to her aching temples. "It's late," she sighed. "And I'm too tired for this conversation right now."

"There's no rush." He turned to smile at her after stopping his car outside the old three-storey Victorian building that housed her flat. "Are you going to invite me in?"

"Harvey wouldn't like it," she shook her head.

There was a sudden tension about him. "Harvey?"

He had been amused at her expense all evening, and now she couldn't resist a little amusement herself. "Dick wouldn't be too pleased either."

Adam frowned. "I didn't know you were sharing your flat with two men."

"Didn't your private investigator tell you that?"

"No," he ground out. "He—What are you laughing at?" he questioned suspiciously when she couldn't contain her humour any longer.

"Harvey's my cat," she explained between giggles.

"And Dick?"

"Moby Dick."

"You have a *whale* in there?"

Fresh laughter convulsed her. "A goldfish," she finally managed to choke out. "But I thought the name might deter Harvey from eating him; so far it's worked."

Adam shook his head tolerantly. "Klutzy, insane,

*adorable* woman," he groaned as he pulled her over to his side of the car before fiercely claiming her mouth. "Life has been so dull since you left me," he rested his forehead on hers as he held her easily in his arms.

"Even a steady diet of caviar can get boring after a while; and I'm *nothing* like caviar!"

"You never, ever bored me; I never knew what you were going to do next!" he smiled.

"That isn't practical for a wealthy industrialist's wife. And I wouldn't stay hidden out of sight as a lover either," she told him before he could point out that he wanted a lover not a wife. "Not that I'm considering becoming one," she added hastily as she realised it sounded as if she were.

"You *are* one." His quick kisses on her mouth stopped her protest. "Sweet dreams, Leonie," he finally released her. "I'll see you tomorrow."

She didn't argue the point with him; so far it didn't seem to have got her anywhere. He would find out soon enough that if he really did want his office decorated that someone else would be in charge of it.

"Good night, Ad— Ouch!" She groaned as her hair seemed to be caught on the button on his shirt. "Adam, help me!" she pleaded, tears of pain in her eyes.

"Sit still, woman," he instructed with patient amusement, his lean fingers working deftly to free her hair. "There you go," he released the last strand, his eyes gleaming with laughter. "I've heard of giving your lover a lock of hair, but this is ridiculous!"

"You're the one that's ridiculous," she snapped, getting out of the car, her exit foiled somewhat as she had difficulty unlocking the door. Her cheeks were red with embarrassment as she turned to speak to him through the open window. "Good night, Adam. Thank you for tonight, it was an interesting experience."

His smile didn't even waver at the coldness in her voice. "One of many," he promised huskily.

Her mouth tightened before she turned on her heel and walked over to the huge front door that was the entrance for all the tenants of the building. She was aware that the BMW hadn't moved away from the side of the pavement, of Adam watching her, congratulating herself on reaching the door without mishap when the keys fell out of her hand straight into the empty milk bottle standing out on the doorstep waiting for collection in the morning.

For a moment she just looked down at her keys inside the bottle in disbelief. Someone ought to lock *her* up for her own safety and throw away the key!

"Are you all right?"

She turned reluctantly to acknowledge Adam's concern at her delay in entering the building. "Fine," she answered brightly as he now stood outside the car, leaning on the roof to look over at her.

How could she nonchalantly pick up a milk bottle and start shaking the daylights out of it! But how could she get in to the building if she didn't God, she felt so *stupid*.

"Leonie, are you sure you're all right?" Adam sounded puzzled as she still hesitated.

"Yes, of course," she answered waspishly, trying to unobtrusively pick up the bottle, the keys inside rattling loudly in the still of the night as she tried to furtively shake them loose.

"What on earth are you doing?"

She was so startled by his sudden appearance at her side, having been so intent on her keys in the bottle that she had been unaware of his approach, that she dropped the bottle. Adam caught it deftly before it could hit the ground, looking down at the keys inside.

"Isn't this a strange place to hide keys?" he frowned as he tipped the bottle up and was rewarded by them falling smoothly into the palm of his hand.

Leonie snatched them from his hand. "I wasn't hiding them," she snapped. "I dropped them."

"Ah."

Her eyes blazed deeply green as she turned on him. "What do you mean 'ah'?" she challenged. "'Ah, I should have guessed'? Or, 'ah, that such an unfortunate occurrence should have happened to me'?"

"Ah, that such an unfortunate occurrence should have happened to you, of course," he said tongue-in-cheek.

Her movements were agitated as she unlocked the door. "I wonder why I have difficulty believing you," she muttered.

"Darling, calm down." He took her in his arms once more. "I really don't mind these little accidents that happen whenever you're around," he soothed.

"I don't remember your saying that the time I caught the bodice of my gown on your father's tie-pin and it took you half an hour to separate us!" She strained away from him, but his superior strength wouldn't allow her to move far, his thighs pressed intimately against hers.

"Dad was the one that was so annoyed, not me," he reminded with amusement. "Look at it this way, Leonie, at least he was a captive audience for that half an hour; you always did say he didn't listen to you!"

She looked up at him in surprise; she had never

heard him talk about his father so disparagingly before. "He used to look straight through me," she said slowly.

"Well he didn't that evening!"

"That gown cost a fortune, and it was ruined," she reminded him.

"It was worth it just to see the expression on Dad's face. Every time I thought about the incident afterwards I burst out laughing," he was grinning even now.

"You never told me that," she accused. "I thought I had embarrassed you once again."

He sobered at the admission. "You've never embarrassed me, Leonie," he shook his head. "You never could."

She was more puzzled than ever now, some of that emotion showing on her face as Adam let her go this time when she moved out of his arms. "I have to go in; Harvey hasn't had any supper yet," she told him in a preoccupied voice.

"You'll have to introduce me to him some time," Adam straightened. "I've always liked cats."

"I didn't know that," she frowned.

"Maybe you don't know as much about me as you thought you did."

She was beginning to realise that, she thought as she slowly went up the stairs to her second-floor flat. She would never have dreamt Adam could behave as light-heartedly as he had this evening, that he could laugh at himself as well as his father, that he could find her mishaps so amusing. She had been married to him for over a year, and he was still an enigma to her.

Harvey was sitting on the window-ledge outside when she entered her flat, coming in through the small open window as soon as he saw her, miaowing plaintively.

"All right, all right," she cut off his reprimand mid-stream. "You aren't the only one that can spend a night out on the tiles, you know," she told him as she opened a tin of food for his supper, groaning as she realised what she had said. "Oh, Harvey, what am I going to do?" She bent down to pick up the bundle of ginger and white fur, burying her face in his side. "Tonight was so perfect," she told him achingly.

The cat gave a loud screech of indignation before jumping to the ground.

"All right," she snapped at his lack of sympathy. "I can see you're more interested in your stomach than in my problems." She put his plate down on the floor, the cat immediately pouncing on it. "I know you catch mice outside so you can stop acting as if you're starving to death," she told him crossly, suddenly rolling her eyes heavenwards. "God, I'm having a serious conversation with the cat now!" She sat down dejectedly in one of the armchairs, oblivious to the passing of time as, his appetite appeased, Harvey jumped up into her lap and instantly fell into a purring sleep, Leonie absently tickling behind his ears as he did so.

Her first meeting with Adam had been totally unexpected. She knew of him of course, her sister Liz having been his Personal Assistant for the last year, but he wasn't at all what she had expected of the wealthy industrialist.

Liz and Nick had been away on holiday for two weeks, still had a week to go, and Leonie was housesitting for them when Adam paid his surprise visit. The sisters had been close in those days, Liz the senior by eight years, having been like a second mother to Leonie since their parents' death three years earlier.

Leonie had opened the door in all innocence that evening, had fallen in love the moment she looked up into that harshly beautiful face, the grey eyes warm, strangely luminous with the black circle around the iris. She hadn't heard a word he said as he spoke to her, having to ask him to repeat himself. He had wondered if Liz were at home even though it were her holiday, had needed to talk to her. Leonie had invited him in as she explained that Liz and Nick had gone away on what they called a ''second honeymoon''.

She had been shy with him, had wished she were wearing something a little more glamorous than an old dress that did little to improve her already plump proportions, her long hair in need of brushing. And then she had cursed herself for the fool that she was, from what little Liz had told her about this man's love-life he was hardly likely to be attracted to a cuddly redhead who barely reached his shoulders no matter what she was wearing!

But Adam had seemed reluctant to leave that evening, even though he knew Liz wasn't there, the two of them talking for hours, until Leonie suddenly realised it was after twelve and she had to go to work in the morning. She had been speechless when Adam asked her out to dinner the next evening.

There had been a week of dinners together, of talking into the early hours of the morning, and each time Leonie saw him she fell a little more in love. Although Adam gave away little of his own feelings, treating her more like an amusing child as he guided her through one mishap after another.

The night before Liz and Nick were due to return home was a magical one, Adam taking her to the ballet, something she loved but could only rarely afford to attend, taking her back to the house he shared with his father. It had been after eleven when they arrived, but even so the lights were on all over the house, the butler greeting them at the door, a maid bringing them a tray of coffee and sandwiches. Leonie had been so nervous she promptly knocked over the plate of sandwiches.

But even that had seemed unimportant as Adam dismissed the incident after helping her put them back on the plate, his eyes almost black as he followed her down on to the rug in front of the fire, his mouth fiercely claiming hers. It was the first time he had done more than give her a polite brush of his lips on hers at the end of an evening, and after her initial surprise at how fierce he was with her she opened her arms and her heart to him.

He could have taken her right then and there on the rug and she wouldn't have cared. But he didn't, his breathing ragged as he pulled away from her.

"Marry me, Leonie," he had groaned. "Marry me!"

"Yes," she gasped her acceptance, on fire for him.

"Soon," he urged.

"As soon as you want me," she promised eagerly.

When her sister and Nick returned the next day she told them she and Adam were getting married, the following Saturday. Liz had been stunned, and Leonie had thought it was because Liz was surprised at her young sister managing to capture such a handsome and sophisticated man. That was what she had *thought* it was, she should have probed deeper!

Adam had taken over her life from the moment he put the engagement ring on her finger that evening, a huge emerald that he said matched the colour of her eyes. She had been happy with his decision that she give up her job, wanting to be with him whenever he could get home from the empire that consumed such a lot of his time, knowing her career would make that difficult. She had even agreed to live in the apartment Adam had always occupied at the top of his father's elegant London home. She had agreed to anything Adam asked of her.

Within two weeks of meeting him she found herself married to a man she barely knew and who she was soon convinced didn't know her. Her wedding night was a fiasco, with her acting the frightened virgin that she was despite Adam's understanding gentleness with her. The pain had been incredible, too much to bear, until finally they had to stop. Leonie had huddled miserably on her side of the bed while Adam slept. The next night had proved as disastrous, and the night after that, until the fourth night Adam didn't even attempt to touch her. She came home from their honeymoon still a virgin, too embarrassed to discuss her problems with anyone. Adam had had so such qualms, making an appointment for her to see a gynaecologist and ordering her to attend when she protested. The doctor had taken away all the embarrassment of her problem, had explained that it was something that occasionally happened, and within a short time the problem had been alleviated.

But the damage had been done, and she resisted all Adam's efforts to get her to join in his passion, until finally he lost all patience with her one night, pinning her to the bed as he held her arms at her sides, ignoring her cries for him to stop as he brought her to the peak of ecstasy. After that night he always made sure she had pleasure too, but he always had to fight her first, to break down the barriers of resistance that

she had built up against him. In the end he became
tired of the fight, hardly ever touching her even
though they shared a bed every night.

She tried to make up for her inadequacies in bed
by being the perfect wife in other ways, but Charles
Faulkner made no secret of his contempt for the
young girl his son had made his wife, and she didn't
even have Liz to turn to for support, feeling too embarrassed to discuss the failure of her marriage even
with her sister.

Her tendency to clumsiness became more pronounced as the months dragged on, so much so that
she became nervous of leaving the apartment and going downstairs for fear of earning the derision of
Adam's father. It was enough of an ordeal that she
had to sit down to dinner with the elderly man every
night, usually managing to knock something over.
She and Adam had intended eating their meals in their
own apartment, but after a week of burnt offerings
Adam had decided his digestion couldn't take any
more and suggested they go downstairs and join his
father for their evening meal. She had been hurt, especially as she was usually such a good cook, but for
the sake of peace—and Adam's digestion—she had
agreed. It was just another brick falling out of the
already crumbling foundations of her marriage.

Adam began to stay late at the office, working he
said. They also stopped going out, a way of stopping
her embarrassing him in front of his friends, she felt
sure. But it just left her more and more to her thoughts
of what had gone wrong between them. It was easier
to try and find something that had gone *right*. The
answer was nothing!

But she decided she wouldn't be a nagging wife,
would make the most of the life they had together.

Much to the disgust of her father-in-law she had offered to organise the decorating and refurbishing of the house; his reply to that was to call in the most well-known interior designing company in London. Next she tried to take an interest in Adam's work; that was met with blank dismissal. After only a year of marriage she was bored, and she was sure—when she wasn't attempting to break one of the family heirlooms or tipping wine over someone—boring! The marriage had been a mistake, and she knew that even if Adam didn't. She had finally had enough after a solid month of not seeing Adam any other time than when he fell into bed beside her, deciding to go to his office and confront him with the fact that she couldn't go on like this any longer.

She had wondered why Adam's secretary tried to stop her going in to his office, especially after telling her he only had Liz in with him. What she had seen and heard had told her exactly why Adam wasn't even trying to make a success of their marriage, and why her sister had been so stunned that he was marrying her at all!

Adam had tried to reason with her when he followed her home, but she had required only one answer to one question; had he been sleeping with Liz just before they met. His answer made her leave him immediately, telling him that he should never have married her, that if he had only wanted a replacement for her sister then an affair would have been a much better idea—and much less complicated to them all. For that was what she was sure she had learnt when she came upon them unwittingly, Liz in Adam's arms, that their decision to end their affair and for Liz to attempt a reconciliation with Nick, had been a failure. And now they were both trapped in marriages they didn't want. But Liz was expecting Nick's child, couldn't leave him now, and Adam was stuck with her young and klutzy sister.

He hadn't been stuck with her for long, although Liz was still married to Nick, their daughter Emma three months old now. And Adam was proposing that they, Leonie and he, had the affair she had once told him they would be better having!

# CHAPTER THREE

"But, David," she protested the next morning. "I told you how badly everything went."

He shrugged off her argument. "Faulkner couldn't apologize enough about your ordeal in the lift. I didn't like to tell him you made a habit of it!"

She had arrived at work this morning all set to tell David how disastrously her appointment with the new President of Thompson Electronics had gone, sure that when he heard all the details that he would be only too glad to put someone else on that job, only to find Adam had already been on the telephone to David this morning, taking all the blame on his own shoulders!

Her pleas with David had been to no avail; he was adamant she work for Adam. And she was just as adamant that she wouldn't, had sworn when she left Adam that she wouldn't take anything from him ever again, and that included this boost to her fledgeling career. "David, I don't want to work with him," she told him flatly.

His eyes narrowed. "Why not?"

She had no intention of telling David that Adam was her estranged husband. Much as she liked the other man, she knew how ambitious he was, and having the wife of Adam Faulkner working for him could give his company the boost into êlite London society that he had been looking for.

"I—I don't like him," she frowned as she knew that was no longer true either. When she had left Adam eight months ago she had never wanted to see him again, had hated him for his behaviour with her married sister. But last night, the pleasure they had finally shared, giving and taking from each other rather than Adam having to force her response, had changed all that. She couldn't hate a man who had given her that sexual freedom.

Some of the remembered sensuality must have shown in her face. "Did he make a pass at you?" David frowned.

A pass! Adam had never made a *pass* at a woman in his life! He was much too controlled for that. "No, he didn't do that," she answered tautly.

David looked relieved to hear it. "Then where's your problem?"

"I've just told you, I don't want to work for him!"

"But he sounded very charming on the telephone."

She grimaced, well aware of how charming Adam could be when he wanted something. He had once wanted her so badly in his bed that he had married her; how ironic that the one thing he had wanted from her had been so disastrous. "Anyone can be charming for the few minutes of a telephone call," she dismissed.

"Then he wasn't charming to you yesterday when you did eventually meet?" David probed.

"Yes, he was," she sighed. "Very charming." Colour heightened her cheeks as she remembered just *how* charming he had been later that evening.

"Then why don't you want to work for him?" David repeated again in exasperation. "I can tell you, he was very impressed with you."

''I made such a fool of myself,'' she said desperately. ''I feel embarrassed.''

David shrugged. ''You always make a fool of yourself sooner or later.''

''Thanks!''

He grimaced. ''But you do,'' he reasoned. ''I've never known you to get through a day yet without something going wrong; and it's usually your own fault!''

''That's what I like, a little sympathy and understanding,'' she glared at him.

He smiled at her anger. ''Trouble just seems to follow you around. Look, I'll tell you what I'll do, I'll call Faulkner's secretary and tell her I'll be joining the two of you for lunch. If I can see any reason, any reason at all, why you shouldn't work for him I'll put someone else on to it. All right?''

It was the best she was going to get, she could see that. And surely she could make Adam drop the tolerant charm for the few minutes it would take David to realise he would be better sending Gary or Sheila on this job, if only for the sake of his company's reputation.

''I'll drive over with you,'' she nodded agreement, feeling a little happier.

David frowned. ''What's happened to the VW, has it broken down again?''

''It's still at Thompson Electronics,'' she told him awkwardly. ''Mr Faulkner insisted on driving me home after my ordeal in the lift,'' she invented.

David smiled. ''He doesn't know you very well if he thinks a little thing like that will shake you up!''

She gave him an exasperated look. ''Actually, I did some work while I was waiting.''

''See,'' he laughed.

She went back to her own desk, her nerves becoming more and more frayed as twelve o'clock neared. Then just as she was tidying her desk in preparation for joining David a deliveryman arrived from a nearby florist's. The single long-stemmed red rose took her by surprise, the bold black script on the accompanying card telling her that Adam had in no way changed his mind about where their relationship was going. "For an interesting experience—one of many", the card read. She crumpled the cryptic message in the palm of her hand, would have done the same with the rose if David hadn't arrived at her office at that moment.

"A new admirer?" He raised blond brows as she thrust the rose into a sadly inadequate glass and pushed it to the far corner of her desk.

She shook her head. "Another apology from Mr Faulkner." There was no point in lying about the sender; knowing Adam he would ask if it had arrived!

"Nice gesture." David helped her on with the fitted jacket to her brown suit, the pale green blouse she wore beneath alleviating its sombre colouring.

"A pity he didn't feel generous enough to send the other eleven," she said with uncharacteristic waspishness.

David's brows rose. "I'm sure he— Watch out!" he had time to call out as the sleeve of her jacket caught the perfection of the single red bud, overbalancing the too-short glass, smashing the latter on the floor, the rose crushed among the heavy glass.

Leonie looked down at the ruined perfection with tears in her eyes, instantly regretting what she had done. For the first time in her life she had committed a deliberately destructive act, had knocked against the flower on purpose, not wanting that reminder of Adam facing her when she got back.

"Careful!" David warned as she bent to pick up the crushed flower, sighing his impatience with her as a large jagged sliver of glass stuck straight into the palm of her hand.

Leonie gasped, automatically pulling out the piece of glass, the blood that instantly flowed from the wound the same colour as the rose she still held. She knelt and watched as it continued to bleed.

"You're dripping blood all over the carpet," David snapped impatiently, taking out a handkerchief to wrap it about her hand, pulling her to her feet. "We had better get you cleaned up before we go anywhere." He led her into his office, the First Aid box kept there.

He took the rose she still clutched and threw it in the bin, concentrating on washing her hand and applying a bandage as the small but deep wound continued to bleed.

Leonie felt sick, and not because of the pain in her hand but because of her deliberate destruction of such innocent beauty. It wasn't in her to deliberately hurt anything. Even when she had discovered how Liz and Adam had deceived her she hadn't wanted revenge or retribution, had felt sorry for her trapped sister, although Adam seemed to be continuing with his life as if it had never happened.

"Are you all right?" David frowned at how pale she had become. "Maybe we should cancel this meeting with Faulkner, you look as if you should go home and rest."

She shook her head determinedly, not intending to delay this confrontation any longer than was necessary; she had already spent one sleepless night, she didn't intend having any more because of Adam Faulkner. "I'll be fine," she insisted, flexing her hand under the bandage; it was a bit sore, but workable.

"Sure?" David still looked concerned.

"Yes," she smiled brightly, standing up. "Shouldn't we leave now, Mr Faulkner is going to think unpunctuality is normal for us."

"For you it is," David mocked as they went down to his car, a white Cortina that he drove with the usual reserve he had to the rest of life.

The cut on her hand was only a throbbing ache by the time they reached Thompson Electronics, the bandage showing no sign of heavy bleeding.

Mrs Carlson greeted them with a smile, instantly informing Adam of their arrival, ushering them straight in to his office.

"Sorry we're late," David greeted the other man, their handshakes firm. "I'm afraid a little—accident, delayed us."

Leonie hung back behind David, feeling uncomfortable about seeing Adam again. The flesh and blood masculinity of him was much worse than she had imagined after the passion they had shared the previous evening, the royal blue three-piece suit and lighter blue shirt he wore making him look devastatingly attractive, his eyes more blue than grey.

His gaze moved surely past David to her flushed face. "What did Miss Grant do this time?" he drawled.

Leonie's blush deepened as David grinned. "A collision with a glass, I'm afraid," he explained.

"The rose you sent me was in it," she put in quickly, challenge in her eyes as she realised he wasn't about to reveal their marital status to David either. ''It had to be put in the bin, I'm afraid,'' she added with satisfaction.

For timeless seconds Adam held her gaze, transmitting a message that made the colour burn in her cheeks. ''The rose can easily be replaced,'' he finally said softly. ''There's only one Leonie Grant.''

''Thank God for that,'' David said thankfully, missing the undercurrent of tension between them, taking the conversation at face value.

Leonie was perfectly aware of the double meaning to Adam's words, her mouth firming frustratedly as she longed to knock that smile off his lips.

''We may as well talk over lunch,'' Adam decided arrogantly. ''If that's all right with you?'' he consulted the younger man as an afterthought.

''Fine,'' David agreed eagerly, seeing nothing wrong in this man taking charge of the meeting.

It was embarrassing how easily David had been taken in by Adam's charm, Leonie thought angrily. He was supposed to be romantically interested in her himself, and yet he seemed to find nothing wrong with the way Adam's fingers closed possessively over her arm as they left the office together, seemed not to notice when Adam moved his thumb erotically against her inner arm.

''What have you done to your hand?'' Adam frowned as he noticed the bandage for the first time, his fingers entwining with hers as he lifted her hand for closer inspection.

''She cut herself with a piece of the broken glass.'' It was left to David to answer for her, her breath catching in her throat at the intimacies Adam was taking with her hand in full view of the other man.

Adam's gaze bored into hers. ''Have you seen a doctor?''

She swallowed hard, shaking her head to clear the spell he was casting over her. "Only David," she dismissed lightly, putting her other hand into the crook of the other man's arm. "But he knows how to take care of me," she added pointedly.

Dark brows met over suddenly icy grey eyes. "Indeed? You have some experience in taking care of Miss Grant, Mr Stevenson?" the question was put innocently enough, but Leonie could feel the tension in the hand that still gripped hers.

"A little." Once again David was innocent of the innuendo behind Adam's words. "I took her to the hospital when she got high using glue in her office one afternoon, and another time when she stuck her letter-opener in her leg."

Adam's eyes twinkled with suppressed humour as Leonie's ploy to imply intimacy between David and herself failed miserably. "I wondered how you had acquired that scar," he said throatily.

Leonie blushed as she remembered the way his caressing fingers had explored the half-inch scar above her knee, how they had explored the whole of her body, pulling out of his grasp to move closer to David. "He's always rescuing this Damsel in Distress," she gave David a warm smile. "I don't know what I'd do without him."

David looked pleased by her encouragement, having received little enough of it the last six months.

"We'll take my car," Adam decided abruptly, striding over to the BMW. "You don't mind if Miss Grant sits in the front next to me, do you, Stevenson, she gets car sick in the back," he said smoothly.

David looked surprised. "I didn't know that."

Neither did she! But short of calling Adam a liar, and possibly alienating him as a client for David she couldn't very well say so, getting ungraciously into the car next to Adam while David sat in the back. She almost gasped out loud when Adam took advantage of their relative privacy in the front of the car to guide her hand on to his thigh, keeping it there with his own hand when she would instantly have pulled away.

His leg felt firm and warm through the material of his trousers, and she could feel the heat rising in her cheeks as both of them acted as if the intimacy weren't taking place, Adam coolly conversing with the unsuspecting David.

By the time they arrived at the restaurant Leonie's nerves were in shreds, her senses in turmoil as she fought against the desire Adam had deliberately instigated. His gaze was silently mocking as he helped her out of the car, although she flushed as she saw his body wasn't quite as controlled, looking away quickly from the evidence of his arousal, her cheeks burning as they entered the restaurant.

She could see David was impressed by the other man, and the restaurant he had chosen, as they studied the menus. She was going to have to do something, and fast, if she wanted David to take her off this job.

"So," Adam sat back after they had ordered their meal. "Is there some problem with Miss Grant coming to work for me?"

David looked disconcerted by the other man's bluntness. "Problem?" he delayed.

Adam shrugged. "Does the owner of Stevenson Interiors usually go to a routine business meeting with his employees?"

"Er—Well—No," David answered awkwardly. "But Leonie is rather new at her job. Not that she isn't good at it," he put in hastily. "She is. But she—

we, wondered if you wouldn't rather have someone more experienced.''

''Just how much experience does Miss Grant have?'' Adam asked softly, his hand somehow locating her knee beneath the table, his fingers caressing.

Leonie's mouth tightened at the—to her—unsubtle double-meaning behind the question. ''Not enough for you, I'm sure,'' she bit out, drawing in a pained breath as his fingers tightened in rebuke.

''I'm sure you'll satisfy me,'' he told her blandly.

''And I'm equally sure I won't,'' she grated.

''I'm not a demanding man, Miss Grant,'' he drawled. ''I simply know what I like.''

So did she after last night, having explored the hard planes of his body then more thoroughly than ever before, Adam encouraging her to do so, to both their delight.

''I like what you've done for me already,'' he continued softly. ''I'd like it to continue.''

Her mouth thinned. ''I don't think I can—work, for you, Mr Faulkner.''

''Leonie!'' David gasped. ''What Leonie means is that she does have a couple of other little jobs that need her attention,'' he quickly invented. ''And anyway, this conversation might be academic.''

Adam looked at him. ''And why should it be that?''

David gave a nervous laugh at the other man's quiet intensity. ''Well, *I* know we're the best, but I'm sure you'll have other quotes in for the work, and—''

''No other quotes,'' Adam told him arrogantly. ''I want Miss Grant to do this for me.''

David flushed with pleasure, and Leonie could understand why. Interior designing was a competitive business, and they lost as many prospective jobs as they won, other companies often undercutting them. If only Adam only had work on his mind!

"In that case," he beamed, "I can get someone else to clear up Leonie's odd loose ends."

"I would appreciate it," Adam drawled. "I need Miss Grant right away."

And he wasn't lying either! His hand had captured hers as she tried to pry his fingers from her knees, guiding it to the throbbing hardness of his thighs. She flinched away from him as if he had burnt her, glaring at him furiously for this subterfuge.

"And, of course, if her work proves as satisfactory this time as last I would consider using her when I have my apartment refurbished," he added challengingly.

"It's a brand new apartment!" She almost groaned out loud as she realised she had revealed to a shocked David that she had been to the other man's home. "Mr Faulkner insisted on taking me home to give me a drink to steady my nerves last night before driving me to my flat," she quickly explained.

"Leonie has a habit of walking into one catastrophe after another," David smiled.

"I've noticed," Adam said dryly. "I feel that my apartment lacks the homely touch at the moment, I'm sure Miss Grant could help me create that,"

She was so angry with him at this moment that if he didn't stop baiting her in this way she was going to pick up his soup and tip it over his head! But maybe if she could show David how Adam kept flirting with her he would realise she couldn't possibly work for the other man; the cold treatment certainly hadn't worked!

"I'm sure there must be a woman in your life who

could do a much better job of that than I,'' she suggested throatily.

His eyes widened questioningly, and then he smiled knowingly. ''I always think this sort of thing is better accomplished by someone who knows what they're doing.''

She blushed as he turned the innuendo back on her. ''I'm sure you're just being modest, Mr Faulkner,'' her voice was husky.

''On the contrary, since my wife left my life has been lacking in a woman's—touch.''

She glared at him in silent rage. And if he really expected her to believe there had been no woman for him since their separation he was insane! Liz might be out of his reach at the moment, but there were plenty of other women who weren't, and God knows he had found little enough satisfaction during their brief marriage.

''How about you, Stevenson,'' Adam turned to the other man. ''Does your life have that special woman's touch?''

''I'm not married,'' David answered in all innocence, receiving a frustrated glare from Leonie at his candid reply.

''Neither am I—now,'' the other man told him in amusement. ''But one doesn't have to be married to have a special woman in one's life.''

David glanced awkwardly at Leonie. ''I suppose not,'' he muttered.

''Just as one can have a special woman in one's life even if one *is* married,'' Leonie put in with sweet sarcasm, looking challengingly at Adam as his expression remained bland.

''Leonie!'' David was shocked at the turn the conversation had taken.

She gave him a scornful look. "We're all adults here, David," she bit out. "And the sanctity of marriage does seem to have lost its meaning to some people. Don't you agree, Adam?" she added hardly.

He shrugged, completely relaxed. "Divorce has been made too easy," came his reply.

"Easy?" she repeated disbelievingly. "You'll excuse me if I disagree!" She glared at him, remembering that she had only been able to be legally separated from him without actually revealing the reason she could no longer live with him, had to wait two years to be free of him.

He gave an acknowledging inclination of his head. "It seems to me that at the first sign of trouble in a marriage now one of the partners runs to the nearest lawyer rather than trying to work the problem out with the logical person, their spouse."

If Leonie could have spoken immediately after that arrogant statement she would have told him exactly what he could do with his theory. As it was, by the time she had overcome her rage enough to be able to talk she had also controlled the impulse, conscious of David even if Adam wasn't. "You believe that's what your wife did, hm?" she prompted hardly.

"Oh no," he denied easily. "My wife was perfectly right to leave me, I was lousy husband material."

Having expected a completely different answer Leonie was once again left speechless. Adam certainly knew how to disconcert her. And he knew it, damn him.

David coughed uncomfortably, obviously finding the conversation embarrassing.

"You'll have to excuse us," Adam turned to him with a smile. "Both being statistics in marriage failure I'm afraid Leonie and I got carried away comparing notes. We'll have this conversation some other time, Leonie,'' there was a promise in his voice. "I'm sure you must have been a much better wife than I ever was a husband.''

Had she been? She doubted it. She had been too young and unsophisticated to cope with the trauma of her honeymoon, had made no effort to bridge the gulf that had arisen between them because of it, had found the physical act between them embarrassing. Then why had last night been so different? Could Adam be right, the lack of a commitment between them made it all so much more uncomplicated, easier to relax and enjoy what they did have?

She looked up to find silver-grey eyes on her, realising he was still waiting for an answer. "No,'' she sighed. "I don't think I could have been.''

His gaze held hers for long timeless moments before he turned to signal for the bill, breaking the mood, his hand finally leaving her knee as they all stood up to leave.

"So when do you think Miss Grant will be able to start work for me?'' he asked David on the drive back to his office, the other man once again in the back of the car, although this time both Adam's hands remained on the steering-wheel; and why shouldn't they, he had no further reason to torment her, he had won. She was going to work for him.

"Monday,'' David answered firmly, ignoring Leonie's dismayed expression. "Is that suitable for you?''

"Very,'' Adam nodded, his mouth quirking triumphantly at Leonie.

She glared back at him. "You will, of course, have

to move out of your office once the work begins,'' she told him tightly.

''I understand that. But you will be supervising the operation personally, won't you?''

''It's the usual practice,'' she conceded grudgingly, knowing that she had to give in, that she had to subject herself to several weeks of working for Adam. But working for him was all she intended doing. If he expected anything else from the arrangement he was going to be disappointed!

''YOU NEARLY LOST us that contract!''

She had been expecting the rebuke from David ever since they had parted from Adam half an hour ago, but he had remained silent as they went down to the car park to their respective vehicles, had waited until they reached the privacy of his office before turning on her angrily.

''All that talk about not being good enough to do the work,'' David continued furiously. ''The man will think I employ amateurs!''

''David—''

''And I could have sunk through the floor when you started talking about the sanctity of marriage. The man's private life is none of our business, Leonie,'' he told her disgustedly.

''I—''

''And just how long did you stay at his apartment last night?'' he added with a frown.

All colour left her face. ''I— What do you mean?'' she forced casualness into her voice.

''The two of you seem pretty familiar with each other's private lives. I've been seeing you for the last six months and yet in one evening that man seems to know more about you than I do!'' he accused.

He had given her the perfect opening for her to tell
him that Adam was her estranged husband, and yet
she couldn't take it. It was much too late for that. The
time to tell him had been this morning, before she
and Adam acted like strangers for a second time, before David would be made to feel too foolish by the
knowledge. He would never forgive her if he was told
the truth now.

"I knew you were separated from your husband,"
David continued forcefully. "But I had no idea you
were actually divorcing him."

She shrugged. "It's the usual conclusion to that
sort of mistake."

"But don't you see, I didn't know," he said heatedly. "And yet you told Faulkner after knowing him
only a few hours!"

"I—er— Maybe the fact that he's separated too
gave us a mutual interest in the subject," she invented.

"How mutual?" David asked suspiciously.

She sighed. "Did I seem as if I wanted to see him
again, even professionally?"

"No," he acknowledged slowly. "But that wasn't
just because you're embarrassed about yesterday."

She stood up, moving restlessly about the room,
wondering what explanation she could give David
that would sound plausible. "I think we have a clash
of temperaments," she spoke softly.

"In what way?"

"In every way I can think of," she snapped. "I
despise everything about the man!"

"Leonie!"

She sighed at her unwarranted vehemence. "He's
a rich playboy who buys and sells everything that he

wants and then doesn't want, including women," she said more calmly. "I despise that type of man."

"Are you sure he didn't make a pass at you?" David frowned, still not understanding.

"Yes," she bit out.

"Disappointed that he didn't?" David sounded puzzled.

Her mouth twisted. "I don't think that question even deserves an answer," she dismissed disgustedly. "Look, I know the type of man he is, David, because—because I was married to one," she admitted gruffly.

His expression softened at the admission. "I'm sorry, Leonie," he said gently. "I had no idea. If you really think you can't work with the man..."

"And how would you explain the change to him after assuring him I was definitely available?" she mocked.

"I could always tell him you broke your neck!"

"Now *that* I'm sure he would believe!" she returned David's smile. "But I won't have you jeopardise the contract in that way. I'm just being silly, of course I can handle Adam Faulkner!"

There was another cellophane-wrapped box from the same florist lying on her desk when she returned to her office, and she opened it with shaking fingers, this single red rose made out of the finest silk, so delicate it looked as if it had just been cut from the garden. The card read "*This* rose won't be crushed— and neither will I." Again it was unsigned, but Leonie knew the sender, only too well.

"An admirer?" Gary grinned at her from the doorway.

She sighed. "You could say that."

Gary sauntered into the room, a few inches taller

than her, with sandy hair and light blue eyes. The two of them had been friends since she first came to work for Stevenson Interiors. He touched the rose. ''He has good taste,'' he murmured, looking at her and not the flower.

Ordinarily she wouldn't have minded his teasing, was always refusing the invitations he made her, both of them knowing that he had been happily married for the last five years. But today she wasn't in the mood for his lighthearted flirting. ''It's been a long day,'' she said abruptly, turning back to her work.

With a shrug Gary left her to it. Leonie sighed, angry with Adam for upsetting her so much that she had been rude to a man who, although a flirt, had always been kind to her. She stood up to go and apologise to him.

# CHAPTER FOUR

"FOILED you, didn't we?" she looked triumphantly at Harvey as he sniffed the silk rose in puzzlement, sitting on the dining-table to eye what looked like a delicious-tasting flower but wasn't. "You won't be able to chew this one beyond recognition," she crowed, as with a disgusted tilt of his nose Harvey jumped down on to the floor.

She had brought the rose home with her, too impressed by its beauty to throw it away as she had the last one. And much to her delight she had found that Harvey, who usually demolished any flowers she brought into the house, had no interest in the delicate bloom.

"Out you go," she opened the window for him. "No, I'm not going out on the tiles again tonight myself," she told him as he hung back reluctantly, obviously not intending going anywhere if he was going to be left on his own for hours again. "Once was enough," she muttered as she left the window open for him.

She stared broodingly at the rose as she tried to reconcile herself to working for Adam as from Monday. The second—indestructible—rose, had been a warning that he was still intent on having an affair with her. Why couldn't he— She looked up sharply as the doorbell rang, instantly knowing who it was.

David was her only, rare, visitor here, and he had gone away for the weekend.

"Adam," she greeted resignedly as she was proved correct.

"Leonie," he returned lightly. "Am I interrupting anything?" he arched dark brows.

"Yes."

"Oh good," he walked past her into the room beyond, his denims fitted tautly to his thighs and legs, his black sweat-shirt doing nothing to hide the bulge of muscle in his arms and chest. He looked about the empty flat, his gaze returning to hers. "I thought you said I was interrupting something?"

"You are," she closed the door forcefully before joining him. "My privacy!"

He grinned, thrusting his hands into the back pockets of his denims. "Nothing is private between us," he dismissed, looking about him appreciatively.

Leonie tried to see the flat through his eyes, knowing the soft peach and cream decor, and the low-backed furniture and fluffy carpets, wouldn't be to everyone's liking. But it was to hers, was all her own work, and she didn't welcome any comments Adam might care to make.

His gaze returned to hers. "I think Dad should have let you decorate and refurnish the house, after all," he drawled. "Maybe then it wouldn't look and feel like a mausoleum!"

"You agreed with the suggestion when he said he wanted to bring in professionals!" she was stung into accusing.

He shrugged broad shoulders. "It was his house. But I didn't come here to discuss the past," he frowned.

"Then why are you here?" she demanded resentfully.

"To take you out."

She flushed. "It's usual to ask first," she snapped.

He shook his head, smiling. "I knew what your answer would be if I did that."

"I'm sure you did," she bit out.

"You'll enjoy yourself," he promised encouragingly.

She blushed. "I'm sure I won't!"

Adam chuckled softly. "Are they very naughty thoughts, Leonie?" he mocked.

"Let's leave my thoughts, naughty or otherwise, out of this," she said sharply. "I have no desire to go anywhere with you."

"Oh yes you do," he contradicted huskily. "And maybe later on I just might take you there. But right now I have it in mind to take you skating."

"Skating!"

"Mm," he nodded.

She frowned. "What sort of skating?"

"Well, hopefully, the sort where we manage to stay upright," he grinned. "Although I have no objection if you get the urge to fall on me!"

"Adam, have you been drinking?" she looked at him suspiciously.

He shook his head. "I'm simply acting like a—"

"Lover," she completed resignedly.

"Exactly. Lovers take their lovers out on mad escapades like this all the time."

"Who told you that?" she derided.

"I read it somewhere," he said with suppressed humour.

"You still haven't told me what sort of skating it will be," Leonie frowned.

"Roller-skating."

"But I can't roller-skate!"

"Can you ice-skate?"

"No." Her sense of humour couldn't be repressed any further, not resisting as Adam pushed her in the direction of the hall to get her jacket. "Can you?"

"Roller or ice?" he quirked dark brows.

"Either!"

"No," he informed her happily. "But just think of the fun we'll have trying!"

And they did have fun, Leonie couldn't ever remember laughing so much in one evening in her life before, let alone with the man who had always seemed so rigidly correct to her. Her tendency to be clumsy wasn't so noticeable with everyone else falling over too, in fact she had almost mastered the sport by the end of the evening while Adam still landed in an undignified heap on his bottom most of the time, and that for a man who had always seemed *so* dignified!

This new irrepressible Adam was impossible to resist, laughing at himself and her in a way she would never have thought he could. If this evening was an example of his indulgence as a lover she didn't know how she was going to continue to say no.

"I'm coming in," he told her when they reached her flat, his expression suddenly serious.

"Adam—"

"I want to look at your hand."

The statement startled her; it wasn't what she had been expecting at all. "My hand?" she repeated incredulously.

"Well I'd like to take a look at all of you," he told her huskily. "But I think we'll start with the hand. Did you think I wouldn't notice the discomfort it's given you tonight?'' he chided as they entered her home.

She had hoped that he hadn't, but she should have known better; Adam noticed everything! Her hand had been aching most of the afternoon but she had put that down to the healing process. The increased pain she had been suffering the last couple of hours seemed to indicate it was more than that, her falls at the rink only aggravating it.

She took off her jacket, holding out her hand for Adam's inspection.

''You may as well sit down,'' he shrugged out of his own casual jacket. ''I'm not going for a while yet.'' He came down on his haunches in front of her, compellingly attractive.

He was very gentle with her as he peeled off the bandage, removing the gauze dressing to reveal a very red and angry-looking cut. Leonie grimaced as he unbuttoned the cuff of her blouse to show that the redness extended in a line up her arm.

''It's infected,'' he mumbled, looking up at her. ''You'll have to go to hospital for treatment, I'm afraid.''

''Couldn't it wait until morning?''

''It could,'' he acknowledged softly. ''But why suffer all night when you could get some relief now from the pain I'm sure you must be feeling?''

His logic always made sense, and he was right, the pain was bad; she doubted she would be able to sleep tonight without something to dull the pain.

''I'll just put a fresh bandage on it and then we'll go,'' Adam stood up decisively as he sensed her consent. ''Do you have a medicine cabinet?''

''In the bathroom,'' she pointed to the appropriate

door. "With my penchant for accidents I'd be insane to be without one," she added self-derisively.

Adam grinned. "I know you can't be feeling too bad when you still have your sense of humour. It was one of the things I always liked about you."

One of the only things, Leonie thought ruefully as he went into the bathroom. The statement had reminded her of exactly who they were, of the fact that they were in the process of divorcing each other; she had been in danger of forgetting that fact with Adam being so boyishly charming.

He was still in the bathroom when the telephone began ringing. God, she had forgotten it was Friday night, hadn't realised it was already eleven-thirty!

"Yes?" she grabbed up the receiver, not in the least surprised when she recognised the caller's voice, giving a mental groan as Adam came out of the bathroom, frowning when he saw she was on the telephone. "Oh yes?" Leonie answered her caller faintly. "How interesting. Look, I'm sorry," she cut in hastily as Adam approached. "But I can't talk just now." She slammed the receiver down, smiling brightly at Adam.

He frowned down at her. "Who on earth telephones at this time of night?" he asked slowly.

She shrugged. "I remember you did a couple of times during the two weeks before we were married."

"That was different," he dismissed.

"Why was it?"

"Because if I couldn't be in bed with you then I wanted to at least talk to you while you were in bed," he told her absently, his thoughts obviously still on the call she had just taken.

"Maybe my caller felt the same way," her voice was shrill at the irony of that statement.

"Is he the one that owns the man's razor in the bathroom?"

Her mouth tightened. "*I'm* the one who owns the man's razor in the bathroom," she bit out resentfully. "For some reason they happen to be cheaper and easier to find than the so-called women's razors are. And please don't ask why I need a razor," she glared at him.

His mouth quirked. "I won't.

"Then let me say I don't appreciate your prying into my bathroom cabinet. The medicine chest is next to it," she snapped.

"And the scissors were conspicuous in their absence," he pointed out softly.

She remembered now, she had used them to cut a broken fingernail, and must have put them back in the wrong cabinet. "Well I don't see that it's any business of yours even if the razor *had* belonged to a man," she told him huffily.

Adam shrugged. "I'm a very possessive lover."

"You aren't—"

"Just as I expect you to be," he continued softly, his gaze compelling.

"Being possessive didn't do me much good while I was your wife," she reminded waspishly.

He shrugged. "I've already admitted what a lousy husband I was."

"And assured me you're a fantastic lover!" she derided harshly.

"And very possessive," he nodded, his eyes narrowed. "Which means I want to know who would call you this time of night?"

She had hoped to divert him off the subject, she should have realised he wasn't a man to be diverted.

"A friend," she dismissed. "I— They work nights," she added desperately.

Adam frowned. "Is that supposed to explain why they would call at eleven-thirty at night?"

"It goes on the company's telephone bill?" she suggested with a grimace for her inadequacy at lying.

"Not good enough, Leonie," he shook his head. "I want to know—" he broke off as the telephone began to ring again, picking up the receiver before Leonie had a chance to do so.

Leonie paled, knowing that the person on the other end of the line wouldn't realise from Adam's silence that it wasn't her he was talking to. She could guess what Adam's reaction was going to be.

"That's very interesting," he suddenly ground out fiercely. "Now let me tell you what I'd like to do to you—" his teeth snapped together as the caller obviously rang off, slamming his own receiver down with suppressed violence. "How long has this been going on?" he demanded to know.

She pulled a face, knowing she couldn't evade answering him. "Ever since I moved in here."

"And how long is that?"

She shrugged. "Six months or so."

Adam's mouth compressed into a thin line. "And is he always so—so—"

"Obscene?" she finished with a grimace. "I think that's how those sort of calls got their name!"

She knew exactly what Adam would have heard when he picked up the telephone, had heard the same revolting filth only minutes earlier. The first time she had received such a call she had felt so sick she was almost physically ill, had felt so threatened she had moved into a hotel for the night. The second time she had been angry, so angry she called the police. They sent someone round to talk to her, but in the end all they could advise was that she change her telephone number. But the calls had still continued. She still felt sick at the disgusting things he said to her each week, but she no longer felt threatened, was sure after all this time that whoever he was he preferred to violate her over the telephone, that he wouldn't actually come to her home and carry out the things he threatened.

"Have you done anything about it?" Adam grated, the nerve pulsing in his jaw telling of his anger.

Leonie sighed. "I've changed my telephone number twice, but it's made no difference."

Adam frowned. "He got your new number both times?"

She nodded. "Even though they're unlisted."

"How often does he call?" Adam's eyes were narrowed.

"Every Friday night at eleven-thirty," she sighed. "There's nothing we can do, Adam, and as long as he stays on the other end of that telephone I can cope with it. Actually, he's getting a little boring now," she grimaced. "His fantasy seems to be stuck in a groove."

"I heard," Adam rasped.

"Interesting idea, isn't it," she dismissed with bravado. "I've told him I think we could do ourselves a mischief, but he—"

"Leonie!" Adam cautioned tightly. "Can't you take anything seriously?"

"I thought you always liked my sense of humour!"

"Not about something like this," he said grimly, his hands thrust into his denims pockets. "The man's a damned fruit-cake, how can you make jokes about it!"

"How?" her voice cracked emotionally. "I'll tell you how! Because every Friday night I live in dread of those calls, and every Friday night at eleven-thirty he calls without fail. In a way it's a relief when he does call, at least then I can relax for another week. You see, I have a theory," her voice was shrill. "That while he continues to call he won't actually come here."

"You think he knows where you live?" Adam frowned.

"I would say it's a logical assumption," she nodded. "If he can get my telephone number three times he can certainly get my address!"

"Then you can't stay here," Adam decided arrogantly.

"Oh but I can," she told him. "I thought about moving, but don't you see," she reasoned at his furious expression, "I'm as safe here as I can be anywhere. This man obviously has the means at his fingertips to find out anything he wants to know about me. If I move he'll know that too, so why go through the bother of it?" She shrugged.

"Then you can't stay here alone," Adam told her grimly.

"Are you offering your services as bodyguard, Adam?" she mocked.

"And if I were?"

She shook her head. "I don't need, or want, a live-in lover."

"Have you been to the police about this?"

"There's nothing they can do. The man doesn't threaten me, he just talks dirty!"

"He *talks* about violating you!"

"And do you realise how many obscene telephone calls are received and reported each year? I can tell you that it's thousands," she said wearily. "The police don't have enough people to follow up on all of them. They asked me all the usual questions, did I know of anyone who would want to do this to me, did I recognise his voice? I don't, and I didn't! It's all I can do to stop myself being sick when he calls. Now can we drop the subject, hm?" she said brittlely.

His mouth tightened. "I think you should move from here," he stated stubbornly, his jaw rigid.

"There's just no point to that," she sighed. "And except for his telephone calls, which will probably continue wherever I live, I like it here. No, Adam, I'm not moving," she told him firmly. "And one of these days he's going to get tired of calling me."

"And what do you think will happen then?"

"Hopefully he'll leave me alone," she shrugged.

"Hopefully!" Adam repeated raggedly. "What if he decides to come here and act out his fantasy?"

She shivered as he put into words what she had tried not even to think about. "The percentage of those that actually carry out the things they talk about is very low," she dismissed.

"You could be one of the victims of that percentage! God, Leonie," he groaned, taking her into his arms as she began to tremble. "I don't mean to frighten you, but I can't bear the thought of some maniac wanting to hurt you."

Her face was buried against his chest, and for a few minutes she allowed herself the luxury of leaning against his strength, of feeling protected. Then she moved back to smile at him brightly. "Maybe the fact that you answered the telephone tonight will frighten him off," she suggested derisively. "I'm sure he didn't get the same satisfaction whispering those things in your ear!"

"No," Adam agreed grimly, shaking off his worry with effort. "Let's hope you're right. Now we had better get you to the hospital— What the hell was that?" he jumped nervously as there was a noise at the window.

Leonie laughed softly. "It's only Harvey wanting to come in." She moved to open the window for the ginger and white tabby-cat to come inside.

Adam looked at him with relief. "After that call my imagination is running riot!" he admitted ruefully, bending down on his haunches to stroke the cat's sleek fur as Harvey strolled over to inspect him.

"Stroking a cat is supposed to be good for the heart and blood pressure," Leonie mocked him.

Adam glanced up at her. "I can think of another redhead I would rather stroke!"

Leonie gave a rueful laugh. "I think I walked right into that one!"

"You did," he straightened. "Any offers?"

She shook her head. "I think one lecher per household is enough—and judging by the amount of females that wait outside for Harvey every night he's it!"

Adam laughed softly, his tension momentarily forgotten. "Bit of a ladies' man, is he?"

"You could say that," she grimaced. "I certainly get the impression the cat population in the area could be on the increase in the next few months!"

"Is he going to need anything before we leave?"

She shook her head. "He's already been fed, he's just home to rest after his exhausting evening out." She moved across the room to check the wire mesh on top of the goldfish bowl that stood on the sideboard.

"So this is Moby," Adam stood at her side watching the fish as it swam into the weeds at the bottom of the bowl.

"I think he snubs his nose at Harvey sometimes," she smiled. "A sort of 'Hah, hah, you can't get me!' look."

Adam chuckled, helping her on with her jacket, careful of her aching hand and arm. "This household is like you; crazy!"

"I like it," she shrugged.

"So do I," he said throatily. "Leonie—" He stepped back as she winced. "Is your hand getting worse?"

"It's—painful," she conceded. But not half as painful as the casual way he kept taking her into his arms! He had been doing it all evening, first at the skating-rink, when he took every opportunity he could to touch her, and now, when the situation was much more precarious, her bedroom all too close.

Somewhere during the evening she had lost sight of the fact that they were adversaries, not lovers. After his disgusting behaviour at lunch today she shouldn't even have been talking to him, let alone have agreed to go out with him. Admittedly, with Adam in this irrepressible mood it was a little difficult to remain angry with him, but she shouldn't have actually enjoyed herself! The same problem still applied to any relationship between Adam and herself; Adam's feeling for her unattainable sister still standing between them.

"Shall we go?" she said sharply. "It's very late, and I have to go out in the morning."

"Where?"

She looked at him coolly as they went downstairs together. "I always visit Liz and Nick on Saturday mornings," she informed him distantly. "Nick would think it a little strange if I didn't make the effort to visit my niece.''

"And Liz?"

"I'm sure you're well aware of the reason that I find it difficult to be with my sister," she bit out, coming to a halt as they got outside. "Thanks for a nice evening, Adam," she dismissed. "Even if I didn't quite manage to skate properly."

"I'm coming to the hospital with you."

"I'm not a child," she snapped at his arrogance. "I'm quite capable of taking myself to the hospital."

"And driving yourself there?" he reasoned softly. "With only one hand?"

She blushed at the truth of that. Unlike his own car hers wasn't automatic; she definitely needed two capable hands for driving, and she certainly couldn't use her injured one. "I can get a taxi," she insisted.

"As I told you yesterday, not at this time of night you won't. Especially now that I know there's some sex-pervert with his eye on you," he added grimly.

God, had it only been yesterday that she and this man had shared so much passion! It seemed as if he had never been out of her life, as if they hadn't been separated for eight months, although she knew this was a different Adam from the one she just couldn't live with any more. This Adam had the power of seduction, a power he wasn't averse to using whenever she proved difficult; which was most of the time!

He took complete charge when they reached the hospital, declared himself her husband as he stood at her side and watched as they cleaned her wound, gave her tablets to fight the infection, and others to kill the pain.

Like this he was more like the Adam she had first fallen in love with, and as they left the hospital together she decided to make it plain to him exactly where they stood in this relationship he had decided he wanted with her. "I accepted your offer to drive me to the hospital, but that's all I accepted," she told him abruptly.

"Why, what do you mean?" he asked with feigned innocence as he opened the car door for her, quickly joining her as he got in behind the wheel.

"I mean you are not spending the night with me," she looked at him with steady green eyes.

"Did I ask if I could?"

"Adam," she sighed. "I may not live with you any more but I do know that you aren't a man that asks; you take."

His expression sobered. "I took because you wouldn't give freely," he rasped.

"And I wouldn't give freely because the more I gave the more you took!"

"I wanted to make love to my wife, I don't consider that a bad thing. Most wives complain their husband doesn't pay enough attention to them in bed!"

"The sexual act didn't hold the same pleasure for me as it did for you," she snapped.

"But that's no longer the case, is it," he reasoned calmly. "Last night you demanded as well as gave."

She blushed at the mention of her wanton responses the night before. "Last night I wanted you too," she admitted. "Wanted to know if I could respond to you."

"And you did."

"Yes."

"Then there's no problem, is there," Adam dismissed.

"Yes, there's a problem," she told him angrily. "The problem is *you,* Adam, I can't deny that last night was a success, but I don't want to repeat it. I don't want to work for you, I don't want to be with you.''

"Too bad, the contract is already signed. And as for being with me, you enjoyed yourself tonight, didn't you?''

She had, she couldn't deny the fun they had had together. "But it wasn't you, Adam,'' she protested impatiently. "You're the man who owns an empire—''

"Several companies,'' he corrected softly.

"It doesn't matter how many,'' she sighed. "You're rich, successful, sophisticated. You aren't really the man that took me roller-skating tonight.''

"Then who was he?'' Adam asked her quietly, not expecting an answer.

And Leonie couldn't give him one. The man she had been with tonight, been to bed with last night, was a man she could like all too much. And she didn't want to like him, knew that if she ever came to truly like Adam rather than just have fallen in love with him that she would be lost.

"I'll see you at nine-thirty on Monday morning,'' he told her as they parted at her door. "You're sure you're going to be all right on your own?''

"My hand is fine now—''

"I wasn't thinking of your hand,'' he said grimly.

"The telephone calls?'' she realised, shaking her head. "He only ever calls that once, at eleven-thirty on a Friday night.''

And it wasn't until she lay in bed that night, Harvey curled up against her side, that she realised that for the first time since the calls began she hadn't even thought about or dreaded tonight's call, that she had been so fascinated by Adam that she had forgotten all about it!

## CHAPTER FIVE

Liz was as beautiful as ever. No, more beautiful. Since Emma had been born three months ago Liz had possessed an inner glow of beauty that far outshone her obvious physical beauty. Her blonde hair was styled attractively close to her head, kept shorter now for convenience sake, having little time to fuss over her appearance now that she had a baby to care for. Her widely spaced hazel eyes were often more green than brown, glowing with the happiness she felt in her new role, her mouth curved into a perpetual smile, her figure having returned to its previous sylph-like elegance, although she wore little that emphasised that fact, her clothes loose and comfortable rather than fashionably styled as they used to be.

Yes, to an outsider Liz looked the perfect wife and mother, ecstatically happy in both those roles. And if Leonie hadn't seen her four-month pregnant sister in Adam's arms she may even have been fooled into believing that image herself.

But she had seen Liz in Adam's arms, had heard her sobbing about when they had been together. Adam had looked up and seen Leonie's stricken face as she watched them from the doorway, but he hadn't come after her straight away, had continued to hold Liz as she cried. In that moment Leonie had realised what a fool she had been, what fools they had all been to think that any marriage other than with the person you loved could possibly work out.

When Adam returned to the house over an hour later her suitcases were already packed, and she was waiting for the taxi to arrive that would take her to a hotel until she could decide what to do with her life now that her marriage was over, the Porsche Adam had given her when they returned from their honeymoon parked outside the house, the keys left on the dressing-table for Adam to pick up, all of the clothes he had given her still hanging in the wardrobe. She wanted nothing he had given her.

He had tried to reason with her, to explain what she had seen, but she had only one question she wanted answered; had he slept with Liz. The guilt on his face had been answer enough. Not that she could altogether blame him for that, Liz was a very beautiful woman, what she couldn't forgive was the fact that he had involved her in their triangle of misery.

She may have left Adam but Liz remained with Nick, both of them adoring the beautiful child they had created between them. But Leonie couldn't help wondering how long that would last, when Liz would decide she had shared Emma with Nick long enough and went back to Adam. Worst of all she wondered how Nick would react to knowing that his wife no longer loved him, that she had stayed with him only because she was expecting his baby. Nick adored Liz, had been in their lives ever since Leonie could remember, his love for Liz evident in everything that he did.

Leonie watched him now as he played on the floor with Emma, the little baby gurgling up at him, her huge green eyes glowing. Nick wasn't a handsome man, but he was strong, in body as well as mind.

Having just passed his fortieth birthday he still remained remarkably fit, his blond hair peppered with
silver giving him a distinguished air. He had lived
next to them since their parents died, had been ecstatic when Liz accepted his proposal.

Leonie loved him like a brother, wished there were
something she could do to prevent the pain and disillusionment he would feel when Liz tired of playing
house and decided to leave him. But he was happy
now, deserved that happiness after the long wait he
had had for Liz; why end that happiness prematurely?

"You'll stay for lunch, won't you, Leonie?" Nick
looked up to smile.

"Er—no, I don't think so," she refused, finding
even this two-hour duty visit per week a strain.

He grinned, straightening, Emma in his arms. "I
can assure you that Liz's cooking has improved since
she's been home full time," he mocked.

"Just for that, Nick Foster, I may decide not to
cook your Sunday lunch tomorrow," Liz pretended
to be offended, but she couldn't help smiling.

"You wouldn't do that to a starving man," he protested.

Liz grimaced at him. "You look as if you're starving," she looked pointedly at his muscular physique.

Leonie's heart ached at the way Liz was able to
banter and share her life with a man she no longer
loved; *she* certainly hadn't been able to do the same
once she knew the truth about Adam and Liz.

"Your mummy is implying I'm putting on
weight," Nick spoke to his daughter of his indignation at the suggestion.

"She isn't implying anything," Liz laughed softly,
taking the baby from him. "She would tell you if you

were. I can't have you running to seed after only a
few years of marriage." She began to feed Emma.

There was nothing more natural than a woman with
a baby at her breast, and yet the sight of Liz and
Emma together in that way twisted a knife in Leonie's
heart. She had suggested to Adam that they have a
baby, had hoped it might help draw them closer together, to give her the confidence in herself as a
woman that she so sadly lacked with the failure of
the physical relationship. But Adam had turned down
the idea, had told her children didn't fit into his plans
for some time to come. No doubt Liz's child would
be a different matter!

She wondered if Liz would feel quite so content if
she knew that Adam was trying to have an affair with
her. Why didn't Liz just go to him now and save them
all a lot of heartache! She stood up jerkily, unable to
take any more. "I really do have to go now."

Liz frowned. "But you've only just arrived."

"I— My hand is aching," she didn't exactly lie,
her hand did ache, despite the pain-killers she had
been taking to ease that.

"How did you do it?" Liz looked concerned.

She shrugged. "Just another of my little 'accidents'," she dismissed.

Nick gave her a teasing smile. "I'm glad you've
never come to me for insurance, it would be embarrassing having to turn down my sister-in-law as too
much of a risk!"

She returned his smile. "I don't think I could have
afforded the premium anyway on my record!"

"You never used to be quite as bad as this."

Her smile became brittle at her sister's observation.
"No," she acknowledged tightly.

"I remember Adam always used to have the effect of making you worse," Nick mused.

"Have you seen anything of him?"

How casually her sister made her interest sound! She had no idea if Liz saw Adam at all, rarely discussed anything personal with her sister, least of all Adam. But she assumed that they would meet occasionally, despite Liz's act of the devoted wife. "I saw him yesterday as a matter of fact," she replied lightly. "He's looking very well."

"He always does," Liz observed affectionately. "Have the two of you—resolved your differences?"

The look she gave her sister was scathing to say the least. "We never will," she said dully, knowing Liz must know that above all people. "Our marriage is over."

"I'm sorry, I assumed because you met yesterday…?"

"I'm going to be working for Adam for a few weeks, nothing more than that," she dismissed.

Hazel eyes widened. "Adam has hired you to work for him?"

"Yes," she bit out. "I may not be any good as a wife but I'm a damned good interior designer."

Liz looked taken aback by her bitterness. "I'm sure you are, it just seems an—odd, arrangement."

Not half as odd as the other arrangement Adam was suggesting! She shrugged. "Adam isn't a man that cares how things look. And I have little say in the matter, David decides who will do what."

"How is David?" Nick asked interestedly.

"Very well." Some of the tension left her at this more neutral subject, looking gratefully at Nick, knowing by the compassion she could see in his deep blue eyes that he understood she would rather not talk about Adam. She had brought David here to dinner one evening, had found him the exact buffer she needed to help her get through an evening with Liz, and the other couple had liked him immensely.

"You see rather a lot of him, don't you," Liz said conversationally.

Leonie at once stiffened resentfully. "I work for him," she reminded abruptly.

"I meant socially, silly," her sister chided.

She looked at Liz with suspicion. What was Liz up to now, trying to absolve her conscience by making sure Leonie had a man in her life when she went to Adam? She was over her own shock and humiliation, needing no man in her life, it was Nick who was going to be devastated.

"I see him occasionally," she dismissed. "Very occasionally. Do you see anything of Adam?" she challenged.

Was it her imagination or did Liz suddenly become very engrossed in feeding Emma?

"Occasionally," Liz replied distractedly, seeing to the baby.

"He came to dinner last week, as it happens," Nick put in lightly. "Strange, he didn't mention that he intended seeing you."

"He meant it to be a surprise," her voice was sharp. "And it was definitely that."

"It must have been," Liz nodded.

Her mouth firmed. "I really do have to be going," she told them determinedly. "I'll see you again next week."

It was Nick who walked her to the door, Liz still busy with Emma. Leonie was just relieved at being able to leave, dreaded these duty visits, sure that both she and Liz were aware of the reason they could no longer get on even on a polite social level.

Somehow knowing she was to see Adam first thing Monday morning made the weekend pass all too quickly. But at least he didn't pay her any surprise visits during those two days; she had half expected that he would, had felt a sense of anti-climax when he didn't.

Her hand was a lot better by Monday morning, the red line of infection having faded up her arm, the wound feeling more comfortable, so much so that she felt able to leave off the sling she had been instructed to wear over the weekend.

"Damn, who can that be?" she muttered as the doorbell rang as she was brushing her teeth, grabbing up her silky robe to pull it on over her lacy bra and panties.

Adam eyed her mockingly. "Either that's toothpaste, or you're foaming at the mouth."

Colour flooded her cheeks as she belatedly remembered to remove the toothpaste from her mouth with the towel in her hand. She had just been so stunned to see him; it was only eight-thirty in the morning. "What are you doing here?" she said ungraciously.

He shrugged, strolling past her into the flat. "You need a lift to work, I'm here to provide it."

Leonie followed him in to the lounge, scowling as Harvey lingered long enough on his way out to rub against Adam's trouser-covered leg, leaving ginger hairs on the dark brown material. "I can drive myself to work," she snapped.

He frowned as she freely used her right hand to prove her point. "You're supposed to rest that."

"I did. I have," she added impatiently. "It's better

now. Or perhaps you don't take my word for it and would like to inspect it yourself?'' she challenged.

"I can see from here that it's in working order again,'' he said dryly, making himself comfortable in one of her armchairs. ''Did you have a good weekend?''

"Did you?'' she returned.

"Very good,'' he nodded. ''Did you visit Liz?''

Her mouth tightened. ''Yes.''

"How is she?''

"Don't you know?''

"If I did, would I be asking?'' he reasoned mildly.

"Probably,'' she scorned. ''After all, you have to keep up appearances. It's Nick I feel sorry for, he just has no idea does he?'' she added disgustedly.

"Leonie, you don't know what you're talking about, so just drop it, hm,'' he was still pleasantly polite.

"I know you were having an affair with my sister when we were married—''

"You know I went to bed with her, it isn't the same thing.'' Steel had entered his voice.

She gave a disbelieving laugh. ''Of course it's the same thing!''

"No,'' he shook his head, his eyes narrowed. ''And one day you're going to want to hear the truth. In the meantime I'd like to concentrate on our affair.''

"I—''

"What did you have for breakfast this morning?''

The question took her by surprise. ''Toast and coffee,'' she answered automatically.

"Dry toast and black coffee?'' he guessed, standing up. ''The more sophisticated hair-style is an improvement, Leonie, but the loss of weight isn't,'' he told her as he went through to the kitchen.

Leonie followed him. ''What do you think you're doing?'' she demanded as he took butter, milk and eggs out of the refrigerator.

''Getting our breakfast,'' he answered dismissively.

''Haven't you eaten?''

He shook his head. ''I thought I'd wait and eat with you.''

''But I told you, I've already eaten.''

''Rubbish,'' he decided, beating the milk into the eggs. ''Go and finish dressing and then come and eat.''

''Adam—''

His gaze was steady. ''I prefer you as you were before you dieted.''

''So you intend fattening me up,'' she protested.

''That's the idea,'' he nodded. ''I should hurry and dress, Leonie, the eggs will be ready in a few minutes.''

''I'll be late for work!''

''I'm your first appointment, and I don't mind if you're late,'' he dismissed with a smile. ''Now off you go,'' he gave her bottom a playful tap.

Leonie gave him an indignant glare before leaving the room. How dare he ignore her all weekend and then calmly turn up here again this morning and attempt to take over her life once again!

Her movements quieted as she wondered whether she were more angry at being ignored the last two days or at the fact that Adam was taking command of her life. The answer made her wince.

''Very nice. Very professional,'' Adam complimented when she rejoined him in the kitchen. ''Now take off the jacket and put it over that chair with mine; I'd like to eat breakfast with a lover, not a business-woman.''

He had effectively robbed her of her line of defence! She had donned the formal oatmeal-coloured suit and brown blouse in an effort to remain distant from the situation he was trying to create. But he had discarded his own jacket and waistcoat, looking ruggedly attractive. With her own jacket removed they looked like any other couple having breakfast together before leaving for work.

"That's better." Adam divided the scrambled eggs on to two plates, putting them on the table with the rack of toast and pot of coffee. He poured a cup of the latter for both of them as he sat down opposite her, adding milk and sugar to Leonie's.

"No—"

"You know you love milk and sugar in your coffee," he stubbornly added another teaspoonful of the latter.

"But it doesn't love me," she grimaced. "Adam, I can't eat that," she protested as he liberally buttered a slice of toast for her.

"Then I'll feed you," he told her throatily, holding the toast temptingly in front of her mouth.

"Something else lovers do?" she rasped irritably.

"All the time," he grinned.

The toast looked so delicious after the strict diet she had kept herself on the last few months. She closed her eyes so as not to be tempted, although the smell tormented her. "I've only just given away all my size fourteen clothes to charity," she pleaded raggedly.

"So I'll buy you some new ones," he dismissed.

Her lids flew open at the arrogant statement. "You most certainly will not!"

"Independent as well as fiery," Adam smiled at

her. "Eat, Leonie." The smile didn't leave his face but his tone was firm.

With an irritated glare in his direction she took a bite out of the slice of toast, savouring every morsel; it seemed so long since she had allowed herself the luxury of butter, only keeping it in the refrigerator for guests. But after tasting the toast oozing with butter it was all too easy to eat the fluffy eggs and drink the sweet syrupy coffee.

She frowned as Adam ate his own eggs. "Why didn't she provide you with breakfast?" she mocked.

"She?"

"The woman you spent the weekend with."

"Ah, that she," he nodded, lifting one of her hands to lace her fingers with his. "I spent the weekend in business meetings, Leonie," he told her reproachfully.

"That's a new name for it!" She glared at him as he refused to release her hand.

He smiled his appreciation of her humour. "Would it bother you if I had spent the weekend with another woman?"

"Would it bother you if I had spent the weekend with another man?"

"Like a knife being twisted inside me," he answered without hesitation.

Leonie gasped, meeting his steady gaze. "Did you really spend the weekend working?" she asked uncertainly.

"Yes."

"Why?"

"So that I had time to spare this week to concentrate on my reluctant lover," he teased.

"And did you spend the weekend alone?"

"My personal assistant—"

"Ah."

"Jeremy," he finished pointedly. "Accompanied me."

"I see," she chewed on her bottom lip. "I spent the weekend alone too."

"I know," he nodded, standing up to clear away the debris from their meal before shrugging back into his waistcoat and jacket.

Leonie glared at him. "If you're still having me followed—"

"I'm not." He held out her own jacket for her.

She shoved her arms into the sleeves, turning to frown at him angrily. "Then how did you know I spent the weekend alone?"

He grinned. "Harvey told me."

"Adam!" she warned tightly.

He bundled her out of the door. "The only man you've been seeing since we separated is David Stevenson, and he mentioned at lunch on Friday that he was going away this weekend."

"Oh." She looked at him resentfully as they emerged out into the street, the BMW parked behind her orange, and rusty, VW. The difference in their cars seemed to echo the difference in themselves, Adam a man of caviar and fresh salmon, Leonie fish and chips and McDonald's. "I'll meet you at your office," she told him abruptly.

"Leonie?" he probed her sudden withdrawal even from arguing with him, frowning heavily.

"We're already late, Adam," she sighed wearily. "And my car isn't the most reliable of machines." She unlocked the door.

"Is that yours?" excitement tinged Adam's voice as he walked over to the VW, touching one fender almost reverently. "I used to have one exactly like it.

I kept it until it just about disintegrated on me,'' he chuckled reminiscently. ''You're lucky to have found one in such good condition.''

''Adam, the car is ten years old! And when did you ever have an old jalopy like this?'' she scorned.

''When I was at college. Dad wanted me to buy something more prestigious,'' he recalled dryly. ''But I'd worked in a bar in the evenings to buy my VW, I wasn't giving it up for anyone.''

He knew exactly how she felt about this rusty old car! He had given her the Porsche during their marriage, and there could be no doubting that it was a fantastic car, but even though she moaned and groaned about the unreliability of the VW she wouldn't exchange it for the Porsche at any price, had worked hard to buy this car for herself. And Adam knew how she felt. Why couldn't he do something, *anything,* so that she could dislike him once more!

''I'll meet you at your office,'' she repeated lightly, climbing into her car.

With a shrug of his broad shoulders Adam strolled back to the BMW, sitting inside the car as he waited for life to spark in her engine. As usual the VW played up, and Leonie was hot with embarrassment by the time the engine roared into life, instantly stalling it and having to start the process all over again.

Mrs Carlson's brows rose questioningly as they entered the top-floor suite together, and Leonie blushed at what the other woman must be thinking about them; she had last seen them going to lunch together on Friday. She felt sure the secretary imagined they had spent the weekend together!

''Mr Spencer is waiting for you in your office,'' she informed Adam coolly, obviously disapproving of the relationship between her boss and an employee, albeit an indirect employee.

"Thanks, Stella," Adam dismissed. "Could you bring in coffee for three?" he requested arrogantly as he ushered Leonie into his office.

A young man stood up at their entrance, his smile warm and friendly as he looked at Adam, cooling slightly as his gaze passed to Leonie, looking her over critically.

Leonie did some "looking over" herself! The slightly overlong blond hair was deliberately styled that way, she felt sure, the face too good looking to be called handsome, his body slender, wearing the cream suit and brown shirt well, his hands long and thin, the nails kept short—and manicured.

Adam met her questioning gaze with suppressed humour. "Leonie, this is Jeremy Spencer, my Personal Assistant," he introduced softly. "Jeremy, this is Leonie Grant, the young lady who is going to transform these offices into something approaching comfort."

Leonie was aware of his amused gaze on them as she and Jeremy continued to eye each other critically.

"Miss Grant," Jeremy Spencer made no attempt to shake hands with her. "I hope you won't attempt to change the decor too much, I think this is exactly Adam already."

She looked around the austere room, knowing that it needed light, that perhaps it would have suited the man she had been married to, but not the Adam she now knew, not the Adam that was her lover. "It is very—masculine," she agreed.

Jeremy Spencer turned back to Adam. "I brought these contracts in for you to sign."

Leonie was ignored by both men during the next

few minutes as they discussed the contract that had obviously been decided upon during the weekend, unable to resist making a comparison between them as they bent over the desk. Jeremy Spencer didn't attract her at all!

He nodded to her abruptly when it came time for him to leave, and Leonie had trouble holding in her laughter until the door had closed behind him. "Really, Adam," she finally spluttered with laughter. "What on earth made you employ *him?*"

Adam shrugged dismissively. "He's harmless. Now come over here, we haven't had our morning kiss yet," he invited huskily.

"Were we supposed to have one?" she delayed mockingly.

"But of course." He strolled over to her, his arms about her waist as he moulded her body to his. "After a weekend apart we shouldn't be able to keep our hands off each other!"

"Then how have we managed to?" she taunted.

"After the way you greeted me this morning I was afraid to touch you until I'd fed you!"

"You aren't afraid of anything," she scorned. "You never have been."

"I'm afraid that if you don't kiss me I'm going to burn up with wanting you," he groaned.

Her breath caught in her throat, her head tilted back to receive his kiss, her lips parting beneath his, her arms moving about his waist beneath his jacket. He felt warm and solid, his smooth jaw smelling faintly of limes.

"Adam, I forgot— Oh." An astounded Jeremy Spencer stood in the doorway, staring at them in disbelief.

"Yes, Jeremy, what is it?" Adam's voice was terse

as he kept Leonie in his arms, the evidence of his arousal pressed against her.

"I—er—I forgot to get your signature on these letters." Jeremy ignored Leonie as he placed the letters on the desk for Adam. "I had no idea I was interrupting—something," he added.

Adam eyed him warningly. "Nothing that can't be continued after you've gone," he dismissed. "I'll sign the letters later," he drawled as the younger man made a hasty departure.

"You've shocked him," Leonie reproved.

Adam scowled. "That's nothing to what he just did to me!"

She laughed softly at his obvious discomfort. "You'll get over it."

"Maybe—for a while," he added warningly. "But it will only be a delay, Leonie, not a reprieve."

She blushed at the promise behind the words. "Isn't it time we got down to business, I do have other clients besides you, you know."

"None that can't wait," he announced raggedly. "I have no intention of discussing anything until I've received a proper good-morning kiss, with a certain amount of feeling."

"That's blackmail," she protested.

Adam grinned. "Terrible, isn't it?" He didn't sound in the least repentant.

"Both lovers have the same physical power," she warned as she moved into his arms, she the one to initiate the kiss this time, moving her mouth erotically against his, feeling the accelerated thud of his heart beneath her hand, moving sensuously against him as he groaned low in his throat, squirming away from him as he would have caressed her breasts. "Good morning, Adam," she greeted throatily.

He let out a ragged breath. ''That was with a 'certain amount of feeling' all right,'' he said ruefully.

She smiled. ''I thought so.''

His eyes narrowed. ''Enjoyed it, did you?''

She was well aware of how aroused he was. ''Immensely,'' she nodded.

''Hm,'' he muttered. ''Let's get down to the business of choosing the decor for this office.''

Leonie worked happily at his side for the remainder of the morning, a satisfied smile to her lips for the whole of the hour it took him to put his desire from his mind—and body; meeting his scowls with a bright smile.

The decisions made about colours and fabrics she had to get back to her office and begin the ordering and arranging, the part Leonie liked the best—apart from the finished result, of course.

''Lunch, I think,'' Adam stood up decisively as she packed away her sample books.

She frowned. ''I hope I haven't delayed you.'' It was after one o'clock.

''I meant lunch for both of us,'' he pulled on his jacket. ''Together,'' he added pointedly.

''Oh I don't usually bother with lunch—''

''I'm fattening you up, remember.'' He closed her briefcase and picked it up, taking hold of her arm with the other hand.

''I'm still full up from breakfast,'' she protested as he marched her out to the lift, blushing as she realised Mrs Carlson had heard her protest. ''Now she must have completely the wrong idea about us,'' she muttered crossly as they went downstairs.

''The right idea,'' he corrected with a smile.

''My car,'' she protested as he led her to the BMW.

''You can come back for it.''

"I haven't forgotten what happened the last time I intended doing that," she glowered at him.

His only answer was a mocking smile. Leonie seethed all the way to the restaurant, resentful of his high-handedness, feeling as if all decisions were taken from her whenever she was in his company. She had found her independence the last eight months, she didn't need him taking over her life a second time. He—

"Come on, dreamer," he chided, the car parked, Adam having opened the car door for her and now waiting for her to join him.

She got out resentfully. "I wasn't dreaming, I— Adam, this isn't a restaurant." She looked up at the tall building that was almost a national monument.

"No, it's a hotel," he acknowledged, guiding her into the plush foyer.

"But they won't serve us here," she whispered fiercely.

"Of course they will," he dismissed.

"No—"

"Have you ever heard of room-service?" he taunted as he led the way over to the reception.

"Room—? Adam!" She came to a shocked halt.

He turned to look down at her with mocking eyes. "I've booked us a room for the afternoon," he announced calmly.

# CHAPTER SIX

"YOU'VE done *what?*" she gasped disbelievingly, staring up at him in horror-struck fascination.

"I've booked us into this hotel for the afternoon," he repeated softly.

Leonie looked about them self-consciously, sure that everyone must know they were here for an afternoon of illicit sex; no one appeared to be taking any undue notice of them. "Adam, you can't be serious," she muttered.

"I am. Very."

"But I—We—I thought only married people sneaked off to hotels for the afternoon!"

"We are married."

"I mean people who aren't married to *each other,*" she glared up at him frustratedly. "Surely you have your apartment for this type of thing?"

"I don't know what you mean by 'this type of thing'," he said softly. "But I have my apartment to live in," he corrected reprovingly.

"But you took me there last time," she said desperately as she noticed one of the receptionists eyeing them curiously, sure they must look very conspicuous as she argued with Adam.

"But isn't this more exciting?" he teased.

It was exciting, there was no denying that. She felt deliciously wicked, could feel the heat in her veins at the thought of spending the afternoon in bed with

Adam. But they couldn't just disappear for the afternoon, they both had responsibilities. "Adam, I have to get back to work, and so do you," she protested.

He shook his head. "I told you, I intend concentrating on my reluctant lover; I cancelled all my appointments for this afternoon so that I could spend the time with you. I also told Stevenson I would need you all day. He agreed."

"Oh, Adam, you didn't," she groaned, sure David would be curious as to why Adam should need her for the whole day when they were only discussing colour and fabrics.

"It's the truth," Adam told her huskily. "And that need is getting out of control," he added pointedly.

Heat coloured her cheeks at his verbal seduction of the senses. "I feel embarrassed even being here," she muttered self-consciously.

"Come on, Mrs Smith," he chuckled as he took her hand firmly in his and strode the short distance to the desk. "Or would you prefer to be Mrs Brown?" he paused with his pen over the registration card.

"I'd rather leave," she groaned uncomfortably.

He shook his head, filling in the form before handing it to the waiting receptionist.

"Good afternoon, Mr Faulkner," the beautiful young receptionist greeted after glancing at the card. "The 'Bridal Suite' has been prepared as per your instructions," she continued warmly. "And if you should need anything else please don't hesitate to call." She held out a key to him.

"I won't," he nodded curtly, taking the key, not glancing at Leonie as she would have pulled away at the other woman's mention of the Bridal Suite.

"Do you have any luggage?" the receptionist asked as they turned away.

"It's following on later," Adam told her smoothly. "A mix-up at the airport."

"Oh, how annoying for you," the young woman sympathised.

"Very," Adam smiled. "Come along, darling," he urged Leonie as she stood numbly at his side. "I know you would like to lie down after the exhausting day we've had."

"Adam, how could you?" she demanded as soon as the lift doors closed smoothly behind them, breaking out of the numbed surprise that had possessed her. She couldn't believe this was happening to her!

"With a telephone call," he deliberately misunderstood her.

"I meant how could you pretend to that woman that we've just got married," she accused. "What are you going to tell her when our luggage doesn't arrive and we leave in a few hours?"

Adam unlocked the door marked Bridal Suite, pushing the door open for her to enter. "I could always tell her you left me," he said softly.

Leonie was too engrossed in the beauty of the suite to detect the rasping edge of truth to his words. Vases of flowers filled every available surface, the olde-worlde decor adding to the feeling of this all being a dream.

"Oh, Adam, it's beautiful," she told him breathlessly.

"You haven't seen the best part yet," he assured her, pulling her towards the bedroom.

"Adam, I know what a bedroom looks like," she blushed at his eagerness to occupy the wide double bed.

"Not just the bedroom," he mocked, throwing open the adjoining door.

The room was as big as the lounge in the flat, two walls completely covered in mirrors, a huge sunken bath dominating the room. But it wasn't that that held her attention. "Champagne," she was already intoxicated without it! "Isn't that a little decadent in a bathroom, Adam?" she teased.

"Very," he confirmed with satisfaction, bending down to turn on the water to the bath.

"Champagne next to the bath is hardly in keeping with the modesty of a newly married couple," she said dryly, wondering what the hotel management had thought of these "instructions" of Adam's. "I— Oh, Adam," her cry of surprise was a mixture of despair and choked emotion. "It's a jacuzzi." She watched as the depth of the water foamed and whirled at the flick of a switch.

Adam sat back on his haunches to watch her reaction. "I think I must have telephoned almost every hotel in London, trying to find a Bridal Suite that had a jacuzzi; most of them thought the 'sweet young things' wouldn't have progressed to sharing a bath just yet!"

"A telephone call" he had said was all it took to arrange this magical afternoon, and yet he had now revealed it had taken a lot of planning, planning she was sure he hadn't consigned to the easily shockable Mrs Carlson. "Why, Adam?" her voice was a husky rasp.

"Well I suppose they thought the bride and groom would be a little shy with each other to start with—"

"Not that, Adam," she spoke quietly. "Why have you done all this?" She hadn't realised at first, had been too fascinated by the idea of an afternoon in bed with Adam to notice the similarities to their failure of a honeymoon. Admittedly they hadn't stayed in a hotel then, but Adam's house in the Bahamas had also been filled with flowers at their arrival, a bottle of champagne cooling in the bedroom, a jacuzzi in the adjoining bathroom.

That night she *had* been embarrassed at the idea of sharing a bath with Adam, her inhibitions making her shy about revealing her body to him so blatantly. Adam didn't have an inhibited bone in his body, had walked about naked almost from the time of their arrival, teasing her when she wouldn't join him in nude bathing on their private beach.

"We have a few ghosts to put to rest." Adam stood up as he saw the painful memories flickering in the bottle-green depths of her eyes.

"Not this way." She shook her head, the memories too vivid to be denied.

"Exactly this way," he nodded firmly, taking her in his arms. "I should never have married you," he murmured. "Another man may have been more understanding about your shy inexperience, may have given you the confidence in yourself as a woman that I never could."

She turned away. "It wouldn't have made any difference," she reminded gruffly.

"Sex isn't everything between a man and woman."

"On their honeymoon it is!" she scorned.

He sighed. "We're here to put those memories to rest, Leonie. Won't you let me try?"

She shook her head tearfully. "I can't be seduced into forgetting that—that fiasco with champagne and a—a damned jacuzzi," she told him sharply.

"I admit it would have been better if we could have returned to the villa, but I had enough difficulty getting you here without arousing your suspicions; the Bahamas would have been impossible!"

"Why should you want to try, Adam?" she sighed wearily.

"I want to replace the bad memories with good ones, erase the bitterness of the past—"

"And can you also erase your affair with Liz?" she scorned.

"There was no affair—"

"Your sleeping together, then," she amended impatiently.

"No, I can't erase that," he acknowledged heavily. "But I would like to explain it one day, when you're prepared to listen. Not today," he refused as she would have spoken. "We'll erase one memory at a time, and today we're starting with our honeymoon."

"I want to leave," she said stubbornly.

"Without testing the jacuzzi first?" he teased.

"Without testing anything," she looked at him coldly.

He shook his head. "I can't let you do that."

"You can't stop me," she derided.

"And what's that starry-eyed receptionist going to think when you walk out after fifteen minutes?"

"That I did leave you," she bit out. "A year too late. If I'd had any sense at all I would have walked out after the honeymoon."

"This is the honeymoon of our affair," he told her huskily, not releasing her.

"Affairs don't have honeymoons," she scoffed.

"This one does," he insisted. "It also has a ring." He took a brown ring-box from his jacket pocket.

"A Woolworth's special, to convince the gullible?" she scorned.

"A Cartier special," he drawled, flicking open the lid to the box, revealing a flat gold band studded with diamonds.

Leonie gasped at its delicate beauty. "I can't take that, Adam," she shook her head.

"Of course you can." He lifted her resisting left hand. "I noticed you no longer wear the rings I bought you," he pushed the diamond ring on to her third finger. "I want you to wear this instead."

She swallowed hard, the ring looking even more delicately beautiful on her slender hand. "Why?" she choked.

"It's an Eternity ring," he told her softly.

"Affairs are usually short-term, Adam," she shook her head.

"Not this one," he said with a return of arrogance. "I want you to move in with me, stay with me."

"We're getting a divorce, Adam," she reminded exasperatedly.

"After the divorce then, if you think that living together might make that difficult. I think I can wait that long, if I can see you every night at my apartment or yours."

"Adam, living together would be like being married!" she protested.

"It would be nothing like it," his voice was harsh. "You hated being married, remember?"

"Yes," she shuddered at the memory of how much pain it had caused her. "I did hate it," she confirmed vehemently.

He nodded. "But you've enjoyed the last few days we've been together, haven't you?"

She would be lying if she said she hadn't; it had been the first time she had felt really alive since she left him. 'Yes...'' she answered guardedly, knowing she was walking into a trap.

"Then wouldn't you like it to continue?"

"It couldn't," she shook her head. "Not indefinitely."

"We could try," he insisted.

"Adam, you and Liz—"

"I'm sick of feeling guilty about Liz and I!" His mouth was tight.

"But what would happen to us when she finally finds the courage to leave Nick?"

"Leave Nick?" Adam looked astounded. "She isn't going to leave Nick!"

"Never?" Leonie frowned.

"Never," he repeated firmly.

"But I thought—"

"I don't care what you thought," he bit out. "Liz is one of those women who make their marriage vows for a lifetime!"

Leonie looked at him sharply, wondering if she had imagined the rebuke behind the words; Adam's bland expression seemed to say she had. "So I'll do as second-best, hm?" she said bitterly.

"You aren't second-best." His voice was harsh. "You never were, you never will be. What happened between Liz and I was already over when I met you. God, I've already admitted I should never have married you, but that doesn't mean we can't be together now. The other night was incredible, you can't deny that!"

"No…"

"And can you deny that you want me now?"

She knew she couldn't, knew he must be as aware of the pounding of her heart as she was. She did want him, the non-committal affair he was offering very enticing.

"Come on." Adam sensed her weakening and took advantage of it, beginning to unbutton her blouse.

"Or the bath will be cold and the champagne flat," he drawled as he slipped the blouse down her arms and moved to the fastening of her skirt. "And we wouldn't enjoy it then—the way I intend us to enjoy it," he added with relish as he stripped her naked.

Colour flooded her cheeks as reflections of herself appeared all over the room, looking very pale next to Adam's dark colouring and the dark suit he still wore. "Are you sure this is a Bridal Suite?" she asked irritably.

"Yes," he laughed softly. "But I think it's for the more—experienced, bride and groom."

"Shouldn't you undress too?" she suggested awkwardly.

"Yes." He looked at her pointedly.

She had had little experience with undressing men, never taking such an initiative during their marriage, their undressing the other night having taken place in a darkened apartment, not broad daylight, with images of them reflected everywhere! Her fingers fumbled a little at first, but her confidence grew as she saw the effect she was having on Adam, her hand trustingly in his as they stepped down into the water together.

It was such a big bath that they could quite easily have sat facing each other, but Adam had other ideas, sitting down to pull her in front of him, pulling her back to lean against his chest, his arms around her waist.

He nuzzled against her throat. "We forgot the champagne," he muttered, the ice-bucket and glasses out of their reach.

"It isn't important." She already felt intoxicated just from his touch, gasping as his hands moved up to cup the fullness of her breasts. "Oh, Adam, I—"

"No, don't move," he instructed as she would have turned in his arms. "I haven't washed you yet." He took the soap in his hand and began to lather her body.

By the time they had finished washing each other the bath was filled with bubbles, all inhibitions gone as they frolicked in the water, Leonie facing him now, leaning against his chest as she lay between his legs. "Do you think we would drown if we made love in here?" The idea had been tantalising her the last few minutes, knowing Adam was as aroused as she was.

"It's too late even if we do," he groaned as his mouth claimed hers.

They didn't drown, but the carpet around the bath did seem very wet when they stepped out on to it, not bothering to dress but wrapping towels around themselves as they carried the champagne through to the bedroom.

Adam dipped a finger in his champagne to trail it between the deep vee of her breasts.

"Oh, Adam…!" she groaned as he licked the wine from her heated flesh, turning in his arms, gasping her dismay as *all* the champagne from her glass tipped over Adam's stomach, dripping down on to the bed. "Oh no," she groaned. "And I was doing so well too!"

"You were," he agreed seductively.

She blushed. "No, I meant—"

"I know what you meant," he chuckled, making no effort to mop up the champagne with the towel he still had draped about his hips. "Care to reciprocate?" he invited. "Your clumsiness may be to my advantage this time."

She knew what he meant, eagerly drinking the champagne from his body, tasting Adam at the same time, feeling the rush of need that engulfed them both as she removed his towel.

"We really should do something about ordering lunch," Adam mumbled contentedly a long time later. "I need to keep up my stamina if you're going to keep attacking me in this shameless way."

"If I'm going to—!" She turned to look at him indignantly, only to find him watching her with one sleepy eye, his mouth quirked in amusement. She relaxed. "Of course, if your age is going to slow you down," she began mockingly. "Maybe I should find myself a younger lover."

There was a deep threatening rumble in his chest as he rolled over to trap her beneath him. "Maybe *I* should just smack your bottom for you," he growled. "My age hasn't slowed me down so far, and—Leonie, did you mean what you just said?" he suddenly asked sharply.

She frowned at his sudden change of mood from lighthearted bantering to serious intensity. "What did I just say?"

"That I'm your lover."

She blushed. "Well you are, aren't you?"

"You didn't seem to think so this morning."

She shrugged. "That was this morning."

"And now?"

"We're in bed together," she stated the obvious.

"And am I your lover?" he persisted, his hand cupping one side of her face preventing her turning away from him.

"Adam, what we just shared was very pleasant—"

"It was toe-curling," he corrected emphatically.

"For you too?" she asked shyly. In her inexperience it had been very special to her, but surely to

Adam, a man with many affairs behind him, it couldn't have meant the same thing.

"Especially for me." His thumbtip moved across her slightly swollen lips. "It was the way I always wanted it to be between us, before a marriage licence and a wedding ring fouled things up."

She looked down at the eternity ring on her finger. "I won't make any demands on you," she told him huskily.

"You never did," he said grimly. "Not even sexual ones."

Her mouth curved teasingly. "Those weren't the demands I was promising not to make," she drawled.

"Thank God for that!" He returned her smile.

She laughed throatily. "Now that I've discovered the—delights of being in bed with you I may never want to get out!"

"Suits me," he murmured as his mouth claimed hers again.

It was after four when they ordered lunch, Leonie groaning at the amount of food Adam had ordered. "I'll get fat," she grimaced.

"I hope so," he nodded. "I really meant it when I said I preferred you more—rounded."

"You mean I really can start to eat again?"

"Please," he said fervently.

They fed each other like starry-eyed lovers, and every time Leonie saw the diamond ring glitter on her finger she felt a warm glow. She wasn't altogether sure what the ring symbolised, they could hardly remain lovers indefinitely, but somehow the ring made her feel as if she really were Adam's lover, and not just a chattel that he took out for display every now and then. Because that was what being his wife had been like; surely being his lover had to be better than that. It *was* better!

"You like the ring?" Adam saw her glowing gaze on it.

"If it enables me to play the part of Mrs Smith, I love it!" she smiled across the table at him.

He laughed softly. "You can play the part of Mrs Smith any time you want to, it's a two-way arrangement."

"You mean if I want to spend another afternoon like this I can just call you and you'll meet me here?"

"Well, not here," he smiled. "We can only play the newly married couple once, but I'll meet you anywhere else that you suggest."

It sounded like heaven after the misery of their marriage. "I think I'm going to like this arrangement," she smiled her anticipation.

"Didn't I tell you that you would?"

"Now don't go and spoil it by saying I told you so," she reprimanded. "I love the ring, and I'll wear it proudly, but it gives you no rights over me other than the ones I choose to give you," she warned.

"Right," he nodded.

She eyed him suspiciously, never having known him be this agreeable in the past. "I won't give up my job."

"No."

"And I won't move in with you."

"Why not?" he frowned, although he made no objections.

She shook her head. "It wouldn't work, Adam. When I lived with you before you swamped me, I became a nervous wreck, terrified of leaving the apartment in the end in case I did something wrong."

"I didn't know that..."

"No," she flushed. "We didn't talk a lot in those days."

"Then we'll make sure we talk now. Do I swamp you now?" he asked slowly, all laughter gone.

"Not while I have my own home to go to whenever I want to. I just couldn't live with you again, Adam."

"Okay," he shrugged. "If that's the way you feel."

"You—you don't mind?"

"No, because I'll move in with you," he stated arrogantly.

"That isn't the idea, Adam," she sighed. "I knew this wouldn't work out," she shook her head. "I think we should just forget the idea, it was a stupid one, anyway."

"If you want us to maintain separate households, then we will—"

"Oh, thank you, Adam," she glowed. "I would prefer it. I don't—"

"—for the time being," he finished pointedly. "Leonie, I can't keep going between two households when I reach sixty!" he said exasperatedly as she looked dismayed. "The strain would probably kill me!"

"Sixty…?" she repeated dazedly. "You expect us to still be together then?"

"Why not? Eternity is a hell of a lot longer than the twenty-one years it's going to take me to reach that age! At least, I hope it is," he frowned.

"Adam, if you think an affair between us will last that long why did our marriage fail after only a year?" she reasoned. "After all, I didn't know about Liz until that last day."

"No, but I did," he answered grimly. "Our marriage never really started, Leonie. I rushed you into it, made all the rules and expected you to abide by them the way that my mother did. But that isn't a marriage, Leonie, it's just legalising the sexual act— and even that didn't work between us then.''

"Is that why you married me, for sex?"

"I married you because I wanted to be with you," he rasped.

"Did you ever love me?" she asked dully.

"What difference does it make," he dismissed. "I couldn't make you happy."

It was a bitter irony that they could now make each other happy, that they were now closer than they ever had been.

"I loved you," she told him softly.

"I know," he acknowledged harshly. "And I hurt you. This way is much better, isn't it?"

She supposed it was— Of course it was! She just couldn't understand how they could make an affair work when their marriage had failed. Unless their expectations were lower, their demands less.

She had married Adam expecting forever, had thought him the man of her dreams, with no faults or blemishes. Hadn't finding that he couldn't banish all the problems of life for her, couldn't reach her physically when she put up a frightened barrier, made him less of a Knight in Shining Armour? She had forgotten she was married to a mere man, that he had needs and fears too, had thought only of herself when the marriage began so badly and continued on its downward slide. Adam wasn't responsible for what had gone wrong on their honeymoon, just as he wasn't solely responsible for the end of their marriage. She had taken his involvement with Liz as the easy way out, when in fact she should have realised she was the one he had married, the one he was trying to share his life with.

Poor Adam, no wonder the idea of marriage had been soured for him; the woman he had chosen for his wife just hadn't been woman enough to try to be his partner in life, to give him the same considerations he gave her.

But she was that woman now, could look back on their marriage with perspective, believed Adam when he said he hadn't slept with Liz after their marriage. Yes, she believed him now, when it was too late, when all he wanted was an affair. But if that was all that could work between them then it was what she wanted too, wanted Adam in her life.

"Much better," she assured him huskily, standing up to take off the towel that was her only clothing. "Shall we go back to bed and see just how much better," she invited suggestively.

Adam needed no second invitation, his own towel discarded long before they reached the bedroom.

## CHAPTER SEVEN

"No, Adam," she said firmly.

After two more days together she had gained enough confidence in their relationship to say what she liked and disliked, and the idea of joining Adam's father for dinner that evening she disliked intensely!

"Why not?" came Adam's calm query over the telephone.

"You can ask me that?" she gasped. "After the way he always treated me?"

"I was as much to blame for that as he was," Adam reminded. "I should have made sure he understood how things are between us."

"And how are they?" she demanded tautly.

"If he wants to continue seeing me," Adam told her softly, "he'll accept you."

Leonie was well aware of Charles Faulkner's love for his only child; she had often felt jealous of the closeness between them in the past. If Adam refused to visit his father because of her it would break the older man's heart.

"Adam, men don't introduce their lovers to their fathers," she derided.

"This man does."

She sighed at his stubbornness. "And what are you going to tell him about us?"

"Nothing."

"Nothing?" she frowned. "Adam—"

"It's sufficient that we're together," he explained arrogantly.

"Adam, I don't want to see your father again," she told him the simple truth behind her objection.

"I'm sure he feels the same way," he sounded amused. "He certainly sounded surprised when I told him you would be accompanying me."

"Then why put either of us through what can only be an embarrassing experience?" She put her hand up in acknowledgement of the night security guard as he passed by on his rounds. She was working late tonight, felt as if she were the only person in the building; it felt good to know Mick was about.

"I thought you said you wouldn't stay hidden as a lover," he reminded softly.

"And I haven't been!" She was angry with him for reminding her of that; the two of them hadn't exactly been keeping a low profile the last few days, Adam calling for her at the office for lunch, a rose, a real one now, continuing to arrive daily. She wasn't trying to hide their relationship, but neither was she willing to hypocritically sit down to dinner with Charles Faulkner; they both knew their dislike was mutual. "I'm not going to have dinner with your father, Adam," she repeated emphatically.

"He's expecting us."

"Then you go on your own," she snapped. "You had no right accepting the invitation without first consulting me."

"You would have said no," he reasoned.

"Obviously," she bit out. "Now could we end this pointless conversation, I have work to do."

"It's after seven," he pointed out.

"And thanks to an insatiable man I know that kept me awake most of the night I didn't get to work until after ten this morning,'' she reminded dryly, smiling at Mick as he passed by her open office door on his way back downstairs.

"Are you complaining?" Adam's voice had lowered sensuously.

"No." She could still feel the warm glow whenever she remembered their nights together, magical nights when they couldn't get enough of each other, seeming intent on making up for the time they had wasted. "But I am saying I have to work late tonight. I don't expect to be able to leave much before eight o'clock, and I am certainly not going to feel in the mood to cross swords with your father when I do!"

"I can tell that," he drawled. "Okay, I'll call him and change it to tomorrow."

"Adam—"

"And I won't come to your apartment tonight so that you can get a good night's sleep and won't have to work late tomorrow," he added huskily.

To say that she felt bereft at the thought of not seeing him tonight would be an understatement, the rest of the evening and night stretched before her like a long black tunnel. But she had a feeling Adam knew exactly how she felt, and she wouldn't give him the satisfaction of knowing how much she would miss him.

"That sounds like a good idea," she agreed lightly. "I can also get a few jobs done around the flat that I've neglected the last few days. And I'm sure Harvey would welcome my undivided attention for a few hours."

"You sound as if you're looking forward to an evening without me." Adam sounded annoyed.

She smiled to herself. She would spend a miserable evening without him, but it would be worth it to know that he didn't realise that. "Well we did agree we would have a certain amount of freedom in this relationship, Adam," she reminded brightly. "And the idea of putting on an old robe, curling up on the sofa with a good book, sounds like heaven."

"It sounds awful," he rasped.

"Only because you don't have an old robe," she mocked. "And you never relax enough to read."

"I prefer other methods of relaxation."

She could just picture the scowl of his face, almost felt it was worth the night without him to have turned the tables so neatly on him. Almost. But she had become accustomed to curling up against him at night, and she knew she would sleep badly tonight. "Take a hot bath and read for a while, Adam," she advised mockingly. "It's just as relaxing."

"Like hell it is!" he exploded. "Is that really what you would compare our lovemaking to, a hot bath and a read?" he demanded angrily.

"I didn't say it was as good," she was enjoying baiting him. "Only that it's as relaxing."

"It's the same thing, damn it," he snarled.

"Is it?" she asked with feigned vagueness, almost laughing out loud at his indignation. "Adam, are we having our first lovers' argument?" She instilled disbelief into her voice.

"Yes," he rasped coldly. "I'll call you tomorrow." He rang off abruptly.

Leonie put her own receiver down more slowly, knowing she had won that round, but at what price. She had denied herself a night with Adam, and the mood he was in now she couldn't even be sure he would call tomorrow. But she wouldn't go to him, had given in to him too much in the past to follow that pattern again. She looked at the ring on her finger; a long-lasting affair he had said. And she believed him. One little argument wouldn't spoil what they had now.

But that knowledge didn't cheer her up at all, and she had little enthusiasm for work now, her concentration level down to nil. She packed up after a few minutes, deciding she would be better off coming in early in the morning.

"Had enough for one day?" Mick sympathised as he unlocked the door for her to leave.

"More than enough," she grimaced at the middle-aged man. "I'll see you early in the morning," she told him lightly, knowing he would still be on duty when she got to work at seven-thirty tomorrow. It must be a long boring night for him.

It was a long boring night for her too. Her bath was relaxing, so was Harvey's decision to spend the evening in with her for a change, but the book might as well have been written in Chinese for all she understood it, putting it down after several minutes; her favourite romance author deserved a more avid reader than she could provide this evening.

Had she fallen into the trap so quickly, wanting more from Adam than he wanted to give? There could be no doubting that they came together as equals now, but would marriage make so much difference to their relationship? Their approach to each other was different this time around, would a wedding ring and marriage licence really "foul up" the relationship, as Adam had claimed it had last time. Couldn't he see that it wasn't those things that had ruined their marriage at all, that it had been their attitudes that were all wrong?

Was she saying she wanted to be married to him again? She knew she had changed since their separation, that she was more self-confident now, had independence in her career if not in her emotions, felt more able to meet Adam on an equal footing, both intellectually and emotionally, and certainly physically. God, how quickly she had changed her mind about being married to him, how she wished she didn't have to spend evenings apart from him like this! Could she accept just an affair now, when she knew she wanted so much more?

THE INSISTENT RINGING of the doorbell woke her up, and with a bleary-eyed glance at the bedside clock she saw it was after three o'clock in the morning. She came instantly awake. She had told Adam that she was sure her obscene telephone caller wouldn't come here while she continued to take his calls, but suddenly she wasn't so sure. And she was very much alone here.

Should she call the police before answering the door, or try to find out the identity of her visitor first? The police certainly wouldn't be very thrilled with her if it turned out to be a false alarm. She decided to do the latter, moving warily to the locked and bolted door, knowing that if someone were really determined to get in that they could break the locks with one blow to the door.

"Who—who is it?" she demanded in a hushed voice, trembling from head to foot.

"Who the hell do you think it is?" rasped an all-too-familiar voice.

"Adam!" Her hands shook as she quickly unlocked the door, almost falling into his arms in her relief, barely noticing he wore casual denims and shirt, his jaw in need of a shave. "Thank God it's you!'' she groaned, her face buried against the warm column of his throat.

His arms tightened about her convulsively as she continued to tremble. ''Who did you think— Oh no,'' he groaned, holding her closer. ''You thought it was him, didn't you?'' he realised, closing the door behind them.

''Yes,'' she shuddered.

''I'm sorry, baby. God, I'm sorry,'' he muttered over and over into her hair, holding her until the trembling stopped and she pulled out of his arms.

''Sorry!'' she glared at him. ''You frighten me half to death and all you can say is you're *sorry!*'' After the relief came her anger, and she was truly furious!

''I'm *very* sorry?'' he said hopefully.

''That doesn't make up at all for the scare you gave me,'' she snapped. ''Just what do you think you're doing here at three o'clock in the morning anyway?'' she demanded to know.

He sighed, thrusting his hands into the back pockets of his already tight denims. ''I couldn't sleep—''

''Well you can take your damned insomnia somewhere else!'' she told him angrily.

''You don't mean that.''

''Oh don't I?'' she challenged recklessly. ''You just turn around and walk out that door. And if you want to see me again you can call at a reasonable time!''

''Have you been able to sleep?''

''Of course, why shouldn't I?'' In fact it was because she had only eventually fallen asleep about an hour ago that was making her so bad-tempered, feeling nauseous with the suddenness of her wakening.

''Because you missed me,'' he suggested huskily.

''Don't flatter yourself,'' she said heatedly. ''I slept

before you came into my life, and I'll sleep the times you aren't with me!''

His mouth tightened. ''You really want me to leave?''

''Yes!'' She glared at him, still badly shaken from her imaginings of him being her obscene caller. ''What we have is a *relationship,* Adam. I'm not some available body you can take to help you fall asleep!''

He recoiled as if she had struck him. ''It wasn't like that—''

''Wasn't it?'' she accused. ''Can you deny you came here to make love with me?''

''That was part of it—''

''I'm beginning to think that might be all of it,'' she scorned. ''Now that I'm not such a non-event in bed you can't do without it, can you?''

A white line of fury ringed his mouth. ''You have improved in bed,'' he bit out contemptuously. ''But I've had better,'' he added woundingly. ''I thought this,'' he twisted up her left hand with his eternity ring glittering on her finger, ''meant we had more than a physical relationship. I thought we had respect and liking, maybe even loving. But I was obviously wrong,'' he thrust her hand away from him. ''I came here because I couldn't sleep until I'd apologised for the senseless argument we had earlier,'' he ground out. ''But you obviously haven't been plagued by the same need. I will leave now, I'm sorry I troubled you!''

The colour had come and gone again in her face as they hurled the hurtful words at each other, knowing she had provoked this scene, a scene that could be the end of them. And suddenly the idea of Adam walking out of her life became too unbearable to contemplate.

"Adam!" She ran to him as he stopped at the door, her arms about his waist from behind as she rested her cheek against his back. "I'm sorry," she said breathlessly. "I shouldn't have said those things."

He didn't move. "The point is, did you mean them?"

"No," she sighed. "I've just woken up after lying awake for hours aching for you," she admitted gruffly. "I'm a bad-tempered witch, and I'm sorry."

The tension left his body in a ragged sigh. "Can I stay?"

"Please," she groaned her need.

He turned to take her in his arms, holding her tightly. "Have you forgiven me for frightening you like that?"

"Of course." She snuggled up against him.

"Has he called again?"

She shook her head. "No, I told you, only Fridays at eleven-thirty."

"I wonder why that is," Adam frowned.

"Maybe that's his night out with the boys away from his wife," she dismissed.

"You think he's married?" Adam's frown deepened.

"I try not to think about him at all," she told him firmly. "And I wish you wouldn't either. He's a sick man who vents his frustration on life by telling me dirty things."

"If I ever find out who he is I'll kill him," Adam ground out.

She smoothed the anger from his face. "We'll probably never know, so let's forget him."

"Yes." He did so with effort. "Shall we go to bed?"

She smiled up at him encouragingly. "I thought you would never ask!"

Their lovemaking was different again tonight, as enjoyable as it always was, but no more so than the closeness they shared afterwards as they lay in each other's arms. As she lay next to Adam Leonie knew that their relationship had transcended the physical, that even though she had no idea of Adam's feelings for her that she loved him, doubted she had ever stopped.

SHE COULD FEEL the tension rising within her as they neared Adam's father's house, wished with each passing minute that she had stuck to her decision not to go there with him for dinner. But her closeness to Adam that morning had compelled her to change her mind, sure at that time that she could survive the ordeal of meeting his father again.

She had changed her mind back again since then, had picked up the telephone a dozen times during the day to tell Adam to cancel the dinner, only to replace it again without speaking to him, sure he would find her cowardly behaviour less than attractive.

Getting herself ready had been a disaster, not realising her nail-polish wasn't dry, finding out that fact when her tights got stuck to it as she tried to get dressed. Then she had torn the hem of her dress with her evening shoe, having to change her make-up tones with the dress, realising at the last minute that she had grey shadow on one lid and green on the other!

By the time Adam arrived to pick her up at seventhirty she was feeling hot and flustered, telling him she couldn't possibly go out, that she thought she

might be going to come down with something. His
method of persuasion had left her even more hot and
flustered—but with a decided glow to her eyes.

The fact that they were now going to arrive very
late didn't seem to bother Adam in the slightest, the
intimate smiles he kept directing her way reassuring
her that she had his support, that he wouldn't let her
down as he had so much in the past.

The Faulkner staff must have been aware of the
break-up of Adam's marriage, and yet the haughty
butler didn't so much as bat an eyelid at Leonie accompanying Adam to dinner, his manner very correct
as he took her jacket.

"Dad doesn't eat little girls for breakfast," Adam
teased her as she hesitated about entering the lounge
where she knew the senior Mr Faulkner was waiting
for them.

"That's only because he knows I'd give him indigestion!" she muttered ruefully.

Adam was still laughing when they entered the
lounge, although Leonie sobered as she sensed the
disapproval emanating from the rigid-backed man
standing across the room from them. Charles Faulkner
was an older version of Adam, still very good looking
despite being over seventy, although the lines of
harshness beside his nose and mouth weren't quite so
noticeable in his son yet. And if Leonie had her way
they never would be!

"You're late," Charles Faulkner bit out critically
without greeting.

"Are we?" Adam dismissed unconcernedly.

"You know you are," his father said harshly, cold
grey eyes turning to Leonie. "What have you been
up to now?" he scorned.

In the past she would have cowered away from

such open contempt, but somehow tonight she knew Adam was on her side, and that gave her the confidence to steadily meet those critical grey eyes. "Good evening, Charles," she deliberately used the informality she had been too nervous to take while living in this house. "I hope you're well," she added politely.

The older man scowled. "I'm as you see me."

Her perusal of his rigidly held body was deliberate and slow. "You're looking very well—considering your age." Her expression remained deceptively innocent, although she could sense Adam was having difficulty containing his amusement.

"And what does age have to do with it?" Charles frowned heavily at the backhanded compliment.

"Well, I remember your once telling me you're just an old man who wants to see his son happily settled before you die," she reminded him of the argument the two of them had had just before she left Adam; it had been one of many occasions when Charles Faulkner had verbally attacked her without Adam's knowledge. She didn't intend to bring those arguments to Adam's knowledge now, she just wanted to warn Charles Faulkner that she wouldn't stand for it a second time. From the look on the older man's face it was working.

"Oh?" Adam sounded suspicious.

"Don't worry, darling," she gave him a bright reassuring smile, enjoying Charles Faulkner being the one to feel uncomfortable for a change; in the past she had never dared to mention his father's cruelty to Adam. "I assured your father I only wanted the same thing."

Adam looked across at the older man with narrowed eyes. "It sounds an—interesting conversation."

"Oh, your father and I had a lot of interesting conversations," she dismissed with feigned innocence. "I've missed them the last few months."

"I'll bet you have," Adam sounded angry.

"Shall we go through to dinner?" his father rasped. "It's been ready almost an hour."

"Then it should be nicely cooked, shouldn't it," his son dismissed hardly.

"Ruined more like," his father muttered, shooting resentful glances at Leonie, which she promptly ignored.

"I've never known Mrs Simmonds to ruin a meal," Adam insisted.

"Always a first time," his father bit out.

The meal was delicious, as they had all known it would be. Emily Simmonds was as taciturn as her employer, but her food melted in the mouth, and it was always perfectly cooked, the Beef Wellington, asparagus tips, and tiny new potatoes that followed the home-made pâte better than could be bought in any restaurant. But the food didn't seem to have improved Charles Faulkner's mood at all.

"You never did tell me why the two of you were so late arriving," he snapped as they were served the chocolate meringue for dessert.

Delicate colour heightened Leonie's cheeks as she left it to Adam to reply; after all, *he* was the one who had delayed them. Even if she had enjoyed it.

"I took Leonie to bed and made love to her," he stated calmly, continuing to eat his dessert in the midst of the furore he had created.

"Adam!" Leonie gasped her dismay, not expecting him to be quite so candid.

His father's mouth was tight. "In my day a man didn't discuss taking his wife to bed."

"Only other women, hm?" his son mocked, the elderly man spluttering his indignation. "But Leonie is no longer my wife." His hand clasped hers, his smile warm.

"You're back together," his father pointed out abruptly.

"And we're staying that way," Adam nodded. "But not as husband and wife."

"You—you mean you're just going to *live together?*" Charles made it sound decadent.

"Not even that yet," his son replied happily. "Not until Leonie is ready for it."

"Leonie!" his father snorted. "In my day a man didn't ask his wife's permission to do anything!"

"I know that," Adam nodded. "And for a while I followed your example. I walked all over Leonie as if she were a piece of the furniture, didn't ask her opinion on anything, didn't even care if she wanted to make love or not. I did, and that was good enough for me."

"Adam...!" She looked at him pleadingly.

"No, Leonie, I have to make my father understand that things are different now." He turned to the older man. "Leonie is a person, with feelings and desires. It took me a long time to realise there was more to a marriage than putting a ring on some lucky woman's finger. Lucky!" he scorned. "Leonie never knew a day's happiness after I married her. I was so busy being the strong man you had taught me to be that I killed the love Leonie had for me. I realise now that mother was just as unhappy with you as Leonie was with me."

His father flushed with rage. "Your mother wasn't

unhappy! I gave her everything, cars, jewels, furs, this beautiful house, the servants, *you!*''

''You didn't give me to mother,'' Adam contradicted impatiently. ''You created me together. And instead of giving things to mother you should have spent more time with her, talked, *laughed.*''

''I had a business to run,'' his father scowled. ''I didn't have time for that.''

''Then you should have made time!''

The two men glared at each other, the similarity between them at that moment unmistakable.

''And I suppose that's what you intend doing, so that you can pander to this—to this—''

''To Leonie, yes,'' Adam bit out.

''And the business will suffer because of it!''

''The business will do just fine,'' Adam corrected. ''That's what delegation is all about.''

''I'm surprised you haven't decided to sell everything off,'' his father scorned.

''I thought about it—''

''Adam!'' Leonie gasped her shocked dismay.

''And decided against it,'' he finished gently, squeezing her hand reassuringly. ''There would have been no point,'' he shrugged. ''I would still have been the same selfish man, and a richer but unemployed one too. So I decided that it was *I* who had to change, not my life.''

''There's nothing wrong with you,'' his father told him tautly. ''At least, nothing that can't be straightened out as soon as you're over this infatuation you suddenly have for your own wife!''

Adam shook his head, his smile sympathetic. ''There's nothing sudden about my feelings for Leonie, I was just too busy to express them before.

Never show any sign of weakness, that's your motto, isn't it, Dad?''

"It's never failed me," the older man ground out.

"Oh it's failed you," Adam contradicted gently. "Mother was never completely happy, never really sure of your love, and I've turned out to be made from your own image."

"There's nothing wrong in that," his father bit out. "You're a successful man, well respected in the business world."

"The respect of complete strangers doesn't mean a lot," Adam told him impatiently.

"I suppose you're going to tell me next that all you want is Leonie," his father derided coldly.

"Yes," Adam answered quietly. "That's exactly what I want. I also want *your* respect for her, and until you can give her that we won't be coming here again."

"Adam." She looked up at him pleadingly.

"It's all right, Leonie," he assured her with a gentle smile, pulling her to her feet at his side. "I'm sure my father knows I mean what I say." The last was added challengingly.

"You're acting like an idiot, Adam," his father rasped. "Can't you see she's a little simpleton? Why, all she's been able to do for the last half hour is gasp your name in varying degrees of incredulity!" he added contemptuously.

"Good night, Father," Adam told him flatly, guiding Leonie to the door.

"Adam!"

He turned slowly at the anguished cry. "Yes?" he bit out coldly.

His father was standing too now, looking more disturbed than Leonie had ever seen him. "Can't you see you're making a damned fool of yourself, and over a young slip of a girl who isn't worthy of you?''

Adam gave his father a pitying smile. ''If this is making a fool of myself I hope I never stop!'' He opened the door for Leonie to precede him out of the room.

''Adam…!''

He ignored his father's second plea, his arm about Leonie's waist as they left the house together.

# CHAPTER EIGHT

LEONIE sat quietly at his side as he drove them back to her flat, all of their nights spent there together, Adam an integral part of her life now.

She was stunned by the evening with Charles Faulkner, had had no idea Adam meant to issue his father such a challenge because of her. She knew Adam had changed since their separation, but she hadn't realised just how much.

And he had done it for her, he had revealed tonight, that was what she found so incredible. He wanted her so much that he was willing to change his whole life for her. Surely that must mean he loved her? It was a word that remained conspicuously absent from their relationship.

But she loved him, more than ever after his defence of her in front of his father, knew that she had never really stopped loving him. And she believed him when he said Liz was out of his life for ever. But she wanted to be his wife again more than anything, wanted the children with him even a long-term affair couldn't give them. Maybe in time...

"Thank you, Adam," she huskily broke the silence.

"For what?" He heaved a ragged sigh. "For subjecting you to even more unpleasantness from my father?"

She put her hand on his thigh. "I've known worse from him."

"I'm sure you have," he ground out. "Just how often did he used to make those digs at you without my knowledge?"

"It's over now, Adam—"

"How often, Leonie?" he demanded stubbornly.

She sighed. "Whenever he could," she admitted. "It was very demoralising." She had no intention of widening the gulf between father and son by telling Adam how often his father had reduced her to tears.

"You should have told me what was going on," he rasped.

Leonie shrugged. "He never said anything that wasn't the truth. It really doesn't matter now," she assured him.

"It matters to me," Adam bit out. "I was such a lousy husband I couldn't even see what a bastard my father was to you!"

"You were not a lousy husband," she defended.

"Yes, I was," he nodded grimly. "God, I hope I'm a better lover than that!"

She felt any hope she may have had of persuading him to resume their marriage slipping away from her. It was obvious that Adam preferred things the way they were. "Yes," she told him softly. "You're a better lover."

She fed the cat when they got in, Adam watching her with brooding eyes as he sat on one of the arm-chairs. He still seemed very disturbed by the incident with his father, and she sat down on the carpeted floor in front of him as she turned to talk to him.

"He'll come around," she said softly.

He looked startled. "You mean Dad?" His brow

cleared. "Yes, he'll come around," he acknowledged heavily. "And I hope he's a wiser man for it."

"But you weren't thinking about him, were you?" she probed.

"No," he admitted flatly. "I was just wondering how you could have stayed with me as long as you did, and what damned arrogance made me assume I could just walk back into your life and get you to accept me as your lover!"

"But I did, didn't I?" She smiled up at him.

"Yes, you did." He shook his head in amazement. "I thought I had changed after you left me, you see I tried to do exactly that, but now I realise I'm still as arrogant, that I haven't changed in that respect at all. What right do I have to expect you to waste one day of your life on me after what you went through when you were married to me?"

"It isn't wasted," she assured him huskily.

"And if I hurt you again?" he rasped.

She shook her head. "You won't."

"How can you be sure?"

"Why should I want to be?" she cajoled. "One thing I've learnt from our marriage, Adam, is that the whole of life is a risk. You simply have to live it the way that is best for you."

He pulled her up to sit on his knees. "And this is best for us, isn't it, Leonie?" he said fiercely.

"Yes," she said softly, hope completely gone. "This is right for us."

She met his kiss halfway, their emotions spiralling rapidly, standing up in unison to go to her bedroom, needing more than just caresses.

They had barely reached the bedroom when the telephone began to ring, Adam frowning heavily as he glanced down at his watch. "Friday, eleven-thirty," he muttered darkly. "He's consistent, isn't he," he ground out, turning to pick up the receiver.

"No, Adam, let me—"

He easily shrugged off her attempt to take the receiver from him, listening to the man in silence for several seconds. "As I said before, it all sounds very interesting," he finally cut in gratingly. "But if you don't stop these calls I'm going to do some heavy breathing of my own—down your damned neck! Do I make myself clear?" He shrugged, putting down the receiver. "He hung up."

"Wouldn't you?" she teased, relieved that the call was over for another week.

Adam sighed. "Leonie, he worries me. I know you say he's harmless, but—"

"He is," she insisted. "And maybe now that he realises I have an aggressive lover he'll stop calling."

"Maybe…" But Adam didn't sound convinced.

"Darling, let's not think about him now," she moved sensuously against him. "Can't you see this is exactly what he wants?" She sighed as she received no response. "Adam, don't let one sick person ruin everything that we have."

He looked down at her with pain-darkened eyes. "If anything happened to you…!" His arms came about her convulsively, carrying her over to the bed to make love to her until she begged for his possession, until neither of them had a lucid thought in their head other than pleasing each other.

Adam still lay next to her when she woke the next morning, and with a contented sigh she realised neither of them had to go to work this morning. She looked down at the man at her side, remembering the incredible night they had just spent together, a night when Adam seemed determined to possess her time and time again, and had.

"Adam…?"

His lids opened instantly she spoke his name, almost as if her voice were all that were needed to wake him. A light glowed in his eyes as he saw the sensuality in her face. "Again, Leonie?" he said huskily.

"Please," she encouraged throatily.

It was after eleven when they woke the next time, Leonie resisting Adam's caressing as she insisted they needed food rather than more lovemaking. It was while they were eating the brunch Adam had prepared that she remembered she should have visited Liz and Nick that morning.

"What is it?" Adam was sensitive to her every mood, fully dressed as he sat across the table from her, although he had told her he intended bringing some of his clothes here the next time he came, sick of dressing in the same clothes he had worn the evening before. He did look rather out of place in the tailored black trousers and white evening shirt, although he had dispensed with the dinner jacket that completed the suit.

"Nothing," she dismissed, not wanting to do or say anything that would dispel the harmony of the morning.

"Leonie?" he prompted reprovingly.

She shrugged narrow shoulders, wearing denims and a cream cotton top. "I should have visited Liz and Nick this morning, but it isn't important. I can call them later."

"There's still time—"

"I'd rather stay with you," she said huskily.

"I have an appointment myself at twelve-thirty." He sipped his coffee.

"Oh?" she frowned, had imagined they would spend the day together.

"Yes." He didn't enlarge on the subject. "And I have to go home and change first," he added ruefully. "So you can still go to Liz's if you want to."

It seemed that she might as well when he put it like that. But she couldn't help feeling curious about who he was seeing at twelve-thirty; he wasn't exactly keeping it a secret, but he didn't seem anxious to talk about it either.

"Well, if you're sure," she frowned.

"I am," he nodded. "I'll come back here around six, okay?"

"Okay."

His sharp gaze narrowed on her. "What's the matter?"

"Nothing," she dismissed with a bright smile.

Adam smiled. "I know you well enough to realise when you're sulking—"

"I do not *sulk!*" she claimed indignantly.

"Yes, you do," he chuckled. "Your bottom lip pouts—like that," he touched the passion-swollen redness with the top of his thumb, "and your eyes get stormy." He looked into the glittering green depths. "Like that. Yes, you're definitely sulking. What is it, Leonie?" he prompted softly.

She shrugged. "I thought we were going to spend the day together, that's all," she admitted moodily.

Pleasure glowed in his eyes. "Tomorrow we won't even get out of bed," he promised. "But today we have our courtesy visits to make, you to Liz and Nick's, I to a business meeting."

"On a Saturday?"

"Sometimes it's the only time that's convenient. But if you would rather I didn't go…?"

"Oh no," she denied instantly, not wanting him to think she was acting shrewish, as he had once claimed a wife's possessiveness could be. "I'll cook us dinner this evening." That way they could spend more time alone together.

"It's about time *you* cooked me a meal." He mocked the fact that he was the one who had once again done the cooking.

"You never used to like my cooking," she reminded softly.

"That isn't true," he sobered. "You used to get yourself in such a state about it if something went wrong that I thought you would prefer to eat with my father. I couldn't have given a damn if some of the food was a bit burnt around the edges!"

"It was usually burnt all over," she grimaced.

"Didn't you know that I didn't give a damn if it was charcoaled?" he rasped. "I didn't even notice what I was eating, I was too busy looking at my wife!"

"Oh, Adam," she choked. "Tonight I'll cook you something really special," she promised. "It's just that I've been too exhausted the rest of the week to be able to crawl from my bed, let alone cook you dinner in the evenings," she teased lightly.

"Tomorrow you won't have to bother," he promised, standing up to pull on his jacket.

"I may starve," she warned.

"You won't." His gaze held hers before he bent to kiss her.

"Man—or woman—cannot live on love alone," she told him.

"We can try," he murmured throatily, shaking his head as he moved away from her. "If I don't leave now, *I* may not have the strength to get out the door."

He gave her a quick kiss on the lips. "I'll see you this evening, darling."

Her flat seemed very empty once he had left, not even Harvey's presence as he jealously followed her from room to room helping to dispel the feeling of loneliness as he usually did. Accustomed to sleeping on the bottom of her bed at night he wasn't too happy about being relegated to the sofa in the lounge this last week.

To Leonie's dismay Nick was out when she arrived for her visit, feeling awkward at being alone with Liz, something she had pointedly avoided since the day she had seen her sister in Adam's arms. But she could hardly leave again just because her brother-in-law was out.

But she didn't know what to talk about to Liz, had felt uncomfortable with her sister since knowing she and Adam had been lovers. Luckily feeding Emma and putting her upstairs for her nap filled the first half an hour, although without the distraction of the baby Leonie felt even more awkward.

"That's a lovely ring." Liz reached her hand across the kitchen table as they sat in there drinking coffee together, admiring the diamond-studded ring on Leonie's slender hand. "It's new, isn't it?" she looked up enquiringly.

Leonie put the offending hand out of sight under the table. "Yes, it's new," she mumbled, wondering why on earth she hadn't thought to take it off before visiting her sister.

"It looks expensive," Liz sipped her coffee.

"I— It probably is," she acknowledged awkwardly.

Her sister's eyes widened. "It was a gift?"

"Yes," she admitted reluctantly.

"Well don't be so secretive, Leonie," Liz laughed reprovingly. "Who's the man?"

She shrugged. "No one important." She instantly felt disloyal for dismissing Adam in that way. "That isn't true," she said quietly, her head going back proudly. "Adam gave me the ring."

"You're back together?"

She wished she could tell more from her sister's expression how she felt about the idea, but Liz was giving nothing away, her expression guarded. "In a way," she finally answered.

Liz frowned at the evasion. "What does that mean?"

She moistened suddenly dry lips. "We're together, but not *back* together if you know what I mean."

"No, I don't," Liz looked puzzled.

"Our marriage was a failure, being with Adam now is nothing like that."

"But you are—together?" Liz persisted.

She drew in a deep breath, not wanting to hurt her sister as Liz had hurt her in the past, their roles somehow reversed now. "Yes," she confirmed abruptly.

Liz let out a long sigh of relief. "You don't know how happy that makes me," she said shakily.

Leonie frowned. "Happy?" It was the last thing she had expected her sister to feel about her reconciliation with Adam. "You realise I know of your involvement with Adam before we were married?"

"Yes," Liz nodded. "I always felt that it was partly that involvement that parted you and Adam."

*Partly!* It was her sister's involvement with *her* husband that had ended the marriage!

"I'm so glad Adam has at last explained to you what really happened between us," Liz said happily. "He has, hasn't he?" she hesitated.

"I know about it," she acknowledged curtly.

"Adam always said that knowing wouldn't make things any better between you, that you had other problems that couldn't be worked out."

"Yes." But they had worked those problems out now! So what was the secret behind Liz's involvement with Adam, how did her sister think Adam could ever condone their actions so that she could forgive them both?

"I couldn't imagine what they were," Liz frowned. "And it wasn't my business to ask. I know how kind Adam is, I couldn't think what could be wrong between you, but Adam insisted that knowing the truth about the two of us would serve no purpose, that things were over between you. I'm so glad he was wrong!"

Leonie had no intention of correcting her sister's assumption that Adam had explained everything to her, knowing that Liz was going to reveal it without realising she was doing so.

"Adam so deserves to find happiness, he was so kind to me. When Nick went through what I can only assume to be his mid-life crisis a couple of years back and had an affair with a young girl at his office I felt so—so humiliated, so—so unfeminine, so unattractive, that I just wanted to crawl away and hide."

*Nick's* affair? This was getting more complicated than she had imagined! She made a non-committal noise in her throat, encouraging Liz to continue.

"Adam made me feel like a woman again, a beautiful woman," she recalled emotionally.

"Wasn't going to bed with you a little drastic?" Harshness entered Leonie's voice. "Offering you a shoulder to cry on might have been just as effective— and less complicated."

"*I* was the one who instigated our lovemaking," Liz admitted heavily. "It could have been any man, I just wanted to prove, to myself, that I was still an attractive woman."

"If it could have been any man why did you have to choose *Adam!*"

She shrugged. "Because I knew he was too kind to rebuff me. He knew I couldn't take any more rejection, acted as if it were what he wanted too, but afterwards we both knew it was a mistake. I still wanted Nick, not Adam, and the only way to get Nick back was to fight for him, to show him how important he was to me, not have an affair myself."

"You obviously won," Leonie said dully, the involvement she had believed to be an affair not an affair at all. Then why hadn't Adam told her that! Because he didn't care enough about her to explain himself…? Somehow his actions now disproved that.

"Yes, although it wasn't easy," Liz smiled tremulously. "Knowing Nick had slept with another woman, was perhaps comparing me to her, was a difficult hurdle to cross."

Leonie didn't need to be told about that torment, she had *lived* it!

"And I knew I could never tell Nick about the night I spent with Adam," she sighed heavily.

"But he had an affair himself!"

"Yes," Liz nodded. "But to be told that I had spitefully slept with another man because he had betrayed me was something I knew he could never accept. Besides, Adam was married to you by this time."

"All the more reason for the truth to come out, I would have thought!"

"And what was the truth?" Liz reasoned. "That

Adam had loaned me his body for a night so that I might feel a whole woman again? Why ruin five lives just to ease our consciences?'' she shook her head.

Because Leonie had a feeling it was that guilty conscience that had ruined her own marriage, *Adam's* guilty conscience that he had once gone to bed with his sister. ''You were never in love with Adam?'' she probed.

''No,'' Liz denied instantly. ''Or he with me. He took one look at my baby sister and fell like a ton of bricks,'' she added ruefully. ''I'd always teased him that it would happen that way for him, and he had always scorned the idea. When I came back from my reconciliation holiday with Nick to be told the two of you were getting married I didn't know whether to be ecstatic for your sake or nervous of losing the happiness I had just refound with Nick.''

''*That's* why you were less than enthusiastic by our news.'' She had thought it was for completely a different reason!

''Yes,'' Liz grimaced. ''I should have known Adam would never break his promise to me. But when I knew I was expecting a baby it somehow seemed important that he reassure me Nick would never find out about that night I had spent with him. Adam assured me no one would hear of it from him.''

And she had walked in on that scene, had misread it completely. Could Liz be right, *had* Adam fallen deeply in love with her the first time they met? And if he had, did he love her still?

''He told me your marriage wasn't working out,'' Liz looked sad. ''That he expected you to leave him any day. I couldn't understand it, the two of you had seemed so much in love. But Adam assured me my behaviour with him had done nothing to cause the rift.''

And he had lied. He had risked their happiness for the sake of her sister's! She knew it as surely as if Adam had told her so himself. But he never would. He *was* kind, had never deliberately hurt anyone in his life. Not even her, she realised now. Two years ago she had been too immature, too starry-eyed, to accept and understand what had prompted him to make love to Liz, a new maturity gave her the insight to realise he had been helping a friend cope with her pain. He couldn't have had any idea at the time that he would fall in love with Liz's young sister, that he would want to marry her even though he knew that, like Nick, she couldn't have taken the truth about him and Liz. When she had found out about the two of them she had acted predictably, hadn't cared that what she had thought to be their affair had taken place before their marriage, that Adam had been completely faithful to her since that time. All she had seen were the black and white facts; Adam had slept with her married sister!

But had he really sacrificed their happiness for Liz's sake? Eight months after their separation they were back together, happier than ever.

And suddenly she needed to tell him she understood the past, that she wanted a future with him, a permanent future, with a wedding ring. There would be no more evasions of the truth between them, she wanted to be his wife, and she intended telling him so.

''He was right.'' She stood up to kiss her sister warmly on the cheek, seeing Liz's surprise to the first instantaneous show of affection she had given her in a long time. ''We had other, much more serious problems.'' Such as not talking to each other about what was bothering them. She intended remedying that straight away!

"I'm so glad you're back together again," Liz hugged her.

"So am I." She gave a glowing smile.

"I hope it works out this time. Adam loves you very much, you know.''

Yes, she finally believed that he did. He had been brought up in a household where love was never expressed openly, found it difficult to show love himself as a consequence, even when he knew it was pushing them apart. While they had been separated he had set about changing a lifetime of emotional repression, of sharing his feelings and fears with another person. The despair he had shown last night when they got back from his father's because he thought he had failed was evidence of that.

It also made her question the affair between them now. What was it he had said the first night they had slept together since their separation, that the affair had been her suggestion? He believed it was what *she* wanted!

It was time they sorted out this mess, to tell each other of their true feelings, for the past and for each other. If an affair were really all he wanted then she would accept that, but she had a feeling they were both living a lie. God, she could hardly wait to see him again!

# CHAPTER NINE

THE telephone was ringing as she entered the flat, and after falling over an awkwardly reclining Harvey as he lay in front of the doorway, she ran to pick up the receiver, sure it was Adam.

"Leonie?"

Her hand instantly tensed about the green-coloured receiver. "Yes?" she sounded breathless.

"You sound as if you've just got out of bed."

"I—"

"Is he still there, Leonie?" that taunting voice interrupted. "Is your lover still in your bed?"

This couldn't be happening. This was Saturday, he never called on a Saturday!

"Leonie?" The man's voice had sharpened angrily as she remained silent.

"Yes! Yes, I'm still here," she gasped, realising that something else was different about this call too. He was using her name! He had never done that before either.

"Did your lover stay the night, Leonie?" he rasped.

"Look—"

"Is Faulkner still there with you?" he cut in furiously.

Leonie felt numb with shock. Not only did this man know *her* name, he also knew about Adam! She felt an uncomfortable tingling sensation down her neck, as if someone were watching her. How else could this man know so much about her and Adam? God, it made her feel sick—and frightened. It was a long time since she had felt physically threatened by this man's calls, but today was different, *he* was different, not talking about the sick things he would like to do to her as he usually did, sounding menacing as he questioned her.

"I said is he there, Leonie?" he grated again.

"I—er—Yes, he's here," she invented desperately, suddenly feeling trapped, out of control of her own life.

"Liar!" the man gave an unpleasant laugh. "He isn't there, is he, Leonie?"

"Of course he is," she insisted. "He—He's in the shower."

"I saw him leave, Leonie."

"You saw—!" She swallowed hard. "Where are you?" Her voice rose shrilly.

"Wouldn't you like to know," he taunted. "Get rid of him from your life, Leonie. You're mine, do you understand?" he growled. "I stood by while that wimp Stevenson tried his luck with you, but Faulkner is a different matter. Get rid of him, Leonie, you won't like what will happen to him if you don't."

"Wh-what?"

"I could love you much better than he ever could," he told her softly.

"What will you do to Adam?" she repeated shrilly.

There was silence on the other end of the telephone, but she knew he was there, knew he hadn't rung off, could sense him there even though he didn't say a word.

"You're in love with him!" The man suddenly exploded.

"No!" she denied desperately. "I just—"

"Yes, you are, damn you," he rasped harshly. "And I can't allow that, Leonie. I would have given you everything, everything," his voice rose. "But you weren't interested, were you? Oh no, you chose Stevenson over me, and now you're in love with Faulkner. You shouldn't have done that, Leonie. I'll never allow another man to have you. Never!" He slammed the receiver down with such force it hurt her eardrums.

She couldn't move, daren't move, felt frozen, her breathing constricted, her hunted gaze darting about the room like a cornered animal.

She had told Adam the man never threatened, but he had threatened just now. She had told Adam she didn't know the man, and yet she obviously did for him to know so much about her. But *who,* who could it be? Every man she had ever met came crowding into her mind, a jumble of male faces that suddenly all looked menacing.

And then she dismissed the majority of them as being too ridiculous; she hadn't seen most of them for years. But that still left so many friends, acquaintances. Two men she knew she could exclude from that list, Adam and David. It couldn't be Adam, she knew that without a doubt, and the man had been so scathing about David he couldn't possibly have been talking about himself.

But there was Tony, the boy she had been seeing casually before she met and married Adam so quickly, several friends of Adam's she had come to know, the man in the upper flat, and the man in the lower one, the men she worked with, the men she had worked for. God, the list was endless, and she couldn't begin to guess which one of them could be this sick.

But she did have to get out of the flat, couldn't stay here and just wait for him to arrive on her doorstep. She had to call Adam, that was what she had to do. It was almost three now, he would be coming to see her soon, and she couldn't possibly let him walk into a trap.

She let his telephone ring and ring, but received no reply, becoming more and more agitated as she didn't. Surely he couldn't still be at his business meeting?

She had to get out of here. She could wait for Adam at his apartment, didn't care how long she had to stand outside; she wasn't staying here.

She moved about the flat picking up her bag and jacket, pushing an unsuspecting Harvey, as he lay asleep on her bed, into his travelling basket; she didn't intend returning here, would have the rest of her things, and Moby Dick, moved to Adam's apartment as soon as she could.

She was just giving one last frantic look round to make sure she had switched everything off when the doorbell rang shrilly. Her breath stopped in her throat, and for a moment she couldn't move. Dear God, what was she going to do? What *could* she do!

She thought of pretending she wasn't here, but the sudden trip she made over the coffee-table, dropping an indignantly screeching Harvey, put lie to that idea. She righted Harvey's basket before moving cautiously to the door, pressing her ear against the white-painted wood. She couldn't hear anything—but what had she expected, heavy breathing!

The doorbell rang again. "Leonie, are you in there?" called a familiar voice. "I heard a thump, have you hurt yourself?"

Relief flooded through her as she ripped open the door. "Gary!" she hugged him before quickly pulling him inside. "Thank God you're here." She felt like crying at the sight of a friendly face after her imaginings.

"I just thought I'd drop by for a coffee while Joan does her shopping," he dismissed in a preoccupied voice, frowning at how pale she was. "*Did* you hurt yourself?"

She shook her head. "Only Harvey's dignity when I dropped him."

Gary looked down at the cat in the travelling basket. "Are you going away?"

"Just to Adam's—Adam Faulkner," she explained with a blush, although Gary must be as aware as the rest of the staff were at Stevenson Interiors that she was seeing Adam. "You see, I've been having these calls, nasty calls," she grimaced. "I think I told you about them once…?"

"Yes," he nodded.

"Well, I was sure he was harmless. But then he called just now, and he never calls on a Saturday, and I—"

"Hey, calm down," Gary chided, his smile gentle. "Why don't you sit down, let me make you a cup of coffee, and then you can tell me all about it."

"No, we can't stay here." She shook her head frantically. "You see, when he called just now he was— threatening. I'm sure he's going to come here," she shivered.

"With me here?" Gary soothed. "I doubt it."

He was a dear, but with his five-foot-eight-inch frame she didn't feel confident she could depend on him if it should come to violence with the obscene telephone caller. But she couldn't say that to him without hurting his feelings.

"I really don't think we should stay here, Gary," she tried to sound calm. "Look, why don't you come over to Adam's with me, he's sure to be back by the time we get there."

"He isn't at home?"

"He had to go to a meeting, and he doesn't seem to be back yet." She was speaking quickly in her agitation. Didn't he realise how dangerous this situation was! "Please, Gary, we have to go," she urged desperately.

"I don't think so."

"But he could be here any minute! He—" her voice trailed off as she watched him walk over to the door, check that it was locked before putting the key into his pocket. "What are you doing?" she asked—but she had a dreadful feeling she already knew!

He looked at her calmly. "Stopping you from leaving."

She swallowed hard. "Gary, this isn't a time to play games. He could be here soon, and—"

"He's already here."

She had guessed that as soon as he pocketed the key—and she had actually *let* him in here! Gary was the man who called her every Friday night, who whispered obscene things he wanted to do to her. She couldn't believe this nightmare, had always believe the two of them were friends.

"Why, Gary?" she asked faintly, feeling weak with nausea that it was him that said such disgusting things to her every week, that he had done so for the last six months, while still continuing to be so friendly at work. God, she had even told him about those calls!

"Why do you think?" he scorned, his eyes narrowed unpleasantly.

"I—I don't know." She watched him warily, but he seemed to be making no move to cross the room to where she stood poised for flight.

"Because I want you, you little fool," he derided mockingly. "I always did, from the moment you came in to my office with David that first morning and promptly fell over the waste-paper basket. You made me feel protective, very much the man as I helped you to your feet. You looked so delicate and defenceless, and I wanted to take care of you." There was a smile to his lips as he recalled the morning they had met. "That month I worked so closely with you was the most enjoyable four weeks of my life," he added flatly.

"I enjoyed it too," she infused enthusiasm into her voice.

His eyes hardened angrily. "You barely noticed me!" he rasped.

"You were married—"

"Yes," he acknowledged harshly. "But so were you."

"I was separated from my husband."

"I remember. I was jealous of any man who had had you and not had the sense to hold on to you. I hated your husband," he stated coldly. "I wanted you, no other man could have you."

"No other man did," she assured him quickly.

"David—"

"We've only ever been friends, nothing more."

"Faulkner?"

She swallowed hard, paling even more, knowing after what he had just said about her husband that she daren't tell him Adam was the man she was married to. ''Adam and I are friends too,'' she dismissed lightly.

''Very good ones from the amount of nights he's spent here with you,'' Gary scorned.

''How did you— Have you been watching me?'' she asked dully.

''I didn't need to,'' he derided. ''Your face when you came into work every morning this week has been enough to tell me just *how* friendly you and Faulkner have become.''

''Gary, you don't understand—''

''Oh, I understand,'' he sneered. ''Like all women you need a man, any man, to make love to you and tell you how beautiful you are one hundred per cent of the time!''

''It isn't like that—''

''That's what Joan said when I found out about the little affair she had been having with a doctor at the hospital,'' he cut in hardly. ''I'd been working hard, just wanted to sleep when I finally fell into bed at night, but the bitch couldn't understand that. Oh no, she had to go and find herself a lover to give her what I wasn't!''

She had met Gary's wife at the Christmas dinner, had found the other woman to be shallow and flirtatious, had been surprised to learn she was a nurse, the wine she had consumed with the meal making her silly and giggly, demanding kisses from all the men in the party, her willowy beauty making them all willing to comply.

''You could have left her,'' she said softly.

''She would take Timmy with her.'' He looked bleak as he spoke of his young son.

''Gary, can't you see that what you—what you're

doing now is wrong?'' she pleaded with his common sense—if he still had any!

"I haven't done anything—yet.''

She shivered in apprehension at the threat behind that last word. ''You made those calls,'' she reminded.

"Not at first,'' he shook his head.

She frowned. ''What do you mean?''

"I didn't make the first couple,'' he sneered. ''And I wouldn't have made any of them if you hadn't started seeing David. You were really upset when you got the first call, remember, told me all about it. But it was David you let comfort you,'' he added harshly. ''David who took you in his arms and told you everything would be all right. And for a couple of weeks the calls stopped, didn't they, Leonie?'' he derided.

"And then *you* began making them,'' she realised dully. She hadn't noticed a change in the voice, had been too disturbed by the first few calls to notice what it even sounded like!

"Yes,'' he admitted with satisfaction. ''It felt strange at first, I didn't quite know what to say. But after a while it just came naturally,'' he smiled his relish.

As he became more and more emotionally disturbed! It was his mentally disturbed state that made him so unpredictable now. She didn't quite now what to do next, or what *he* was going to do either!

"You always made such a joke about asking me out, Gary,'' she tried to smile, although her face felt stiff. ''I didn't realise you were serious.''

"And if you had you would have accepted, hm?'' he scoffed at her attempt to placate him.

"I may have done,'' she answered sharply.

"You may have done,'' he repeated derisively, his

gaze mocking. "Don't lie to me, Leonie." His eyes hardened to blue pebbles. "Joan is always lying to me." His hands clenched into fists at his sides. "And I don't like it!"

She could see that, swallowing hard at the anger emanating from him. "I'm sure she loves you, Gary," she encouraged. "Every marriage has its problems, I'm sure Joan regrets her lapse with the doctor."

"She still sees him."

"Oh." Leonie chewed on her bottom lip.

"Once a week," he spoke almost to himself, not seeming to see Leonie at all at that moment. "She tells me she's working at the hospital that night, but I've checked; she's seeing him."

"Fridays," Leonie realised weakly.

"Yes," he bit out, focusing on her again.

"She can't really care for him, Gary, otherwise she would have left you to go to him," she pointed out desperately.

"He's married too," Gary scorned. "This way they both have the best of both worlds!"

And Gary's jealousy and pain had acted like a sickness, growing, spreading, until he latched his unwanted love on to another woman—who also turned out not to want him.

"For a while I thought about killing both of them," he continued matter-of-factly. "But then I met you, and realised I could have the same arrangement Joan has. You should have gone out with me, Leonie, I would have been so good to you. Now all we'll have is this one night together."

"Wh-what do you mean?"

"Well you know who I am now," he shrugged.

"You—you're going to leave London?"

He seemed amused by the idea. "No," he drawled.

Leonie felt faint as his meaning became clear to her. She couldn't believe this were really happening—it happened on television, in films, *not* in real life!

"Gary, you're making a mistake," she told him breathlessly. "I—I'll forget all about this if you—if you'll just leave," she urged desperately.

He shook his head. "As soon as I got out the door you would call the police."

She would too, knew she would have to. Gary was a danger to other people as well as to himself. But by the sound of it she wasn't going to get the chance to call anyone.

"It would be your word against mine," she reasoned.

"And Faulkner's," he grated. "It was him who answered the last two calls, wasn't it?"

She flushed her guilt. "Gary—"

"We've talked enough," he snarled. "I didn't come here to talk!"

She knew exactly what he had come here for, and the thought of it terrified her. "Gary, can't you see this is wrong?" she pleaded. "Do you really want to make love to a woman who doesn't love you?"

"Why not?" he scorned. "That's what I do at home!"

"But that's Joan, Gary," she said softly. "Things could be different between us. We—"

"Don't try the psychological approach, Leonie," he scoffed. "I've seen those bad films too!"

"I've always liked you, Gary," she insisted.

"Then you're going to get the chance to prove it, aren't you?" he taunted. "And for God's sake shut that cat up!" he rasped as Harvey scratched frantically at the basket to be let out.

Leonie weighed up the possibility of winning a fight against Gary, instantly knowing that she wouldn't, not even with desperation on her side. Gary may be short and stocky, but muscles bulged in his arms and legs. He could overpower her in a few minutes, possibly sooner.

She moistened dry lips. ''If I let him outside he'll stop,'' she suggested desperately. ''He— He's likely to keep scratching if I leave him in the basket.''

Gary's mouth twisted. ''By all means throw the damned cat out. But don't try and scream,'' he warned gratingly. ''You wouldn't like the way I silenced you,'' he promised.

Leonie had a feeling *he* would enjoy it immensely, her hands shaking as she carried the wicker basket over to the window, all the time measuring the distance between herself and Gary, a plan formulating in her mind. He was too close, although as Harvey clambered thankfully out of the window the empty basket in her hand gave her an idea.

''Hey, Gary,'' she called, at the same time launching the basket at him, knocking him momentarily off-balance, his language voluble as she climbed outside on to the ledge that Harvey used to get to the neighbouring buildings.

Only it wasn't as easy for her to balance there as it was for Harvey, the nine-inch-wide ledge that seemed more than adequate for his wiry frame suddenly seeming too narrow for her to negotiate with any degree of safety.

''What the hell do you think you're doing?'' Gary's furious face appeared at the open window, his hand reaching out to clasp her ankle.

She had seen the move coming and scuttled a short distance along the ledge, sighing her relief as she realised she was out of his reach, leaning back against the rough brickwork of the wall behind her as she swayed giddily, the ground seeming a very long way down.

"You stupid bitch," Gary's face was contorted with fury. "Get back in here."

"Are you joking?" she gave a shaky laugh, her eyes still closed as she fought back feelings of faintness. "You *have* to be joking, Gary!"

"You'll fall and break your damned neck!"

She turned to look at him, breathing heavily in her anger. "Surprisingly enough," sarcasm sharpened her voice, "I would find that infinitely more preferable to being attacked by you. Isn't that strange!" she bit out contemptuously.

Some of the bravado left him as he realised she was serious, taking on the look of a man who just didn't know what to do next. "Leonie, please come back in here," he encouraged softly.

"No!"

"I promise not to touch you, damn it!"

"You think I believe you?" she derided harshly. "I wouldn't trust you—Oh!" she gasped as dizziness washed over her once again.

"Are you all right?" Gary sounded desperate. "Leonie, for God's sake get back in here."

"I can't," she shook her head, pushing into the wall behind her, biting her lip as she became afraid to look anywhere but straight ahead.

"I won't hurt you," he promised vehemently.

"Don't you understand," she grated between clenched teeth. "I can't move!"

"What is it? Is your foot stuck somewhere? Maybe if I—"

"No!" she cried her panic as she heard him attempting to climb out on to the ledge. "Don't come near me," she warned desperately.

"But if you're stuck—"

"I'm not," she shuddered. "I—I have vertigo!" Two floors up, and she was terrified! Heights had never bothered her before, although she did have to concede that the circumstances of her being out here on a nine-inch ledge may have contributed to the fact that she now couldn't move back into the window and couldn't attempt to reach the neighbouring building either! The thought of moving at all terrified her, frozen to the spot.

"Then let me help you—"

"Don't come near me," she warned as Gary would have joined her out on the ledge. "If you come out here I—I swear I'll jump!"

"But you can't stay there!"

"Why can't I?" she was near to hysteria.

"Leonie, you have to come in some time," he encouraged.

"And face a raving sex-maniac?" she shook her head vehemently. "No, thank you!"

"It was only a game—"

"Remember, Gary," she bit out grimly, "I watched the same bad films."

"You would rather stay out there, possibly fall, than come back in here with me?" he sounded exasperated.

"In one word, *yes!*"

"You stupid—"

"Bitch," she finished curtly. "I've noticed that seems to be your favourite word for a woman who won't do things your way," she scorned. "No wonder Joan found herself another man!"

"You know nothing of my marriage to Joan," he snarled.

"I know that the failure of it has involved me," she bit out. "And I—" she broke off as the telephone in her flat began to ring. "It's Adam," she breathed. "It has to be Adam. If I don't answer that Gary, he'll know there's something wrong."

"Why should he?" he dismissed logically. "He'll just think you're still out."

He was right, of course, but she had to try. "No," she insisted. "He said he would call me. If I—if I don't answer he'll think something has happened to me."

"Then come in and answer it," Gary invited softly.

God, the phone would stop ringing in a minute, with the caller—*possibly* Adam, thinking she just wasn't at home!

"I didn't think you would," Gary said smugly.

"You—you're insane!" She told him angrily as the telephone stopped ringing, the silence it left unnerving.

"I thought you had already concluded that," he dismissed. "I'll be waiting inside if you should change your mind about coming in," he told her conversationally.

When she finally dared to turn her head it was to find him gone from the open window. "Gary," she called sharply. "Gary?"

There was no answer. Was he playing a game with her, waiting for her in silence inside her flat? If he thought she was lying about the vertigo, that believing him gone, she would climb back inside, he was wrong. She really couldn't move!

"Gary," she called again. "Gary, please answer me."

He had gone, she was sure of it. God, what could the time be, about three o'clock? That meant she had another three hours before Adam was due to arrive. She wasn't sure she could balance on this ledge for that amount of time. But if she couldn't, that left only one way off it, and that was down!

# CHAPTER TEN

IT was amazing how traffic could pass by and not even realise there was a young woman balancing precariously on a second-floor ledge above them! It was a street that had little or no pedestrians, and the people in their cars were too engrossed in their own lives to look up and see Leonie.

One really bad moment came when Harvey decided to make his way back along the ledge, rubbing against her legs in greeting, not understanding when she wouldn't move out of his way and allow him into his home. He became quite agitated by her refusal to move, and with his usual stubbornness refused to go back the way he had come. Leonie vehemently decided that his wandering days were over if she ever got off this ledge.

And so were someone else's if she survived this! Her fury turned to Adam. If they had been living together as husband and wife instead of conducting this ridiculous affair this wouldn't have happened to her. And if an affair were all he wanted he could find some other woman to have it with, she would be his wife or nothing!

What time was it now? She felt as if she had been on this ledge for hours. Surely it must be almost six by now? She was too afraid to even raise her arm and look at her wrist watch! But as if in answer to her question she could hear a clock striking the hour, one,

two, three, four, five—she waited for the sixth bell—
nothing happened. Five o'clock, it was only five
o'clock! She wasn't sure she could stay balanced here
for another hour.

Suddenly she heard a noise in the flat behind her,
freezing, almost afraid to breathe. Gary had been
playing a game with her all along, he was still in there
waiting for her.

"What the—! What the hell are you doing out
there?"

She turned sharply at the sound of that voice, regaining her balance with effort, feeling shaken as the
world swayed up to meet her.

"Be careful, damn it," Adam rasped. "You almost
fell then."

"You don't say," she scorned shakily. "You aren't
supposed to be here for another hour," she accused.

"What?" he frowned his disbelief, in the act of
climbing out of the window.

"It's only five, you said you wouldn't be here until
six," she stupidly reminded. Had she lost her mind?
What did it matter what the time was, he was *here!*

"Well if that's the way you feel about being rescued," he ground out, climbing back down. "I'll
come back in an hour!"

"Adam!" she screamed her fear that he would really leave her alone again out here. "Oh, Adam," her
voice broke on a sob. "Don't leave me. Please, don't
leave me!"

"It's all right, Leonie," he soothed, sounded closer
now. "I'll be with you in a second, and we'll go in
together."

"We might fall," she cried.

"We won't," he told her calmly.

She felt his fingers on her arm, clasping her hand

now as she clung to him, feeling his strength flow into her. "Adam," she sobbed, still not turning. "Oh, Adam!" Sobs wracked her body.

"That bastard!" he grated feelingly. "He didn't tell us he had left you out here."

"Gary? You mean Gary?" she prompted. "Did you get him?"

"We got him—"

"How?" she breathed raggedly. "I had no idea it was him, I even invited him in thinking he could help protect me after the man called again. Oh God, Adam, I've never been so scared in my life!"

"I can imagine," he cut in harshly. "And once I have you safely inside you can tell me exactly what happened here this afternoon. But right now I have to get you inside."

"I can't move," she shook her head.

"Of course you can." he soothed.

"No."

"Leonie, you will move," he instructed coldly. "Do you understand me?"

Her bottom lip quivered emotionally. "There's no need to shout at me."

"I'll shout at you a lot more than this if you don't soon get yourself moving," he rasped. "It's damned windy out here."

She turned to glare at him. "Do you think I don't know that?" she snapped furiously. It may have been a warm day but the wind had started to blow about an hour ago, increasing in intensity the last ten minutes or so. "I've been stuck out here for hours," she told him angrily. "I've probably caught pneumonia."

"You probably deserve to," Adam said callously.

"No one in their right mind balances on a ledge like this one for hours!"

"That's just the sort of remark I should have expected from you," Leonie eased along the ledge behind him, glaring at him as she allowed him to catch her under the arms and lift her inside. "You don't— Oh!" Her legs gave way as she realised where she was, Adam catching her deftly before she fell.

"It's all right now, Leonie," he soothed, smoothing her hair as he held her. "I have you safe."

She shuddered as she realised she was at last off the ledge. "You deliberately made me so angry that I didn't know what I was doing," she accused between her tears.

"As long as it worked I don't care what I did," Adam was trembling. "I've never been so scared in my life as when I came in and saw your open window and realised you were out there."

"I tried to use psychology with Gary," she remembered with a quiver. "It didn't work."

Adam's arms tightened about her. "He's safely in police custody now."

"When? How?" she frowned.

Adam led her over to the sofa, sitting her down before pouring her a drink, standing over her while she drank the brandy. He took the empty glass from her fingers, sitting down beside her to pull her into his arms. "Did he hurt you?" he asked gruffly.

She knew exactly what he was asking. "No," she assured him softly. "Now tell me how you knew it was Gary? Is he really in police custody?"

"Yes," Adam sighed his relief. "The police arrested him when he arrived home two hours ago. I was with them, and when they knocked on the door he just crumpled. He told them everything when they took him to the police station. But he didn't tell us he had left you perched out on a ledge,'' he frowned his anger.

"It's over now, Adam," she touched his thigh.

"Thank God," he breathed. "Having you followed told us nothing—"

"You're still looking for the grounds to divorce me?" she pulled away from him, her expression pained. "I hope your detective told you that you're my only visitor! Can you be named in your own divorce?" her voice rose shrilly.

"Leonie—"

"I don't think you can, Adam." She stood up, moving away from him. "So we had better stop our affair so that I can find a lover you *can* name. Maybe I should have just let Gary do what he wanted to do after all," her voice broke. "Then you could have named *him.*"

"Leonie—"

"Silly me thought that climbing out on that ledge was better than being violated," she said self-derisively. "If I had just let him go ahead I could have saved us all a lot of trouble. You really should have told me—"

"Leonie, if you say one more word, *one more word,*" he repeated icily, "I'll put you over my knee and beat the living daylights out of you."

"I wonder why I never realised how gallant you are." Her eyes flashed. "I've just escaped attack by a sex-maniac by balancing on a ledge for more than two hours and you intend to beat me!" She gave a choked laugh. "And to think I'd decided, if I ever got off that ledge, that I was going to talk to you about what went wrong in our marriage. It looks as if I needn't bother. Although you'll have to provide the evidence for the divorce, the thought of taking a lover nauseates me!''

''Leonie…?''

''Although I know it won't be Liz,'' she looked at him accusingly. ''All this time you've let me believe the two of you were lovers, and you were lying! Liz told me the truth today.''

''If she said we didn't sleep together then *she* lied,'' he bit out.

''I know you went to bed together, before we were married. I also know now that it only happened the once. And Liz told me it wasn't done out of love on either of your parts.''

''I still slept with your sister,'' Adam told her flatly.

''You helped a friend when she needed it,'' Leonie amended abruptly.

''By making love to her!''

''Do you want a whip to beat yourself with?'' Leonie scorned. ''What you did wasn't wrong.'' She shook her head. ''Misguided, perhaps, but not wrong. I've believed all this time that you were in love with Liz.''

''I never was,'' he denied softly.

''I know that now!''

He sighed. ''The night I made love to her should never have happened, I knew that. Never more so than when I met you,'' he rasped. ''I think I fell in love with you on sight, and yet my guilt about Liz stood between us.''

Leonie moistened suddenly dry lips. ''You *did* love me?''

''Yes.''

''You never once told me that.''

He frowned. "Didn't I? But surely it must have been obvious," he dismissed impatiently.

His emotionally repressed childhood again! "I ought to hit you over the head with something!" she snapped.

"Why?" he looked dazed.

"Because I loved you from the moment we met too," she glared at him. "But my inexperience, my clumsiness, my naiveté, seemed to be driving you away!"

He shook his head. "Your inexperience enchanted me, your clumsiness amused me, and your naiveté enthralled me!"

"Then why couldn't you bear to be near me!"

"Because of Liz," he admitted heavily. "I was terrified that one day you would find out about that night I spent with her, and that you would hate me for it."

"Why couldn't you have just told me about it before we were married?" she sighed.

"I'd promised Liz. Although, believe me, if I had thought you could accept what happened I would have broken that promise," he added grimly.

"You thought me too immature to understand," she nodded. "I believe I was," she acknowledged heavily. "But I understand now."

His eyes were narrowed. "You do?"

She gave a ragged sigh. "Liz told me about Nick, his affair, how you tried to help her through it."

His mouth twisted. "I'd like to say it was all a question of helping Liz, but it wasn't. I couldn't have made love to her if I hadn't desired her."

"I understand that too," Leonie nodded. "But you didn't love her, or want to marry her."

"God, no."

"I thought you did, you see. That day I saw you

together at your office, I thought you had married me because Liz had decided on a reconciliation with Nick rather than marriage to you, that you both now realised your mistake, but that it was too late for you to be together, because Liz was expecting Nick's child. I believed I was a very second, second-best,'' she admitted miserably.

''You were never that.'' Adam shook his head. ''The night I met you I was driving past Liz's house and saw the lights on. My first thought was that it was burglars. Then you opened the door!'' He gave a tight smile. ''I fell, God how I fell. And yet Liz stood between us. I rushed you into marriage before I could talk myself out of it, knew I had to have you even if I lost you later. But our problems began straight away.''

''I was a failure in bed,'' she sighed.

''You weren't a failure,'' he rasped angrily. ''You were a very young girl with a problem you were too embarrassed to even talk about. And by the time we had dispensed with that problem your barriers were well and truly up, you were self-conscious about lovemaking to the point where you didn't even like me to touch you. You can't know what that did to me! But my own guilt about Liz made it impossible for me to reach you. I knew I was driving you further and further away from me, but I didn't know how to stop it. When you decided to end the marriage I knew I couldn't stop you.''

''And now?''

''Now I'm giving you what you want,'' he shrugged. ''An affair.''

''While you divorce me,'' she said bitterly.

''For God's sake, I wasn't having you followed so

that I can divorce you!'' Adam grated. ''I was protecting you, because of those telephone calls.''

''A lot of good that did me,'' she scorned, not believing him.

Adam flushed at the rebuke. ''There was a flaw in the plan. On Saturdays I met with the detective to get his report. We met at twelve-thirty today for lunch.''

''So that was who you were meeting?'' she realised.

''Yes,'' he bit out. ''And while he was telling me that he had followed through investigations into the two men that live here, into the people I work with, and the people you work with, coming up with Gary Kingsfield as the caller, *he* was here threatening you! No one was here watching you, damn it,'' he admitted tersely.

Leonie could see the humour in the situation now that she knew Adam wasn't trying to divorce her. ''That was the flaw?'' she couldn't hold back her smile any longer.

''It isn't funny,'' Adam growled. ''He could have—could have—''

''But he didn't,'' she soothed. ''And unless I'm mistaken, he's done me a favour.''

''I can't think what,'' Adam scowled.

She walked into her bedroom without answering, coming back seconds later, opening her hand in front of him to reveal a thin gold band, and another ring with the stone of an emerald. ''Will you marry me,?'' she invited softly.

His startled gaze was raised to hers. ''The affair…?''

''Is not what I want,'' she said with emphasis. ''I only said that in the heat of the moment, because I was hurt. I'll grant you the last couple of weeks have been exciting, that first night, the afternoon at the hotel, the rose every day. But can't we still have that and be married?''

Adam looked confused. ''I don't understand.''

''Do you still love me?''

''Yes,'' came his emphatic answer.

She felt the glow begin inside her. ''And is an affair really all you want?''

He flushed. ''I thought after an appropriate time, when you'd got used to my being around all the time, that I would ask you to be my wife again.''

That's what she had thought, had finally come to know the workings of her husband's devious mind. ''I want to be your wife now,'' she told him softly. ''And I want you to be my husband.''

''Are you sure?''

''As sure as I was when you first asked me to marry you,'' she smiled. ''We've made mistakes, Adam, terrible, destructive mistakes, but we still have so much, still love each other so much. Don't you agree?'' she looked at him anxiously.

''Gary Kingsfield will never hurt you again, you know. He should go to prison for some time once the police know how he threatened you today.''

''I don't care about Gary,'' she dismissed impatiently. ''I'm talking about us. *Will* you marry me?''

''Give yourself time to get over the shock of this afternoon—''

''That does it!'' she glared at him, pushing the two rings on to her finger next to the eternity ring herself. ''Now we are officially married again,'' she told him crossly. ''And you will be a good, and always *truthful,* husband,'' she warned.

He raised dark brows. ''I will?''

''You will,'' she told him firmly. ''I'll continue to

work, we'll lunch together when we can, you'll come home to me at five-thirty every evening, and we'll live together at your apartment. Your new one, I mean. I don't think we would be welcome at your father's again,'' she grimaced.

''He called this afternoon and invited us over for dinner next week,'' Adam put in softly.

Leonie became still. ''Did you accept?''

''I thought I'd ask you first—''

He was learning, this arrogant husband of hers! ''Then accept,'' she instructed. ''I hadn't finished with the outline of our future,'' she reproved sternly.

''Sorry,'' he said, but there was a devilish glint in his eyes.

''Apology accepted,'' she said primly. ''Now I will decorate your apartment as you once suggested I should, and one of those rooms will be a nursery—''

''Children,'' he said softly. ''Are we going to have children?''

''Three,'' she nodded.

''Why three?'' he frowned at the odd number.

''Why not?'' she frowned.

Adam shrugged. ''Why not? And when do you plan to have the first of these offspring?''

''Well I thought I needed a bit more practice at the basics first,'' she told him thoughtfully.

''Believe me,'' he drawled, ''you don't need any more practice.''

She smiled. ''But it might be fun, don't you think?''

''I'm sure it will,'' he nodded, taking her into his arms. ''Oh, Leonie, I do love you,'' he groaned. ''I'm sorry I was such an idiot when we were together last time.''

"And I'm sorry I was so stupid and left you," she sighed.

"I'm not," he shook his head. "We needed the separation," he explained at her frown. "Otherwise we might never have realised how much we love each other."

She rested her head against his chest as they held each other silently for a very long time, each cherishing the fact that they had at last managed to find happiness together.

"Oh, Adam," Leonie greeted him at the door, her face glowing. "It's triplets!"

The briefcase slipped out of his hand, his face paling. "Are you sure?"

"Of course I'm sure," she said impatiently, pulling him into the house they had shared with his father for the last four months, since Leonie had become pregnant and Charles Faulkner had humbly asked them to. "I've seen them."

Adam swallowed hard. "You have?"

"Yes," she laughed exultantly. "Your father is delighted."

"He is?"

"I must say, you seem less than pleased," she told him crossly.

He looked dazed. "I just never thought— One seemed enough to start with," he finished lamely.

"One?" she frowned. "I don't think that's very usual, they usually come in four or fives."

Adam frowned. "Leonie, what are you talking about?" he sounded puzzled.

"Suki has had her kittens," she sighed her impatience with him. "Harvey is proudly sitting next to the basket, as if he did it all himself, and your father gave a cigar to Chambers.'' She giggled as she remembered the look on the butler's face when Charles Faulkner pushed the cigar in his breast pocket.

"Dad is excited about his prize Siamese giving birth to Harvey's kittens?'' Adam sounded disbelieving.

She nodded. "He says he's going to keep one of them,'' she announced triumphantly. "Adam,'' she frowned. "Just what did you think I was talking about when you came in?''

He looked down at her slightly rounded stomach. "Well…''

"Adam!'' she gave a shocked laugh. "I've had a scan, there's only one in there.''

He took her into his arms. "One can never tell with you,'' he nuzzled into her hair. "That one came as a complete surprise.''

"I think we practised too much,'' she mocked.

"What shall we call it now?'' he said as he led her up the stairs to their bedroom.

"Well, we can't allow all that expertise to go to waste,'' she teased as she began to undress him.

"No,'' he agreed as he undressed her.

"So we'll just say we're practising for the next one,'' she murmured as they sank down on the bed together.

"By the time we're ninety we should be perfect,'' Adam groaned.

Leonie giggled. "We're perfect now, but so what…''

Everything was perfect, their love for each other, the fact that Charles Faulkner seemed to have accepted her as a member of his family since she was carrying his grandchild.

"By the way,'' she caressed his chest. "I've

booked Mr and Mrs Smith a room at The Savoy to-morrow afternoon.''

Adam gave a throaty chuckle. ''I think we're going to have to stop being afternoon lovers soon.'' He looked down at her with tender eyes, one hand lightly cupping her rounded stomach. ''As it is our baby was conceived in a hotel room.''

''I remember,'' she smiled. ''I remember every minute we spend together.''

''So do I,'' he told her gruffly. ''So do I—and I thank God for all of them! I'm so proud to have you for my wife, darling.''

And his pride and love for her were all that mattered.

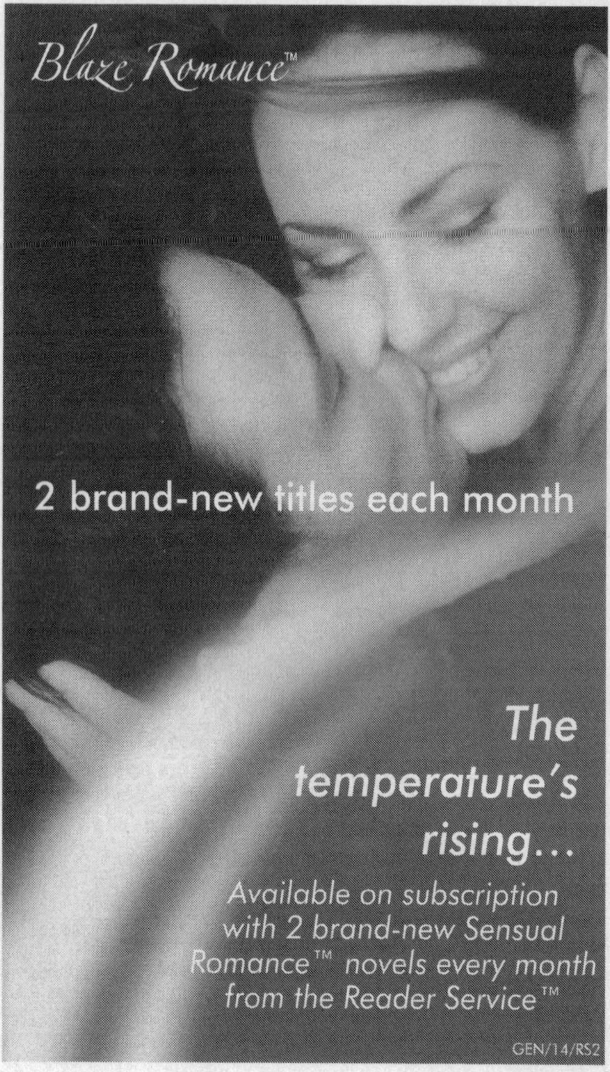

Blaze Romance™
2 brand-new titles each month
The temperature's rising...
Available on subscription with 2 brand-new Sensual Romance™ novels every month from the Reader Service™
GEN/14/RS2